Geology of the Grantham district

The district of south and central Lincolnshire which is described in this memoir includes the towns of Grantham and Sleaford, and the outskirts of Newark-on-Trent. From the Trent–Witham lowlands in the west of the district, the ground rises eastwards to the escarpment of Lincoln Edge, beyond which it slopes down to the fens east of Sleaford. Partially covered by Anglian to Recent drift, gently tilted Jurassic strata from the Lias to the Oxford Clay crop out, resting more or less concordantly on Trias and Permian at depth. These Jurassic formations were deposited on the relatively shallow marine East Midlands Shelf, which shows evidence of temporary emergence. The deposits, consisting mainly of mudstones and limestones with some ironstones, have in the past provided brick clays, building stone and iron ore.

In contrast, the Carboniferous strata, at depth, show considerable structural and sedimentological diversity, which has been revealed by exploration for coal and hydrocarbons. Seismic evidence from below potentially coal-bearing strata indicates a major pre-Carboniferous structure, the Sleaford Low, and a considerable thickness of early Carboniferous strata which has not been penetrated by boreholes. The Sleaford Low is separated by a major fault zone, the Barkston Fault, from the Foston High to the south. From boreholes drilled on the high, samples have been obtained of the igneous and metamorphic basement, inferred to be of Lower Palaeozoic and/or Precambrian age.

During the Quaternary period, the Anglian glaciation and the effects of subsequent glacial and interglacial stages modified the landscape both by erosion and deposition. The resulting terraces of sand and gravel are described and the evidence for their ages is discussed. Some of these deposits may be of commercial interest.

The memoir also describes the tectonic history of the district, its hydrogeology and its geology-based economic potential.

D1615437

Cover photograph
Belton House, now in the care of the National Trust, was built in the 17th century using Lincolnshire Limestone. The Limestone has been worked along its crop in Lincolnshire and Leicestershire since Roman times, providing material for local buildings and was also in demand farther afield, in East Anglia and in the south-east of England. This high quality building stone is known as Ancaster Stone. it weathers well and has good cutting qualities for sculptural work. The stone used in Belton House was probably worked from nearby quarries at Heydour and Wilsden MN 27979. (Photograph taken by P A Tod with permission of the National Trust.)

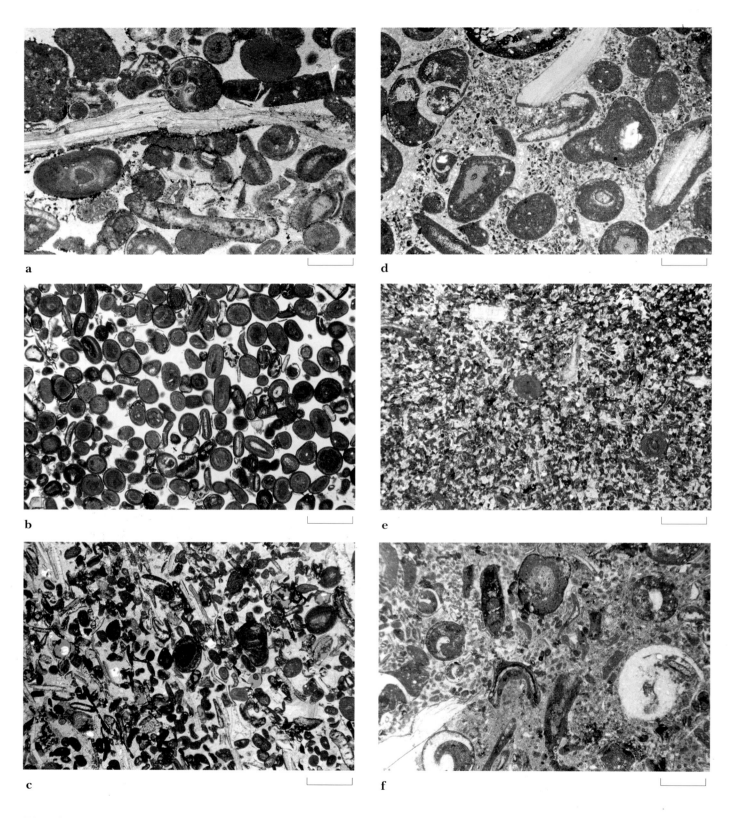

Plate 1   Lincolnshire Limestone Formation. Selection of photomicrographs illustrating some typical lithologies of the formation. All thin sections stained for calcite (pink), ferroan calcite to dolomite (shades of purple and blue) and voids (clear blue dyed impregnation medium). All sections seen in plane-polarised light to a common magnification: scale bar represents 1 mm. (See p.viii for detailed description.)

Petrography and photography by G K Lott.

BRITISH GEOLOGICAL SURVEY

N G BERRIDGE
J PATTISON
M D A SAMUEL
A BRANDON
A S HOWARD
T C PHARAOH
N J RILEY

Geology of the Grantham district

Memoir for 1:50 000 Geological Sheet 127
(England and Wales)

CONTRIBUTORS

Clay mineralogy
C J Mitchell

Economic geology
P M Harris

Engineering geology
A Forster

Geophysics
Z K Dabek

*Hydrocarbons and
geothermal energy*
D W Holliday

Hydrogeology
J Davies

Petrography
G K Lott

Stratigraphy
K Ambrose
B M Cox
H C Ivimey-Cook
J B Riding
M G Sumbler
G Warrington
C N Waters
I P Wilkinson
S R Young

In memory of
Madeleine Dorothy Anne Samuel
1949–1996

London: The Stationery Office   1999

ISBN 0 11 884530 6

Bibliographical reference

BERRIDGE, N G, PATTISON, J, SAMUEL, M D A, BRANDON, A, HOWARD, A S, PHARAOH, T C, and RILEY, N J. 1999. Geology of the Grantham district. *Memoir of the British Geological Survey*, Sheet 127 (England and Wales).

Authors

N G Berridge, BSc, PhD
J Pattison, MSc
M D A Samuel, BSc
A Brandon, BSc, PhD
A S Howard, BSc, PhD
T C Pharaoh, BSc, PhD
N J Riley, BSc, PhD
British Geological Survey, Keyworth

Contributors

B M Cox, BSc, PhD
Z K Dabek, BSc, DipAdvStud
A Forster, BSc
P M Harris, MA, CEng, MIMM
D W Holliday, MA, PhD
H C Ivimey-Cook, BSc, PhD
G K Lott, BSc, PhD
C J Mitchell, BSc
J B Riding, MSc, PhD
M G Sumbler, MA
G Warrington, DSc
C N Waters, BSc, PhD
I P Wilkinson, BSc, PhD
S R Young, BSc, PhD
British Geological Survey, Keyworth

J Davies, BSc
British Geological Survey, Wallingford

Other publications of the Survey dealing with this district and adjoining districts

BOOKS

Memoirs
Geology of the country around Ollerton (Sheet 113), 1967
Geology of the Nottingham district (Sheet 126), in preparation.

British Regional Geology
Eastern England from the Tees to The Wash (2nd edition)

Mineral Assessment Reports
No. 20 Newark upon Trent, east SK85, 1976
No. 27 Lincoln, west and south SK95, 96, 97, 1977

MAPS

1:1 000 000
Solid (pre-Quaternary) geology, Sheet 2
Pre-Permian geology of the United Kingdom (south)

1:625 000
Geological map of Great Britain (solid) Sheet 2, 3rd edition, 1979
Quaternary geology of the United Kingdom, South, 1977
Bouguer gravity anomaly map of the British Isles, Southern Sheet, 1986
Aeromagnetic map of Great Britain, Sheet 2, 1965

1:126 720
Hydrogeological map of north and east Lincolnshire, 1967

1:63 360 or 1:50 000
Sheet 113 (Ollerton) 1966
Sheet 114 (Lincoln) (Provisional) 1973
Sheet 115(Horncastle) (Provisional) 1993
Sheet 126 (Nottingham) 1997
Sheet 142 (Melton Mowbray) 1976
Sheet 143 (Bourne) 1964
Sheet 144 (Spalding) 1992

Printed in the UK for The Stationery Office
J89713   C6   8/99

CONTENTS

PREFACE

In 1990, the British Geological Survey embarked upon a major programme of geologically surveying (or resurveying) Britain in order to bring the standard of mapping up to the level of detail and precision that will be required in the next century. This is a long-term programme, extending over 15 years; it is also an expensive programme. More important however is that it is a very cost-effective programme in that it will enable government at all levels, together with the private sector, to sensibly plan for future land use.

The Grantham district is part of the rural north-east Midlands of England, lying mainly in south-west Lincolnshire and including parts of Nottinghamshire and Leicestershire. The economy is primarily based on agriculture which is strongly dependent upon geological factors. In addition there are significant mineral resources. Building stone is exploited within the district, there are potential resources of aggregate and abundant clay in the Lower Lias which is suitable for brick-making and has been used in the past. The Marlstone Rock and Northampton Sand formations have been worked for ironstone, but quality and accessibility put them out of economic consideration at present. The hydrocarbon potential has been investigated using seismic reflection techniques and deep drilling.

This memoir describes the surface and subsurface rocks and deals with geological structure. A particularly detailed account is given of the Lias Group, interest in which was stimulated in the 1980s by the need to evaluate the Fulbeck airfield area as a potential site for radioactive waste disposal. Geological analysis was largely instrumental in proving its unsuitability for this purpose.

The Lincolnshire Limestone forms the Lincoln Edge escarpment, the dominant topographical feature of the area. The limestone is the main aquifer of the district, and is sensitive to groundwater pollution from agricultural chemicals and landfill in the numerous quarries throughout its outcrop. It is the source of a high-quality building stone, the Ancaster Stone, which is still worked.

The district is known to have been affected by only one glaciation, the Anglian, but it was later traversed by several major river systems at various periods during the Pleistocene. Each left tracts of sand and gravel; some of these deposits are of potential economic value as sources of aggregate, others are of poor quality or too thin to work. The Ancaster Gap in the Lincoln Edge escarpment probably carried the River Witham to The Wash by a more direct route than the present-day course.

The district is not free from potential geological hazards. The Lincoln Edge escarpment is prone to landslip. Some mudstone formations, particularly the Blisworth Clay, are liable to desiccation contraction, and the Northampton Sand, though very thin, may be above average for radon emission.

Many of the above factors are of possible relevance to farmers in planning the management of their land, to planners in their choice of site or route stability, to hydrogeologists in groundwater and pollution management, or to insurers in assessing the risk factor imposed by the geology in specific case studies.

I would like to dedicate this memoir to the memory of Madeleine Samuel (neé Hughes). She joined the Survey in 1971 where she had a varied career working in hydrogeology, mineral assessment and information systems. Latterly, she trained as a field geologist and surveyed part of the Grantham district. She was largely responsible for the compilation of this memoir. Sadly, she did not survive to see the fruits of her labour. She died of cancer on 29 July 1996, aged 46.

Peter J Cook, CBE, DSc, CGeol, FGS
Director

British Geological Survey
Kingsley Dunham Centre
Keyworth
Nottingham
NG12 5GG

Plate 1

a. 'Blue'-hearted 'Weather Bed' from Gregory's Quarry (cover picture). E66182. [990 410]. Oo/pelsparite (Folk, 1959) or ooidal/peloidal grainstone (Dunham, 1962). Moderately sorted grains include micritic ooids, peloids, bioclasts and intraclasts. The cement is dominated by poikilotopic ferroan calcite spar postdating an earlier fringing cement of acicular non-ferroan calcite.

b. 'Ancaster Stone' from Bed 25 (c.7 m from top of face) at Copper Hill Quarry, Ancaster (Plate 5) [9774 4261]. E66150. Oosparite (Folk, 1959) or ooidal grainstone (Dunham, 1962). Well sorted grains include dominant micritic ooids with subordinate abraded bioclasts. Cement is dominantly non-ferroan calcite spar that succeeds an earlier diagenetic isopachous calcite fringe to each grain.

c. 'Freestone' from Gregory's Quarry (cover picture) [990 410]. E66184. Oobiosparite (Folk, 1959) or ooidal and bioclastic grainstone (Dunham, 1962). Akin to b (above), but showing a higher proportion of bioclasts, ferroan rather than non-ferroan calcite spar cement, some deformation of the micritised ooids and extensive secondary dissolution of ooids.

d. Bed 10 (17.7 m from the top of the section) at Copper Hill Quarry, Ancaster [9776 4259]. E66157. Oopelsparite (Folk, 1959) or bimodal ooidal/peloidal grainstone (Dunham, 1962). Large grains similar to those of a (above), but here suspended in a fine-grained grainstone matrix with abundant ferroan calcite spar cement. The matrix grains include quartz sand (colourless) as well as the dominant calcite peloids. It is unclear whether the spar cement has replaced primary lime-mud matrix (NB27 below).

e. Bed 11 (16 m from the top of the section) at Copper Hill Quarry, Ancaster [9776 4259]. E66156. Biopelsparite (Folk, 1959) or peloidal grainstone (Dunham, 1962). A well-sorted, very fine sand grade carbonate grainstone with micritic, non-ferroan, peloidal grains and bioclastic debris set in slightly ferroan calcite spar cement. Sparse sand-grade quartz also present.

f. Bed 21, 5.1 m above the base of the section in Ropsley Quarry [0024 3641]. E66175. Oosparite-oomicrite (Folk, 1959) or ooidal grainstone-packstone (Dunham, 1962). Comparable with d (above), with a bimodal grainstone fabric patchily cemented by ferroan calcite spar, but the greater part of the field of view shows apparently primary micritic mud.

ACKNOWLEDGEMENTS

In this memoir, the sections on the Scunthorpe and Brant Mudstone formations have been written by A Brandon, the Marlstone Rock, Whitby Mudstone and Oxford Clay by J Pattison, the Northampton Sand, Grantham Formation, Lincolnshire Limestone, Rutland Formation and Blisworth Limestone by N G Berridge, and the Blisworth Clay, Cornbrash and Kellaways Formation by M D A Samuel. Additional information on the Dyrham Siltstone, Marlstone Rock and Northampton Sand Formation were provided by M G Sumbler. The drift geology sections were written by N G Berridge and J Pattison. In the concealed geology section, the part concerning the Pre-Carboniferous geology was written by T C Pharaoh, the Carboniferous by N J Riley, the Permian by J Pattison and the Triassic by A S Howard. T C Pharaoh also wrote most of Chapter Two, with a geophysical interpretation by Z K Dabek. The greater part of the economic geology section was written by P M Harris, with D W Holliday, and the hydrogeology by J Davies. Contributions on palaeontology and stratigraphy were made by M A Calver, M Mitchell, B Owens (Carboniferous), J Pattison (Permian), G Warrington (Permian and Triassic), H C Ivimey-Cook (Triassic: Penarth Group; Jurassic: Lias, Inferior and Great Oolite groups), B M Cox (Jurassic: Ancholme Group), J B Riding (palynology) and I P Wilkinson (calcareous micropalaeontology). The petrography of the Jurassic limestone formations has been studied by G K Lott and the clay mineralogy of the Lias and Oxford Clay by C J Mitchell. A Forster has made a study of the landslips on the Lincolnshire Limestone scarp.

The memoir was compiled by N G Berridge and M D A Samuel and edited by E R Shephard-Thorn, A A Jackson, J I Chisholm (Carboniferous) and M G Sumbler.

Grateful acknowledgement is made to numerous organisations and individuals who supplied information during the resurvey. In particular, we wish to thank UK NIREX Ltd, British Coal, British Petroleum, Enterprise plc, the National Rivers Authority and Lincolnshire County Council for supplying borehole and seismic data and for permission to publish it. The permission of the Yorkshire Geological Society to reproduce Figure 19 from Brandon et al. (1990), and of the Geological Society of London to reproduce Figure 3 from Ebdon et al. (1990), is gratefully acknowledged. We are also grateful to local landowners, especially the farmers and quarry owners, for their cooperation in providing access for the surveyors.

NOTES

The word 'district' used in this memoir indicates the area included in the British Geological Survey 1:50 000 Series Sheet 127 Grantham.

National Grid references are given in square brackets throughout the memoir. The two-letter prefixes have been omitted for the localities within the district: those beginning with 8 or 9 are in the 100 km square SK and those beginning with 0 or 1 are in the 100 km square TF.

ONE

Introduction

This memoir describes the geology of the district covered by the 1:50 000 Series Sheet 127, Grantham. The district lies mainly in south-western Lincolnshire but includes small areas of Nottinghamshire and Leicestershire on its western side. Grantham, on the southern edge of the district, is the largest town, with about 30 000 inhabitants. It has long been important as a communications centre and an engineering town on the main road and rail routes between London and the north. The market town of Sleaford, in the east of the district, has a population of about 10 000. Newark-on-Trent is just beyond the north-west corner (Figure 1b). Apart from these towns, the district is mainly rural, with scattered villages. Local industry is mostly agriculture-related.

Jurassic formations, dipping very gently towards the east, underlie the district. The more resistant limestone, ironstone and sandstone units within the succession have created west-facing scarps, most prominent of which is the 'Lincoln Edge', formed by the Lincolnshire Limestone. It extends from north to south through the centre of the district, as the western edge of an upland area which reaches over 130 m above OD in the south and 90 m in the north. It is breached only by the 'Ancaster Gap', a winding, but generally west–east-aligned valley extending from near the village of that name to the town of Sleaford. Immediately west of the Lincoln Edge is a parallel scarp, which is less continuous, but only slightly less prominent, formed by the Marlstone Rock. Between it and the western edge of the district is a lowland area,

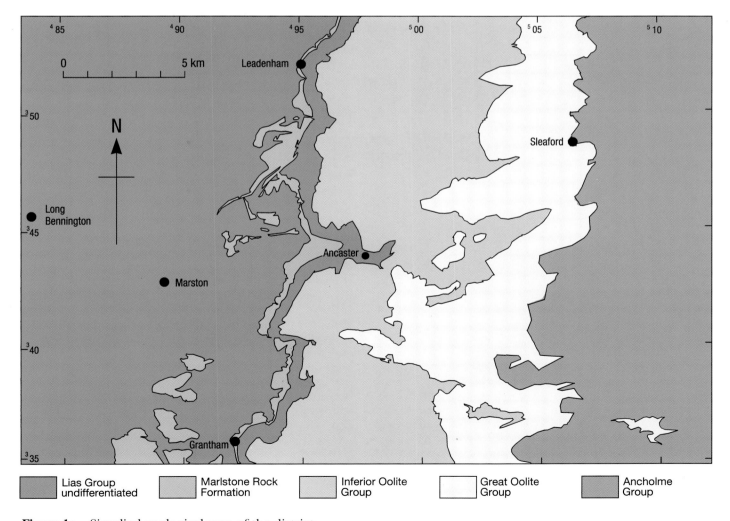

Lias Group undifferentiated   Marlstone Rock Formation   Inferior Oolite Group   Great Oolite Group   Ancholme Group

Figure 1a Simplied geological map of the district.

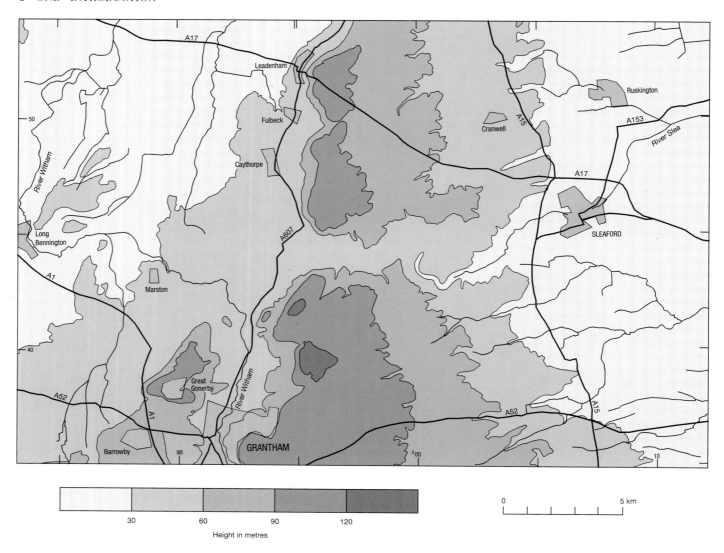

Figure 1b Topographical map of the district.

at about 14 to 50 m above OD, underlain by the Lower Jurassic Brant and Scunthorpe Mudstone formations. This plain is diversified by low scarps formed by thin limestones and sandstones within these formations, and by belts of country underlain by the sand and gravel of river terrace deposits.

From Lincoln Edge, the high heathland formed by the dip slope of the Lincolnshire Limestone slopes gently eastward. Farther east, that formation is overlain by younger strata, mainly comprising mudstones, limestones and sandstones, as the level of the ground gradually falls to between 9 and 21 m near the eastern edge of the district. This area is mostly underlain by the Oxford Clay and borders the Lincolnshire Fenland. The drift here includes broad spreads of sand and gravel, glacial till capping low hills, and some peat in the north-east of the district where the ground falls to about 3 m above OD.

Almost the whole district is drained by the River Witham and its tributaries. That river's famously erratic course enters the district at Grantham; it flows for 7 km

to Barkston before turning to a generally westward direction for 12 km to Long Bennington and then roughly north-north-eastwards for a further 12 km to leave the district at Beckingham. From there, the river follows a long loop to the north and east, passing through the Lincoln Edge at Lincoln. Locally, the principal tributaries of the Witham are the Foston Beck and River Brant, which flow northwards across the Lias deposits in the west, and the River Slea, which drains the Ancaster Gap and flows eastwards to Sleaford and beyond to join the lower Witham. A small part of the south-western corner of the district is drained by the River Devon, a tributary of the River Trent.

The dominant land-use in the district, as elsewhere in Lincolnshire, is arable farming with wheat, barley, oil-seed rape and sugar beet as the dominant crops; potatoes and pulses, especially peas, are also common. There were several Second World War airfields in the district, most of them now disused, but Cranwell College, the RAF officer training centre, remains.

The principal mineral workings locally have been of ironstone from the Marlstone Rock, brick clay from both the Brant Mudstone and Oxford Clay formations, and aggregate and building stone from the Lincolnshire Limestone. The latter, notably from the Ancaster area, has yielded stone for the construction of many buildings in Lincolnshire and beyond, including the handsome high-spired churches which are a characteristic feature of the local landscape. The Lincolnshire Limestone is also an important source of groundwater for the eastern part of the district.

HISTORY OF RESEARCH

Early references to the local geology include William Smith's geological map of Lincolnshire (1821) and papers by the Reverend P B Brodie (1850, 1875), largely about the Jurassic rocks around Grantham. The primary geological survey in the region took place during the 1870s and 1880s. The resulting map for this district, produced by W H Holloway, S B J Skertchly, W H Penning, J W Judd, W H Dalton and A J Jukes-Browne, was published at a scale of one inch to the mile on (Old Series) geological Sheet 70 in 1886. An accompanying memoir (Jukes-Browne, 1885), and the memoir for the adjacent district to the south (Judd, 1875), established many of the Jurassic formational names still in use.

Early in this century the Lias of the region, and Lias sections in this district, were described by Trueman (1918 and 1917 respectively). From about the same time a local amateur geologist, Henry Preston, who helped to establish the Grantham museum, collected material for it from both the Jurassic strata and Quaternary gravels.

The Geological Survey returned to the district during the Second World War, when D A Wray, F B A Welch and W D Evans resurveyed the Marlstone Rock and Northampton Sand outcrops as part of a national assessment of ironstone resources. The resulting memoirs (Hollingworth and Taylor, 1951 and Whitehead et al., 1952) published details of local sections.

Just after the war, the first drilling of deep boreholes in the region took place to investigate the possible easterly extension, into Lincolnshire, of the Nottinghamshire coal and oil fields. These boreholes and the associated geophysical investigations provided much information about the deep geology of the region (Falcon and Kent, 1960; Howitt and Brunstrom, 1966; Kent, 1967 and 1968a).

P E (later Sir Peter) Kent combined his professional interests as an oil geologist with a life-long personal study of the Jurassic rocks at outcrop in Lincolnshire. He published many papers on individual sections and boreholes as well as descriptions of the Lincolnshire Limestone (1966) and the Grantham Formation (1975). He also co-authored 'The geology of Lincolnshire' (Swinnerton and Kent, 1949; 1976), wrote a new Survey regional guide of Eastern England (Kent, 1980) and contributed to a review of East Midlands geology (Sylvester-Bradley and Ford, 1968).

A partial revision of the Lincolnshire Limestone in the northern part of the district was undertaken by W D Evans in 1952, and of the Marlstone Rock outcrop by V Wilson in 1954, and six-inch to one-mile maps along the southern edge of the district were revised by R B Wilson in 1952 and by R J Wyatt in 1961 and 1969. The results of these and the previous resurveys, together with revisions of the Lower Lias stratigraphy by P E Kent, were incorporated in a revised edition of the 1:50 000 scale geological map for the district, compiled by P M Allen and published in 1972.

More recent studies of the Jurassic of the district include works on the Lincolnshire Limestone (Ashton, 1980) and the Lias (Brandon et al., 1990). The usefulness of geophysical borehole logs in correlating Upper Jurassic sequences in Lincolnshire has been demonstrated by Penn et al. (1986).

A leading figure in post-war studies of the Quaternary geology and geomorphology of Lincolnshire has been Professor Allan Straw who has written about both the local glacial tills (1958, 1969, 1991) and the evolution of the river systems (1963). The complex history of the River Witham and its deposits within and beyond the district are closely related to those of the River Trent. Those relationships and the several terrace surfaces and gravel deposits associated with either or both rivers have been discussed by Clayton (1953), Pocock (1954), Posnansky (1960) and Brandon and Sumbler (1988; 1991).

The present resurvey, upon which this memoir and the accompanying 1:50 000 scale geological map are based, commenced with the mapping, at the six-inch scale, of the south-east corner of the district by T P Fletcher and J H Powell in 1978. It continued in 1986–87, with the NIREX-funded resurvey, by A Brandon and M G Sumbler at the 1:10 000 scale, of the area around Fulbeck airfield. The rest of the district, except for the western margin, was resurveyed at 1:10 000 scale between 1989 and 1992 by N G Berridge, J Pattison, M D A Samuel, K Ambrose, A Brandon and M G Sumbler. The western margin was resurveyed in 1992, as part of the re-mapping of the adjoining Nottingham (Sheet 126) district, by A Brandon, A S Howard, C N Waters and S R Young. Full use was made of all archival material, including commercial data subject to the owners' approval. Further details are available in specific papers and reports, particularly in the BGS Technical Report Series (Appendix 2).

OUTLINE OF GEOLOGICAL HISTORY

The oldest rocks proved in the Grantham district are those from Foston 1 and Cox's Walk boreholes, but their ages are uncertain. Foston 1 Borehole encountered metasedimentary slaty siltstone, and Cox's Walk Borehole proved altered andesite and dacite lava with a composition typical of mature volcanic arcs. It is not certain whether these are Precambrian Charnian rocks, or Lower Palaeozoic rocks which were folded and deformed by the Caledonian orogeny, around 400 million years

(Ma) ago. Elsewhere in the region, tuffs are reliably dated both as late Precambrian and as Ordovician.

The two boreholes mentioned above are both sited in the south of the district, on a structural 'high' where Carboniferous strata are relatively thin. A basin of deposition, the Sleaford Low, lay immediately to the north of this high during Carboniferous times, extending across the district and beyond it, in a west-north-westerly direction. The basin was bounded on its southern side by a major fault, the Barkston Fault, which probably originated earlier and was reactivated in the Carboniferous period. A similar and larger basin, named the Widmerpool Gulf, lay in echelon to the south-west. Both basinal structures were situated on the northern margin of the London–Brabant Massif which existed at that time.

Syndepositional movement took place on the Barkston Fault. Coarse clastic wedges were deposited during tectonically active periods, alternating with the prograding carbonate ramps characteristic of more quiescent periods. Carbonate deposits of ramp or shelf type accumulated throughout Dinantian times, reaching about 2500 m in the thickest part, at the southern boundary of the basin.

The Namurian was a time of erosion in the area, but some sand and mud were deposited locally. This was followed in Westphalian times by the deposition of fine-grained sands, silts and muds in delta-top and river flood-plain environments. These are the Coal Measures. The presence also of steeper slopes is indicated by coarser-grained sands deposited in channels and braided streams. There was some development of seatearths and coals, but marine flooding did not occur frequently in this district, as it did to the north-west. Igneous activity early in the Westphalian included some volcanicity, with the extrusion of basaltic lavas, as well as the emplacement of sills.

Uplift during the Variscan orogenic movements created a more irregular topography and brought further erosion. Locally, much of the Westphalian succession is missing. A second phase of sill intrusion occurred during later Westphalian (Bolsovian) times. Deposition of coarse basal conglomerates and breccias occurred. Finer-grained deposits overlie these, including sandstones, siltstones, thin mudstones and, increasingly rarely higher in the succession, seatearths with some thin coals. Erosion occurred at times, and reddening which is present in the higher beds of the Barren Measures indicates that the climate became more arid.

The district was close to the equator during the Permian period, and appears to have been a hilly desert area with, initially, entirely terrestrial sedimentation consisting of piedmont gravels and siliciclastic 'red-beds' of sandstones with subordinate mudstones. Wind-blown sands accumulated in the low-lying areas, for example, in a basin, possibly part of the Widmerpool Gulf, which is believed to have been present near the south-west of the district. Much of the rest of the district seems to have been occupied by higher ground, so that deposits are thin.

Later in Permian times, the southern shoreline of the Zechstein Sea lay across the district during the first three of the five major depositional cycles of the Zechstein succession. Each cycle brought a marine transgression, covering the north of the district, followed by evaporation of the sea from the shallow basin. The landscape also included lagoons and probably ephemeral rivers and alluvial flats. Upper Permian rocks thicken northwards through the district and are very variable. They include marine argillaceous and siliciclastic deposits and carbonates, and terrigenous deposits such as breccias and conglomerates, sandstones, siltstones and red mudstones. Reworking of earlier Permian sediments is believed to have taken place. Evaporites were rarely formed in this district because of its position at the margin of the Zechstein Sea.

Following the last Zechstein depositional cycle directly to affect sedimentation in the district, the climate remained arid or semi-arid. Accumulated wind-blown sand was redistributed by a seasonal braided river complex which flowed from the west or south-west, depositing the sands of the Sherwood Sandstone Group.

Fluvial sandstone marks the lower part of the Mercia Mudstone Group. Overlying mudstones were deposited in seasonal lakes and mudflats. Persistent beds of gypsum in the upper part of the group may be the result of hypersaline seas which developed in the southern North Sea Basin and possibly flooded this area before evaporating. The mudflat environment thus passed into one of supratidal sabkhas. A widespread marine transgression ensued in late Triassic times and the depositional environment of the Grantham district became lagoonal before passing into fully marine conditions.

The district lies on the East Midlands Shelf, which became established in Mesozoic times as a relatively stable area extending from south of the Market Weighton Block (Figure 2) or 'high' to the northern edge of the London–Brabant Massif, and eastwards to about 40 kms offshore from the Lincolnshire coast. During the Early Jurassic, the East Midlands Shelf was a slowly subsiding area of generally more uniform shallow-marine sedimentation, with the depositional environment primarily one of low energy. Mudstones form the chief lithology for this period. Limestones occur as varying proportions of the succession. Some were formed by diagenetic processes. Others show laminations and are bituminous, suggesting very tranquil and anaerobic conditions. Deposition was generally slow, apparently with some reworking, suggested by phosphatisation of ammonites and the boring of limestone nodules. Some intercalated bioclastic limestones are traceable over much of the shelf area. These indicate formation in a higher-energy environment, with wave and current action effective over large areas.

To the south of the district there was a gradual passage towards sandier facies near the London–Brabant Massif. In the middle of Early Jurassic times, a northerly source of sediment contributed more silt and fine sand to the limestone beds. A break in sedimentation subsequently occurred, with some erosion. An unusual ferruginous oolite overlies this unconformity, and the mudstones subsequently deposited are similar to those below, but tend to show increased ferruginous content. This was probably derived from the north and north-west, where shallowing allowed the formation of lagoons and conditions suitable for the precipitation of iron. Primary bioclastic limestones are rare and very thin in this part of the succession.

Towards the end of Early Jurassic times, a marine regression occurred. Local shallowing in the southern part of the district preceded the deposition, in high-energy conditions, of the sandy limestones and ferruginous sandstones of the widespread Marlstone Rock Formation. A short-lived return to a relatively deep marine environment followed, but local variations in conditions produced variations in the faunas of the Whitby Mudstone Formation deposited at this time.

The Mid-Jurassic was a time of very much less-uniform conditions of deposition, which included shallow-marine and paralic sedimentation and some local emergence. Gentle uplift and partial erosion of the mudstones took place before another temporary trangression occurred. Variable sediments, including ironstones, sandstones, siltstones and mudstones, were deposited in marginal to nonmarine conditions, forming the Northampton Sand and Grantham formations. A marine barrier bar–lagoonal complex was subsequently established, and carbonate sediments of the Lincolnshire Limestone accumulated. These include some siliciclastic material, particularly near the base, and reef knolls developed locally. The lower part of the formation shows a degree of rhythmic sedimentation, and was formed in a relatively low-energy environment, with some indications of moderately high-energy periods of activity. The upper part was deposited in a generally high-energy environment, with a large proportion of coarse-grained ooidal lithologies and much channelling into the lower beds.

A regression of the sea followed, and brackish to marine mud, silt and sand were deposited with a slight unconformity on the Lincolnshire Limestone. The beds show a rhythmic sedimentation pattern, in which a relative rise in sea level was followed by gradual accumulation of mud with local development of carbonate beds, passing up into sediments which supported rooted plants in semi-emergent conditions. More fully marine conditions followed, with the accretion of the shell-fragmental limestone, the Blisworth Limestone.

A further period of mud deposition, in brackish to marine, mainly lagoonal conditions, followed. There are some indications of volcanic activity, the source being probably at a considerable distance from the area, because some of the clay minerals present in the Blisworth Clay are believed to derive from volcanic ash.

A renewed transgression of the sea occurred across the district. At first the water was shallow and the environment was of moderate energy, and a thin but extensive shell-fragmental limestone, the Cornbrash, was formed. During gradual deepening, with moderate terrestrial influence but reducing energy, the mud and fine sand of the Kellaways Formation were deposited, followed by considerable thicknesses of mud which formed the Oxford Clay. The climate was warm, and the area sheltered at first so that the lower deposits formed are particularly rich in organic content, although this was later reduced by increased circulation in a more extensive sea. The fauna was abundant and varied.

Cainozoic inversion/uplift and further erosion subsequently removed all evidence of later Mesozoic sedimentation. However, it is probable that folding and faulting took place later in Jurassic times, and probably also at the end of the Cretaceous.

Drainage would have been originally eastwards, in response to the eastward-dipping surfaces, but later a drainage pattern developed in which the larger watercourses tend to flow parallel to the strike, along softer beds.

During the Quaternary, climatic conditions are known to have fluctuated between warm and cold, but the Anglian glaciation is the only one known to have reached this district. Erosion by ice and by greatly increased volumes of surface water from seasonal melting, greatly affected the landscape, and cut deep valleys. Till, which caps hills particularly towards the east, was deposited during this period of glaciation. Later cold and warm periods have, by their effects on sea level and fluvial regimes, also affected erosion and deposition. Among the products have been bodies of sand and gravel, distinguished by the various levels at which they occur and their characteristic compositions. In the east of the district, layers of peat overlie estuarine sediments.

TWO

Structure

Permian and Mesozoic strata of the district rest unconformably on Carboniferous rocks, and were laid down on the north-western edge of a persistent high, the London–Brabant Massif (Figure 2). In Carboniferous times, the area was part of a basin complex. The history of fault development during Carboniferous basin evolution suggests reactivation of thrust faults or shear zones within the Caledonide basement. These structures have subsequently had some influence on those in the exposed Mesozoic rocks. The Caledonide basement was severely deformed during the Caledonian Orogeny and a penetrative cleavage was developed (Pharaoh et al., 1987a).

A major structural domain, the East Midlands Platform (Fraser et al., 1990) underlies this region. Within the district, features on this platform include the Nocton High in the north-east, and the Sleaford Low, in the centre of the district, separated by the Barkston Fault from the Foston High in the south (Figure 2, 4). The western boundary of the Foston High is delimited by the Denton Fault, in the extreme south-west. This is a southeasterly extension of the Eakring Fault (Ebdon et al., 1990) and shows a significant Variscan reverse throw. The Belvoir Coalfield occupies the footwall of the Denton Reverse Fault and lies at the eastern end of the Widmerpool Gulf.

CARBONIFEROUS BASIN EVOLUTION

The evolution of the Carboniferous basin complex of the East Midlands is now much better understood as a result of detailed seismostratigraphical studies of reprocessed, high-quality, seismic reflection data (Ebdon et al., 1990; Fraser et al., 1990). These studies have demonstrated that Dinantian sedimentation in this region is characterised by alternating phases of rift-related tectonism and quiescence. In the Widmerpool Gulf to the south-west (Figure 2), six sequence units (EC1-6) have been recognised within the Dinantian syn-rift phase, and two sequences (LC1-2) within a late Brigantian to late Bolsovian post-rift phase (Figure 3). Each of the sequences EC1, 3 and 5 show a wedge-shaped geometry, with thickening towards the basin-bounding fault and thinning up-dip, on the hanging wall. Other depositional features associated with this rifting include strong onlap, coarse clastic wedges, drowning of hanging-wall carbonate margins and footwall uplift (Ebdon et al., 1990). They are interpreted as tectonically driven sequences arising from periods of lithospheric extension. Intervening sequences, EC2, 4 and 6 reflect the development of prograding carbonate ramps, typically thinning towards basin-marginal faults (Figure 3). They are interpreted as still-stand, or regressive sequence tracts, deposited during tectonically

quiescent periods. In late Brigantian times, there was a minor inversion event along north-north-west-trending faults (Ebdon et al., 1990). This occurred after the deposition of sequence EC6 and before sequence LC1; the latter was controlled by thermal subsidence. The initiation of the Eakring inversion anticline and other comparable structures dates from this time.

The seismic reflection data available for this study have not been reprocessed and are of poor quality compared to those described by Ebdon et al. (1990) and Fraser et al. (1990). In addition, the borehole control on the Dinantian sequence in the Sleaford Low is sparse. Thus, it has not proved possible to carry out such a detailed seismostratigraphical analysis in the Grantham district. In particular, it has not yet proved possible to recognise the slowly subsiding sequences (EC 2, 4, 6) associated with phases of tectonic quiescence, as recognised in the Widmerpool Gulf. Such still-stand and regressive sequences may be present, but are masked by the wedge-like thickening which occurs towards the bounding fault (Figure 5).

East Midlands Platform

The platform rises gently towards the Nocton High in the north-east (Figure 2) and features the Sleaford Low in the centre of the district. This is separated by the Foston High from the Belvoir Coalfield in the south-west. Bassingham 1 Borehole [9208 6060] (Appendix 3), located 6.5 km to the north of the district (Figure 4) (Fraser et al., 1990) penetrated 478 m of Dinantian strata, ranging in age from Chadian to Asbian (Riley, 1993) and is overlain by 191 m of Westphalian, Langsettian to Bolsovian strata. Regional seismic interpretation indicates the presence of a further 400–500 m of Dinantian strata (probably Tournasian) overlying the Caledonide basement in the vicinity of Bassingham 1 Borehole making a possible total of over 1100 m of Dinantian strata.

Sleaford Low

The Sleaford Low is an asymmetric half-graben lying in the hanging wall of the west-north-west-trending Barkston Fault (Figure 4). It may be regarded as a small-scale analogue of the Widmerpool Gulf. Seismic reflection data indicate that the Dinantian sequence thickens southward and is about 2500 m thick adjacent to the Barkston Fault (Figure 5). Other boreholes within this district which prove Dinantian strata are Gables Farm [0460 4327], Hurn Corner [0907 4118] and Westfield Lane [9199 4172]. These proved upper Dinantian (Brigantian) strata high in the hanging wall of the Barkston Fault. Brigantian strata die out to the north of the fault, and Namurian

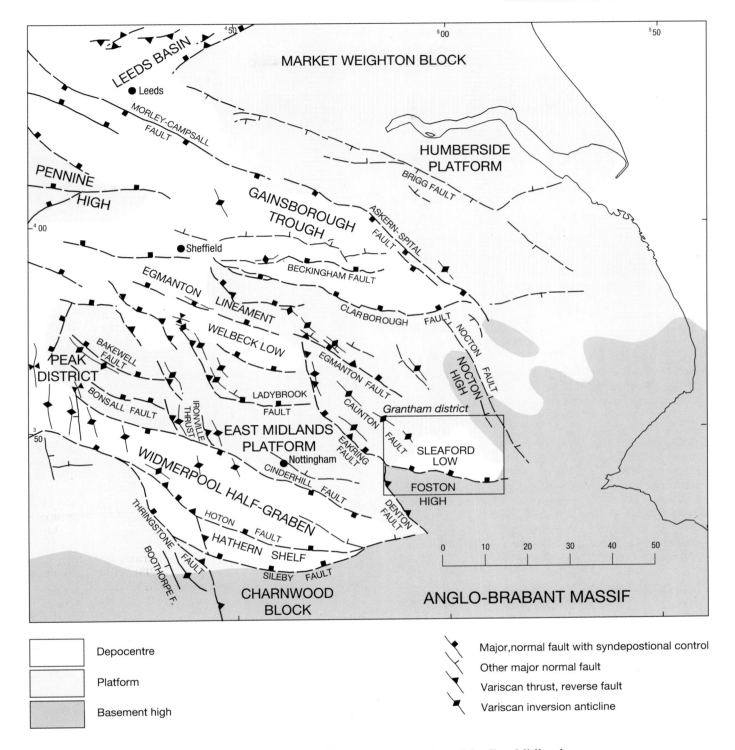

Figure 2 Principal tectonic elements of the Carboniferous basin complex of the East Midlands and eastern England: incorporates sub-surface mapping of Dinantian structures and half-grabens published by Ebdon et al. (1990) and Fraser et al. (1990), as well as unpublished BGS mapping.

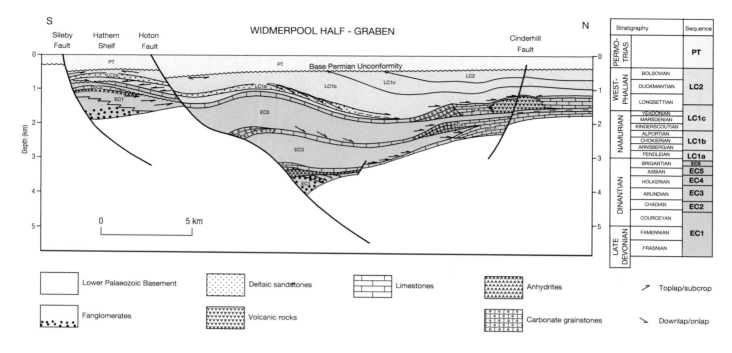

Figure 3 Diagrammatic representation of a seismostratigraphical interpretation of the western part of the Widmerpool half-graben. Reproduced by kind permission of Ebdon et al.(1990) and the Geological Society of London.

rocks rest on strata of early Asbian age at Mareham Grange Borehole [0845 4328] and of Holkerian age at Burton Lodge Borehole [1142 4384].

Namurian strata are absent (or very thin) throughout the Sleaford Low. In the east of the district, a significant intra-Westphalian break (mid-Bolsovian) is recognised (Riley, 1993), and late Bolsovian strata rest unconformably on Langsettian beds; strata of Duckmantian age are absent in Burton Lodge Borehole.

Foston High

Dinantian strata are thinner on the Foston High (Figure 6) and have been penetrated by two boreholes. Cox's Walk Borehole [8411 3808] proved 58 m of Holkerian strata (Riley, 1993), resting unconformably on sub-Carboniferous basement. Namurian strata are thin; only 22 m of late Marsdenian–Yeadonian strata are present. In Foston 1 Borehole [8489 4145] a similar thickness of Dinantian strata rest unconformably on the Lower Palaeozoic basement, and Silesian strata are absent.

Belvoir Coalfield

This coalfield lies at the eastern end of the Widmerpool Gulf, to the west of the Denton Fault in the south-western extremity of the district (Figure 2, 4). Dinantian strata have been proved in boreholes to the west of the district and show that Namurian and Westphalian strata are thicker than in the Sleaford Low and the Foston High. Plungar 8A Borehole [7745 3336] proves the

fullest sequence, comprising 422 m of Dinantian strata, ranging in age from Chadian (and possibly late Courceyan) to Arundian and possibly younger (Riley, 1993). Namurian strata are 124 m thick in Plungar 8A. In Bottesford 4 [7859 3881], Westphalian strata are 470 m thick. Within the district, Stenwith [8335 3683] and Bennington G1 [8376 4157] boreholes prove over 200 m of Westphalian strata.

STRUCTURAL INTERPRETATION

Seismic reflection lines oriented north–south across the Foston High and Sleaford Low (Figures 5 and 6) demonstrate early Dinantian syndepositional throw on the Barkston Fault. There is a marked reduction in thickness southwards, across the fault, and a more gradual thinning northwards on the dip slope of the hanging wall. Other subsidiary faults within the Sleaford Low may also exhibit Dinantian syndepositional throw. This interpretation is based on tracing the 'Arundian Shale Marker' horizon southward from the Bassingham 1 Borehole (Figure 5), and indicates that the most dramatic thickening onto the Barkston Fault, and hence the greatest syndepositional movement, occurred in early Dinantian (possibly Courceyan to Chadian) times. Less pronounced thickening also occurs in the Arundian–Holkerian sequence. Brigantian strata are apparently preserved only in the south of the Sleaford Low, close to the Barkston Fault. This, together with the absence of Namurian strata in the low, suggests a widespread

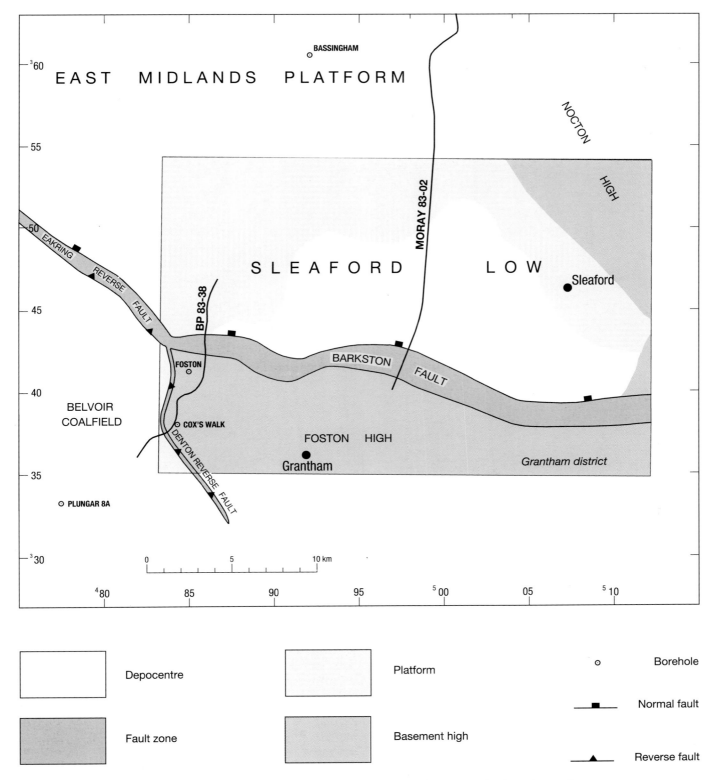

Figure 4 Carboniferous structural elements within the district: also shown are the locations of seismic reflection profiles MORAY 83-02 (depicted in Figure 5) and BP 83-38 (depicted in Figure 6) and the locations of boreholes proving pre-Carboniferous basement.

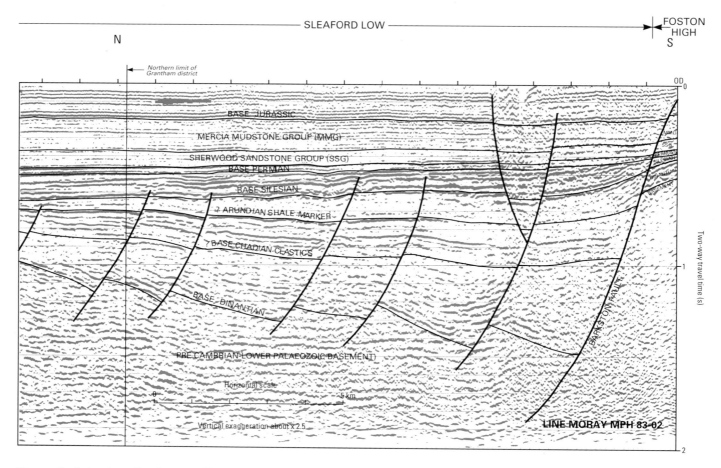

Figure 5 Seismic reflection profile MORAY 83-02 and interpretation (path of seismic line is shown on Figure 4).

inversion of the Sleaford Low in pre-Westphalian times. Further uplift and erosion of the low occurred in mid-Bolsovian times, prior to deposition of late Bolsovian (possible Etruria Formation equivalent) strata, and as a result of Variscan (end Westphalian to Stephanian) orogenic movements.

On the Foston High (Figure 6), lower Dinantian rocks are absent and Holkerian strata rest unconformably on pre-Carboniferous basement, as proved by Cox's Walk Borehole. The absence of Courceyan to Arundian strata is due either to the existence of the Foston High through-out early Dinantian times, or to pre-Holkerian uplift resulting in erosion of the early Dinantian sequence. The presence of thin Namurian strata on this high may indicate that pre-Westphalian (possibly Namurian) inversion of the high was less severe than in the low.

In the Belvoir Coalfield, west of the Denton Reverse Fault, early Dinantian subsidence appears to have been slower than in the Sleaford Low. Relatively thick Silesian strata west of the Denton Fault, as proved in Bottesford 4 and other boreholes, contrast with the thin Silesian sequence of the inverted Foston High and Sleaford Low to the east of the fault. Figure 7a demonstrates the effect of fault-controlled subsidence in Dinantian times with a

maximum depositional thickness in the south against the Barkston Fault. In Silesian times, the depocentre had shifted to the north-east (Figure 7b). Also apparent is the effect of Variscan inversion, concentrated along a north-north-west-trending axis, sub-parallel to the Eakring–Denton Reverse Fault System and to the Nocton High. Up to 600 m of uplift (at base Silesian level) occurred during this inversion event. The Eakring–Denton Fault is probably a reactivated thrust or shear zone within the Caledonide basement.

Most of the rift-related thickening in the Sleaford Low appears to have been achieved by late Arundian times. It is possible that the pre-Holkerian footwall uplift of the Foston High recognised above may have occurred con-temporaneously with the significant footwall erosion recognised by Ebdon et al. (1990) along the southern margin of the Widmerpool Gulf during the EC3 rift phase. Mild inversion of the Sleaford Low prior to the deposition of sequence LC1 in late Brigantian times, and strong Variscan inversion on the Eakring–Denton Reverse Fault System is comparable to the geometry and history of inversion observed in the Widmerpool Gulf. Fraser and Gawthorpe (1990) recognised that the greatest Dinantian syndepositional throws occurred on

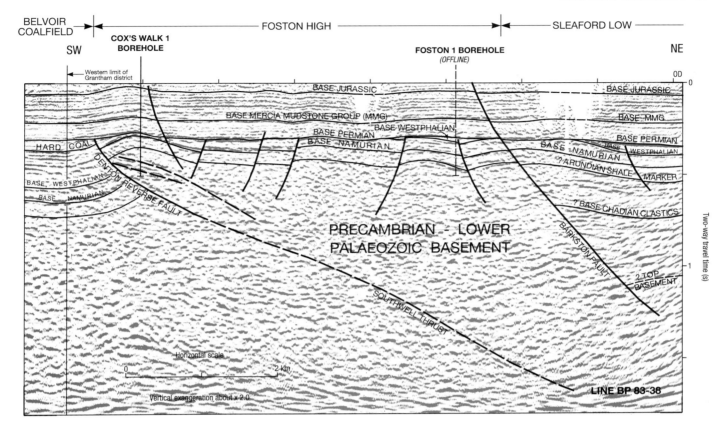

Figure 6   Seismic reflection profile BP 83-38 and interpretation (path of seismic line is shown on Figure 4).

west-north-west- and north-west-oriented faults, for example the Hoton and Askern–Spital faults (Figure 2). In the Grantham district, the Barkston Fault exhibits analogous history. Variscan inversion produced long wavelength inversion anticlines in the hanging wall-blocks of these faults (Figure 3). By contrast, north-north-west-trending faults, for example the Eakring–Denton Reverse Fault and Ironville Thrust (Figure 2), show less Dinantian syndepositional growth and are characterised by shallower detachments and tight inversion anticlines adjacent to the faults, for example at Eakring and Welton.

PERMIAN–MESOZOIC BASIN EVOLUTION

Permian strata lie unconformably across the Carboniferous basin complex overstepping a subcrop of Dinantian and Namurian age on the Foston High, and of Westphalian age in the Sleaford Low and Belvoir Coalfield. By Permian times, the Carboniferous structures were already concealed beneath younger strata and the district lay on the Eastern England Shelf, marginal to the Southern North Sea Basin. Some of the Variscan faults

were reactivated and show minor amounts of normal movement affecting Permo-Triassic strata (Figure 7c). Subsequent to the Variscan Orogeny, reactivation of the Barkston Fault led to the development of an echelon system referred to as the Foston–Syston–Dembleby Fault system, which shows a normal displacement of up to 40 m of Mesozoic strata (Plate 7). Another east-trending fault, lying about 10 km north of the Barkston Fault, with no apparent surface expression, shows a normal downthrow to the south of up to 30 m at the base of the Permian. Some north-west-trending faults show a minor throw of Permo-Triassic strata, but do not affect Jurassic strata. The presence of a low-amplitude, anticlinal structure affecting Permian, Triassic and early Jurassic strata, in the hanging wall of the Denton Fault (Figure 6), indicates a small component of post-Jurassic, probably Cainozoic, inversion on the fault. Most of the faults affecting Jurassic strata have an east–west orientation.

REGIONAL GEOPHYSICS

Regional gravity and aeromagnetic data are available for the Grantham district from the BGS databanks

Figure 7 a. Structure map on the top of the pre-Carboniferous basement.
b. Structure map on the top of the Dinantian/base of the Silesian.
c. Structure map on the base of the Permian.

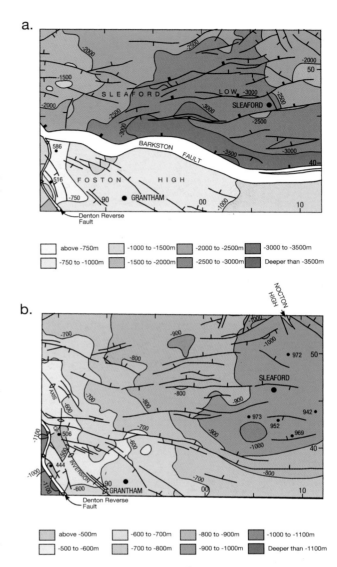

(Appendix 4). Maps based on these datasets (Figures 8a and 8b) indicate the presence of many well-defined anomalies which are related to the structures defined by geological and seismic evidence. The interpretation of these anomalies leads to an improved understanding of variations within the pre-Carboniferous basement, where little other information is available, and also indicate the regional importance of some structures. The interpretations were carried out using physical property data derived largely from borehole geophysical logs (Appendix 4).

Seismic reflection data have been used to define structures in the Mesozoic and Carboniferous sequences. In the area to the west of Grantham, seismic refraction profiles provide information on the pre-Carboniferous basement (Whitcombe and Maguire, 1981).

Main gravity and aeromagnetic anomalies

The Bouguer gravity anomaly field is dominated by highs at Nocton, Foston and Spalding, and by an extensive low at Newark which extends to the east as a trough separating the Spalding and Nocton highs (Figure 8a). The highs coincide with topographical highs in the higher density, pre-Carboniferous basement where Carboniferous rocks are reduced in thickness or are absent (Foston). The Newark Low forms a pronounced feature on the gravity map of the East Midlands but its origin remains uncertain. Evidence from boreholes and seismic surveys (Table 1) largely rules out the possibility that a basin of Lower Carboniferous rocks is responsible and the two main remaining alternatives are a granite or a basin of low-density pre-Carboniferous rocks (Rollin, 1978; Evans and Allsop, 1987; Cornwell and Walker, 1989). If the source is a granite, it will occur in the Grantham district only in the north-western corner at depth. The gravity high at Nocton coincides with a pronounced aeromagnetic anomaly, strongly suggesting that the basement ridge is underlain by a large basic intrusion.

The source of most of the aeromagnetic anomalies will be within the pre-Carboniferous basement, the only other magnetic sources being possible volcanic rocks within the Carboniferous sequence, similar to those occurring to the west. The character of the aeromagnetic anomalies changes across the line of the Barkston Fault. To the south, the map (Figure 8b) is dominated by sharply defined anomalies consistant with source rocks lying at, or near, the shallower pre-Carboniferous basement but to the north the anomalies have longer wavelength or, in the north-west, are largely absent. This change in anomaly character suggests a corresponding change in the nature of the basement rocks across the fault.

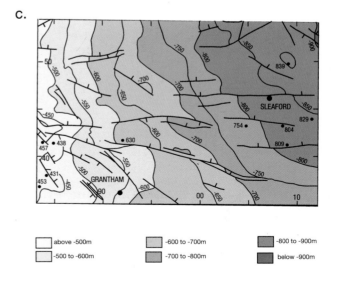

a.
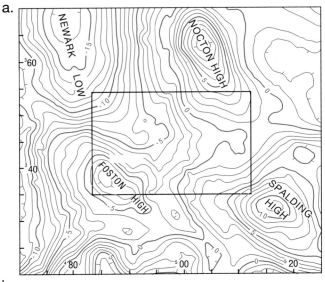

b.
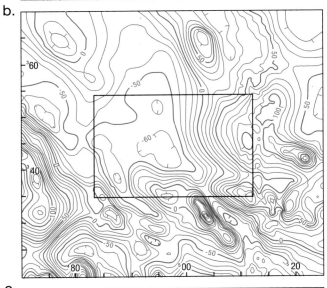

c.
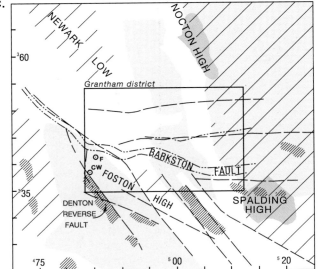

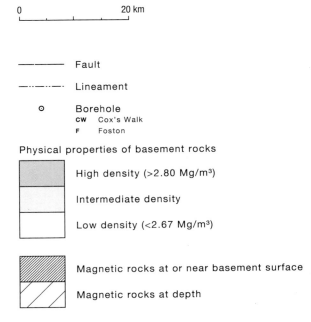

Figure 8a.   Bouguer gravity anomaly map with contours at 1 mGal intervals based on data reduced using a Bouguer correction density of 2.5 Mg/m³. Rectangle indicates Grantham mapsheet.

b. Aeromagnetic map with contours at 10 nT intervals.

c. Compilation map showing main results of interpretation of regional geophysical data.

Table 1
Borehole depths (m) at seismic interfaces.

Borehole name	Redmile 2	Harston	Gt Ponton 1	Newark 1	Helpringham
	[8070 3609]	[8452 3166]	[8940 3053]	[8290 5244]	[1753 3884]
Datum (OD) m	58	105	135	22	8
					245
1 Top Penarth Mercia Mudstone	103	245	324	369	—
2 Top Sherwood Sandstone Sherwood Sandstone	344	472	551	278	579
Top Permian Zechstein Lower Permian	428	550	623	392	676
		568	635	426	
3 Base Permian	475	577	647	523	729
	478				761
Wesphalian	volcs	sills	lavas	sills	762
	646				
Top Namurian Namurian		973	864	707	
4 Top Dinantian		1040	945	733	
		1080	970	745	
Dinantian **5 Base Carboniferous**					

The vertical bars extending down the columns of Table 1 indicate the intervals logged using a Compensated Formation Density tool.

Both the Bouguer gravity and aeromagnetic maps show anomalies with north-west or west-north-west trends, characteristic of the concealed Caledonide structure of eastern England (Pharaoh et al., 1987a; Lee et al., 1991). The data also provide evidence for the existence of geophysical lineaments in the form of linear anomalies or anomaly truncations/displacements.

The Grantham district lies between two broad zones of magnetic basement rocks, also with a general north-west trend, regarded by Wills (1978) as reflecting ridges of Precambrian rocks. The magnetic anomalies in the east of the district form part of the more northerly of the two ridges and extends from the Lake District to The Wash.

Data interpretation

Several interpretation procedures were applied to the observed aeromagnetic and Bouguer anomaly fields in order to improve interpretation of the main anomalies. First and second vertical derivatives of the gravity field were found not to produce additional significant features but the same procedure with the aeromagnetic data considerably improved the definition of the margins of rock units.

The Bouguer gravity anomaly data reflect density variations from several rock groups in the district (Table 2), including the effects of variations in the thicknesses of the lower density Mesozoic cover and in the underlying intermediate density Carboniferous sequence. These effects were removed from the observed data by calculating their gravity responses from the known thicknesses and densities of the rock units to produce a stripped gravity anomaly map. The anomalies remaining should then reflect density variations in the pre-Carboniferous basement; in the Grantham district most of the anomalies apparent in Figure 8a are preserved, indicating the dominating effect of basement lithological variations. This observation is supported by the improvement in the relationship between the stripped gravity and the aeromagnetic data. The stripped gravity data were further interpreted by iteratively varying the densities of the basement rocks with the upper surface of the model defined by the base of the Carboniferous structure contours. The densities calculated in this way vary between 2.62 and 2.82 Mg/m³, and indicate a range of rock types from acid to basic composition.

The observed aeromagnetic anomalies were also interpreted as variations in the magnetic susceptibility of the basement but with the upper surfaces set at 1 km or 2 km below OD. The combination of interpreted densities and

Table 2 Densities of the major lithostratigraphical units.

Interval	Base seismic reflector	Density (Mg/m³)
Lower Jurassic	Top Mercia Mudstone	2.38
Mercia Mudstone	Top Sherwood Sandstone	2.38
Sherwood Sandstone	Base Permian	2.49–2.55
Silesian	Top Carboniferous Limestone	2.51
Dinantian	Base Carboniferous	2.66–2.70

magnetic susceptibilities provides some control on the nature of the basement lithologies.

Results of interpretations

The interpretation results are summarised in Figure 8c. These include a general classification of the basement rocks based on their physical properties and the recognition of geophysical lineaments, probably representing major faults.

South of the Barkston Fault the geophysical evidence suggests that the basement probably comprises a series of blocks of contrasting composition and defined by north-west-trending faults. The intermediate density indicated for the block in the south-west is consistent with that for indurated, possible Lower Palaeozoic, sedimentary rocks, such as the slates proved in Foston 1 Borehole. These are replaced by lower-density rocks to the west and, to the east, by a narrow elongated belt, also of lower-density rocks. These areas where lower-density rocks are indicated also contain some magnetic anomalies, suggesting that if quartzites occur they must contain some intrusions. Slates (?) probably re-occur to the east, but the gravity high at Spalding and the associated magnetic anomalies point to the existence of a large basic mass.

The sources of the linear magnetic anomalies south of the Barkston Fault are not clearly defined; volcanic rocks similar to those proved in Cox's Walk Borehole are a strong possibility, although the location of the borehole lies at the margin of one of these anomalies. Carboniferous volcanic rocks are alternative sources for some of the anomalies. The rocks responsible for the magnetic anomalies are not regularly associated with pronounced gravity anomalies, suggesting either that they have limited size or, more probably, that they have densities similar to those of the adjacent sedimentary rocks. Lavas with the intermediate composition indicated by the petrology of the Cox's Walk samples would be consistent with this interpretation.

North of the Barkston Fault the pre-Carboniferous basement in the east of the district appears to be essentially a continuation of that to the south, but with the magnetic basement probably occurring at greater depth. The Nocton anomaly is probably due to an oval-shaped basic intrusion rising nearer the basement surface over the margin of this deep magnetic basement. To the west the basement is characterised by both a low density and low magnetisation. Slates are considered unlikely, but the possibly Cambrian quartzite proved farther to the north and north-west of the district would be likely to have the lower density required. Quartzites occur at the basement surface at Nocton, suggesting that they must thicken considerably to the west if they are to explain the gravity low there. Quartzites could also be responsible for the east–west-trending low passing through Sleaford.

The possibility that the main gravity low at Newark might have a granite source has already been mentioned.

Geophysical lineaments

The regional geophysical data for the Grantham and adjacent districts are characterised by a series of well-defined geophysical lineaments (Figure 8c), mostly with north-west or west-north-west trends. These correspond in many cases to faults mapped either at the surface or, using seismic data, at the base of the Carboniferous. The Barkston Fault is particularly clearly defined by the truncation of aeromagnetic and gravity anomalies, although its gravity response appears to be smaller than that due to basement lithological variations. Regional geophysical data from a wider area suggest that the Barkston Fault is part of a major lineament at least 200 km long, extending from the Peak District into Norfolk (the Grantham lineament of Cornwell and Walker, 1989; Lee et al., 1990, 1991).

South of this structure the pre-Carboniferous basement of the Foston and Spalding highs is clearly dominated by north-west–south-east lineaments, including the major Eakring Fault. The regional geophysical anomalies indicate the importance of both north-west and west-north-west trends (Lee et al., 1991); the trace of the Barkston Fault reflects the effects of both these structural grains.

North of the Barkston Fault geophysical lineaments are less well defined, due mainly to the absence of anomalies with near-surface origins. However, deep-seated faults with the east–west trends mapped on geological evidence are thought to form the margins of the gravity low passing through Sleaford.

STRUCTURES IN THE EXPOSED STRATA

The Jurassic rocks dip to the east at about 1° and are cut by faults of generally minor throw. The Barkston Fault is traceable across the district as a series of offset echelon elements linked by cross faults. This reactivated, deep-seated fault is termed the Foston–Syston–Dembleby Fault at surface (Berridge, 1993), after villages it passes through or near. Barkston lies above the fault plane at depth, but because of the northward dip of the fault its surface outcrop is at least a kilometre south of the village (see Plate 8). The dominant trend of the surface faults in the district is north-east to south-west.

Minor dome and basin folding is clearly discernible in parts of the district, particularly in the Lower Lias around Stubton, Dry Doddington and Allington. Locally, there is evidence of gentle but somewhat brittle folding in more competent rocks higher in the sequence, in the Lincolnshire Limestone at Ropsley Quarry, for example (Plate 4). There is a possibility that some steep local dips may be related to drag adjacent to faults, for example, at Oasby where the Rutland Formation exposed near the fault shown in Plate 7 dips 10° south-west and 5° north-east on either side of a minor fault adjacent to the main Foston–Syston–Dembleby break.

Some warping of strata may be related to superficial cambering and/or valley bulging.

East of Oasby, for example, an east–west interfluve is flanked by Blisworth Limestone dip slopes to both north and south, suggesting cambering. A more probable instance of cambering is shown along the base of the Lincolnshire Limestone at Lincoln Edge escarpment and, most noticeably (see horizontal section on 1:50 000 map) around the Marlstone Rock outlier from Barrowby to Great Gonerby.

Superficial structures also include disruption by landslip (described later) and cryoturbation processes. The latter include the buckling of both drift and surface hard rock, and the downward 'piping' of surface material into former ice-wedge crevasses. At Castle Quarry, Ancaster [9868 4327], funnel-shaped fissures in Upper Lincolnshire Limestone contain brashy soil and also grey clay, probably from overlying Rutland Formation which has otherwise been removed by erosion at this locality. Fissuring in limestone may, of course, be related to groundwater solution rather than cryoturbation, and this is certainly the origin of numerous swallow-holes that have been mapped in the district. The typical swallow-hole site is in a minor valley in the Rutland Formation, where the valley approaches the outcrop of underlying Lincolnshire Limestone. Good examples are to be seen at a location [9935 4049] south-south-east of Realstone Quarry, Wilsford Heath, and at another location [0101 3633] east of Ropsley Quarry. At Heydour Lodge Farm, north-west of Ropsley Quarry, a swallow hole [9969 3727] occurs where the dip slope of the Upper Lincolnshire Limestone is locally capped by till.

THREE

Concealed strata

PRECAMBRIAN AND CALEDONIDE BASEMENT

The nature of the pre-Carboniferous basement in the Grantham district is poorly known and its age uncertain. It has been proved by two boreholes on the Foston High (Figures 4 and 7).

Foston 1 Borehole [8489 4145], drilled by the D'Arcy company in 1943, proved 134 m of well-cleaved purple slate with olive-green layers and quartz veins, beneath Dinantian strata. These 'slates' were compared petrographically with the greywackes occupying the highest unit of the Charnian Supergroup of Charnwood, and a Precambrian age was inferred (Kent, 1967). The subcrop map of Kent (1967) shows a northward prolongation of the (?Precambrian) metamorphic basement of the Midlands Massif in the vicinity of the borehole.

In thin-section, the Foston core is seen to be a metasiltstone, with a penetrative slaty cleavage associated with the growth of white mica and chlorite in strong preferred orientation, crosscut by a crenulation cleavage (Plate 2a). Pharaoh et al. (1987a) determined a white mica-crystallinity value of 0.22° 2θ for the Foston slates, indicating greenschist facies metamorphic conditions. Although similar mica-crystallinity values were obtained for Charnian metapelites (Pharaoh et al., 1987a), an early Palaeozoic age was inferred for the Foston protolith, as elsewhere in the East Midlands, for example at Eakring [SK 6762 6132], Stixwould [TF 1885 6530] and Bardney [TF 1191 6862] (Kent, 1967), and metamorphism during the Acadian phase of the Caledonian Orogeny was invoked. Geochemical data for a hand-picked cuttings sample of slaty siltstone from the Foston 1 Borehole is presented in Table 3. The sample has a higher content of high field strength (HFS) elements, such as Zr and Nb, than Charnian magmatic and sedimentary rocks (compare with Pharaoh et al., 1987b), which suggests that the correlation with Charnian greywackes proposed by Kent (1967) is now suspect.

Cox's Walk 1 Borehole [8411 3808], drilled by the National Coal Board in 1975, proved 243 m of andesite and dacite lava (Pharaoh et al., 1991) unconformably overlain by Dinantian strata. The uppermost few metres comprise altered rhyodacitic and rhyolitic lavas. The volcanic rocks are well jointed and fractured, show abundant chloritic alteration and are cut by veins and brecciation bearing calcite and pyrite (Plate 2b). Penetrative fabrics are absent and primary igneous textures such as amygdales (Plate 2c), trachytoid alignment of plagioclase (flowage texture), autolithic fragments and zoning in plagioclase are well preserved.

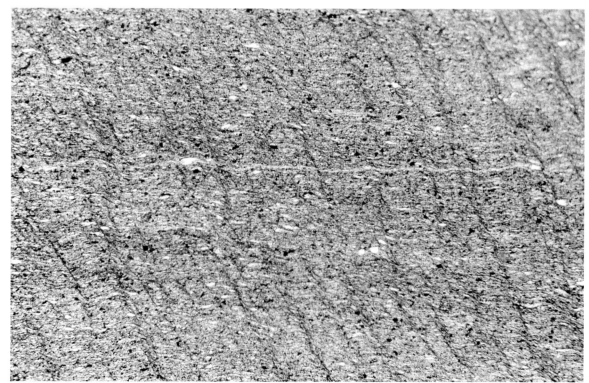

Plate 2 Thin-section photomicrographs of borehole core samples from the pre-Carboniferous basement of the Grantham district.

a. Slaty siltstone from Foston 1 Borehole (E20152). Slaty cleavage (sub-parallel to the long axis of the photograph) is cut by a thin quartz vein and a crenulation cleavage. Plane-polarised light, field of view 3.75 mm × 2.5 mm.

Plate 2

b. Porphyritic basaltic-andesite lava from 643.0 m depth in Cox's Walk 1 Borehole (E47693). Primary trachytoid (flowage) alignment of plagioclase is visible between cross-cutting veins bearing calcite and chlorite. Plane-polarised light, field of view 7.5 mm × 5.0 mm.

Plate 2

c. Porphyritic basaltic-andesite lava from 642.5 m depth in Cox's Walk 1 Borehole (E47692). An amygdale 4 mm long is filled with calcite and chlorite.

The lavas are of basaltic-andesitic, andesitic, dacitic and rhyodacitic composition (Figure 9a) and exhibit a calc-alkaline fractionation trend (Figure 9b). Two of the samples (BLF8511A, BLF8523A) exhibit relatively high content of total iron (>16 wt.%), MnO (>0.35 wt.%) and loss on ignition (>10 wt.%). Sample BLF8523A also exhibits relatively low content of 'mobile' elements such as Sr, Rb, K and Ba (Table 3, Figure 10a). These geochemical features are considered to reflect the hydrothermal alteration of these particular samples. Geochemical patterns normalised to mid-ocean ridge basalt (MORB)

values (Pearce, 1982) shown in Figure 10a exhibit strong enrichment in large ion lithophile (LIL) elements, for example, K, Rb and Ba together with Th, and slight enrichment in Ce, with respect to Nb and other high field strength (HFS) elements. The spread of LIL elements observed in Figure 10a confirms that the content of these elements may have been modified by alteration in basaltic and andesitic compositions. However, the enrichment in Th and Ce is considered an original magmatic feature, and is characteristic of magmas erupted in mature volcanic arcs (Pearce, 1982). The dacitic and rhyodacitic lavas (Figure 10a, ii and iii) show less dispersion of the LIL element pattern, suggesting that alteration is less significant in the more felsic compositions, and retain the Th and Ce enrichment with respect to Nb. The rhyodacites display a depletion of P and Ti which is compatible with the removal of these elements within phases such as apatite and titanomagnetite fractionating from the felsic magma. The volcanic arc affinities of the felsic volcanic rocks are confirmed on the Nb-Y diagram (Figure 10b).

A Charnian age for the lavas was inferred in the original borehole lithological log. However, there are significant geochemical differences; the Charnian calc-alkaline lavas have a much lower content of HFS elements such as Nb and Zr (Pharaoh et al., 1987b). The Cox's Walk lavas have yielded a Rb-Sr isochron age of 466 ± 11 Ma (mid-Ordovician), which Pharaoh et al. (1991) preferred to interpret as the age of eruption, as no penetrative deformation is developed. However, recent U-Pb zircon dating studies (Noble et al., 1993) have demonstrated that Rb-Sr ages from the deep basement of eastern England are easily reset by metamorphic and hydrothermal alteration, and thus cannot be reliably interpreted as emplacement ages. Some of the concealed volcanic rocks (for example, felsic ash-flow tuffs proved in Glinton Borehole [15020 05260], south of the district) are of late Precambrian age, while other occurrences (for example, the tuffs proved in North Creake Borehole [TF 85668 38637] in Norfolk) are reliably dated as Ordovician (Noble et al., 1993). As a result, the Rb-Sr isochron obtained for the concealed volcanic rocks

a.

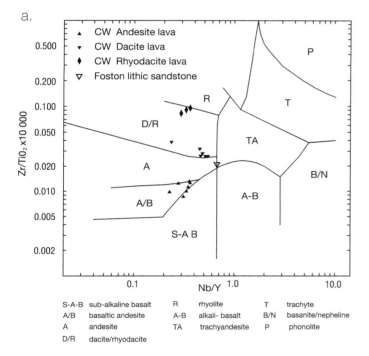

S-A-B sub-alkaline basalt   R   rhyolite   T   trachyte
A/B   basaltic andesite   A-B alkali- basalt   B/N basanite/nepheline
A   andesite   TA   trachyandesite   P   phonolite
D/R   dacite/rhyodacite

b.

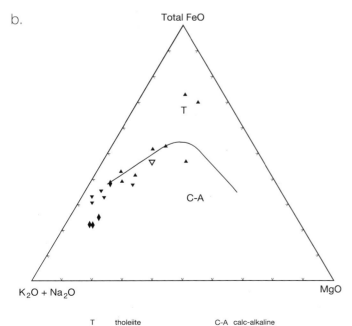

Figure 9 Geochemical data for pre-Carboniferous lavas proved in Cox's Walk 1 Borehole.

a. plotted on the Zr/TiO_2-Nb/Y covariation diagram; field boundaries after Winchester and Floyd (1977).

b. plotted on the Igneous AFM diagram; field boundary between tholeiitic (T) and calc-alkaline (C-A) fields after Irvine and Baragar (1971).

Key

S-A B	subalkaline basalt
A/B	basaltic andesite
A	andesite
D/R	dacite/rhyodacite
R	rhyolite
A-B	alkali-basalt
TA	trachyandesite
T	trachyte
B/N	basanite/nepheline
P	phonolite
C/P	comendite/pantellerite

Table 3   Geochemical data for pre-Carboniferous lavas proved in Cox's Walk 1 Borehole and slaty metasiltstone proved in Foston 1 Borehole.

Sample no.	BLF8505	BLF8506	BLF8507	BLF8508	BLF85Notts	BLF8511	BLF8511A	BLF8512	BLF8513	BLF8516	BLF8518	BLF8523A	BLF8520	BLF8521	BLF8522	Fo2390
Locality	Cox's Walk 1	Cox's Walk 1	Cox's Walk 1	Cox's Walk 1	Cox's Walk 1	Cox's Walk 1	Cox's Walk 1	Cox's Walk 1	Cox's Walk 1	Cox's Walk 1	Cox's Walk 1	Cox's Walk 1	Cox's Walk 1	Cox's Walk 1	Cox's Walk 1	Foston 1
Lithology	Altered rhyodacite lava	Altered rhyodacite lava	Altered rhyodacite breccia	Altered rhyodacite lava	Altered rhyodacite lava	Basaltic rhyodacite lava	Altered basaltic andesite lava	basaltic andesite lava	Andesite lava	Dacite lava	Dacite lava/tuff	Altered rhyodacite lava	Dacite lava	Dacitic lava/tuff	Dacitic lava/tuff	Lithic sst or tuff
Depth	566.35	567.35	568.35	569.6	629.0	642.5	642.5	643.0	662.1	687.4	699.8	704.45	739.7	741.0	743.3	728.5
SiO_2	77.91	79.67	78.63	77.61	65.18	46.53	46.70	46.18	55.14	58.69	64.95	42.20	62.48	62.79	62.89	63.53
TiO_2	.10	.10	.12	.14	.65	1.75	1.18	1.69	1.35	.53	.57	1.07	.66	.63	.65	.83
Al_2O_3	12.41	12.38	12.86	13.63	15.09	16.69	10.40	15.62	16.06	14.70	17.49	12.81	17.21	17.19	17.50	16.75
Fe_2O_3	2.11	1.07	1.41	1.20	5.20	9.94	16.92	8.45	7.74	5.74	3.66	16.46	5.07	4.10	4.77	7.20
MnO	–	.01	.01	.01	.08	.24	.35	.20	.17	.17	.10	.38	.15	.09	.08	.14
MgO	.34	.41	.50	.41	1.80	3.07	3.00	2.10	4.14	.98	.75	4.29	.69	.55	.44	2.28
CaO	.21	.18	.16	.14	2.31	6.96	4.58	9.85	4.45	6.44	2.35	10.40	2.52	3.05	2.32	.67
Na_2O	.11	.09	.13	.26	3.63	2.78	.18	2.75	2.80	4.55	3.04	1.86	5.91	6.13	6.06	2.07
K_2O	2.60	2.96	3.20	3.15	2.30	2.21	2.50	2.29	1.02	1.38	2.93	.28	1.76	1.62	2.15	3.01
P_2O_5	.03	.02	.02	.03	.24	.36	.22	.32	.20	.16	.18	.17	.19	.19	.19	.08
LOI	3.88	3.13	3.40	3.20	3.60	9.75	13.90	10.50	6.95	6.73	3.63	10.48	3.35	3.48	2.88	3.40
Total	99.77	100.10	100.53	99.82	100.20	100.45	100.08	100.11	100.16	100.22	99.76	100.54	100.14	99.97	100.07	100.15
Trace elements in parts per million																
Ba	304	324	399	354	305	265	254	229	116	623	577	108	420	407	465	651
Co	12	12	6	13	12	39	43	29	25	17	13	35	21	16	32	32
Cr	22	242	8	63	27	89	77	78	154	5	23	58	67	9	7	117
Cu	4	1	1	2	5	69	49	97	76	5	7	111	16	59	3	8
Mo	4	–	–	2	–	–	–	2	1	–	–	–	–	–	–	–
Nb	8	8	9	9	12	16	10	14	8	12	13	7	13	13	12	16
Ni	12	3	2	3	7	77	46	49	29	3	9	44	2	–	2	37
Pb	45	31	19	24	4	14	12	8	8	9	5	6	6	9	3	17
Rb	84	83	98	97	77	64	62	60	25	40	84	8	51	50	68	107
Sr	51	59	58	70	82	136	74	137	115	153	126	98	165	215	222	102
Ta	8	–	–	14	–	–	2	–	–	–	–	–	9	7	8	9
Th	15	14	13	9	9	5	–	6	5	6	7	2	70	7	–	–
V	22	8	15	30	46	234	224	200	213	47	54	240	70	70	66	92
Y	33	24	30	7	51	45	36	38	23	25	29	31	25	24	26	24
Zn	95	23	3	115	86	103	59	80	76	70	50	116	67	70	52	78
Zr	–	91	100	51	249	226	145	209	150	145	181	104	173	166	173	174
La	32	25	–	42	9	–	21	34	13.31	–	–	–	30	43	–	46
Ce	–	25	9	16	–	43	87	24	28.46	26	50	41	62	–	34	–
Nd	–	–	–	–	–	–	–	28	14.95	–	–	–	–	–	–	–
Yb	–	–	–	–	–	–	–	–	2.10	–	–	–	–	–	–	–

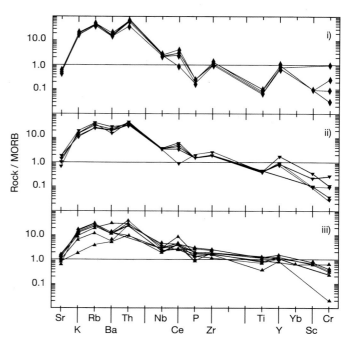

Figure 10a. MORB-normalised geochemical patterns for pre-Carboniferous lavas proved in Cox's Walk 1 Borehole. MORB-normalisation values from Pearce (1982): i, basaltic-andesite and andesite lavas; ii, dacitic lavas; iii, rhyodacitic lavas.

b. Geochemical data for pre-Carboniferous felsic lavas proved in Cox's Walk 1 Borehole plotted on the Nb-Y variation diagram. Field boundaries after Pearce et al. (1984).

Key

VA + syn-col volcanic arc and syn-collision felsic magmas
WP within-plate felsic magmas
OR ocean-ridge felsic magmas

Symbols as in Figure 9

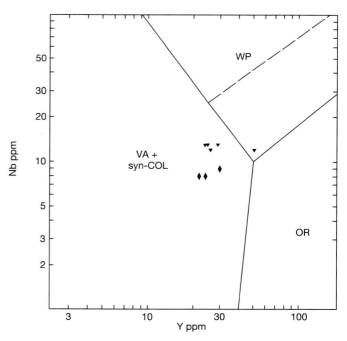

proved in Cox's Walk Borehole cannot be reliably interpreted as the age of eruption.

Maps of geophysical potential field data (Figure 8c) suggest that the pre-Carboniferous basement of the Foston High is compartmentalised into blocks with distinct magnetic and density properties, oriented in a north-north-west direction, and oblique to the west-north-west-trending Barkston Fault which forms the principal controlling element of the Carboniferous Sleaford Low. The north-north-west potential field trend is parallel to that of the Denton Reverse Fault, as well as faults with less significant displacements within the high (Figures 7b, c). The north-north-west grain is interpreted here as the structural grain established by the Caledonian Orogeny, and reactivated during the Variscan Orogeny.

The nature of the deep basement underlying the Sleaford Low in the Grantham district (Figure 7a) is not known. Quartzite and lithic arenite of supposed Cambrian age (Kent, 1967) was proved in Eakring 146, Nocton 1 and Bardney 1 boreholes, which lie to the north-west and north of the district. The trend of the geophysical potential fields in the pre-Carboniferous basement to the north of the Foston High is muted by the thick Carboniferous sequence of the Sleaford Low. As a consequence, the structural grain of the basement in this district is less certain.

The evidence for the age of the pre-Carboniferous basement in the Grantham area is therefore equivocal. A late Precambrian age has previously been inferred (Kent, 1967), on the basis of lithological comparisons between the Foston slates and Cox's Walk volcanic rocks with counterparts in the Charnian Supergroup. Pharaoh et al. (1987a; 1991) have published petrographical, geochemical and isotopic data which appear to contradict such a correlation; they prefer to interpret the volcanic and metasedimentary basement of the district as part of the concealed Caledonide volcanic arc and deformation belt of eastern England.

CARBONIFEROUS

The Carboniferous rocks of the district are entirely concealed beneath younger strata, but their economic importance in coal and oil exploration has provided a considerable amount of information in the form of seismic surveys (Figures 5 and 6) and boreholes. A generalised sequence based on selected boreholes is shown in Figure 11, and correlation of the boreholes is shown in Figure 12.

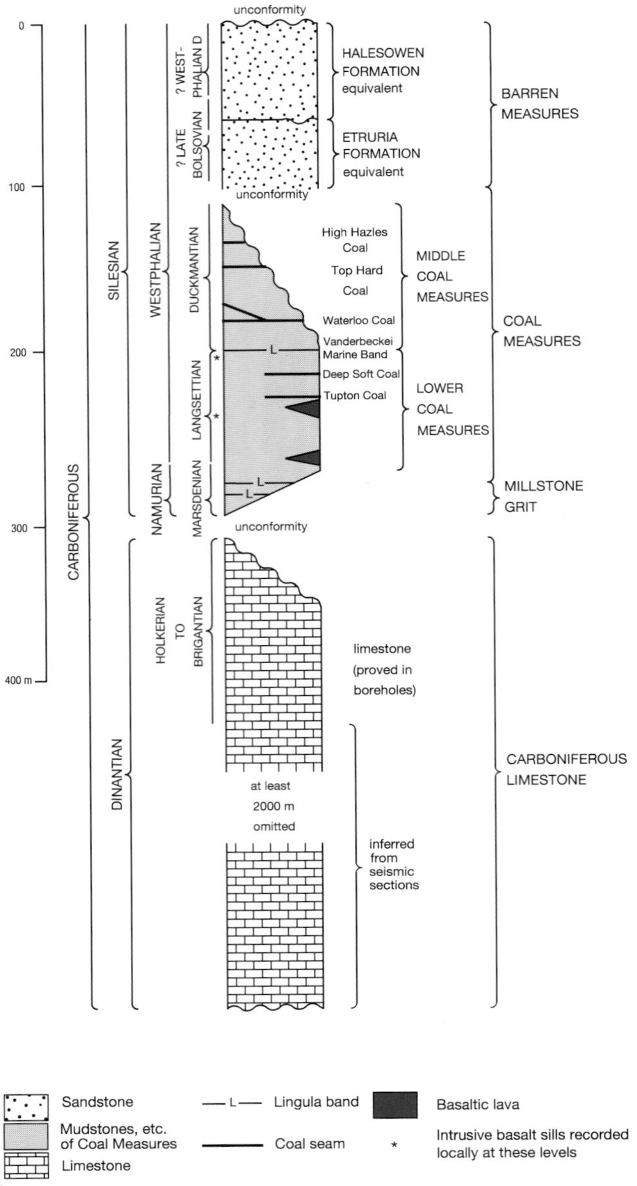

Figure 11 Generalised section of the Carboniferous rocks of the district, based on borehole and seismic data.

During the Carboniferous Period, the district lay on the northern margin of the London–Brabant Massif (also known as St George's Land). As a result, the sequence is thinner than in adjacent areas to the north-west, and contains several unconformities. The basal Dinantian unconformity is developed on a variety of older Palaeozoic and Precambrian basement rocks. The oldest Dinantian strata, the Carboniferous Limestone, are 70 to 150 m thick where proved in boreholes. However, seismic evidence suggests that the maximum thickness is much greater, reaching about 2500 m in the Sleaford Low. The Dinantian sequence is truncated by the basal Silesian unconformity.

The oldest Silesian rocks are sandstones and shales, the Millstone Grit, of late Namurian age, and are up to 20 m thick. They are present locally, and elsewhere Lower Coal Measures of Langsettian age rest directly on Dinantian strata. The Lower Coal Measures reach a maximum thickness of around 80 m and are overlain conformably by Middle Coal Measures of Duckmantian age, with a maximum thickness of 95 m. Only the early Duckmantian Stage is represented; the top is truncated by an unconformity at the base of the Barren Measures.

A widespread unconformity at the base of the Barren Measures locally cuts out the entire Middle Coal Measures. There is some evidence that a further unconformity occurs within the Barren Measures. The Barren Measures are possibly late Bolsovian to Westphalian D in age.

Dinantian

CARBONIFEROUS LIMESTONE

The oldest Carboniferous rocks proved are limestones of Holkerian age, developed in carbonate ramp and platform facies of the East Midlands Shelf (Strank, 1987). Preliminary observations suggest that they are comparable with sequences well known at outcrop to the north-west, in the Derbyshire Dome. Asbian and Brigantian limestones have also been recognised. Strata older than Holkerian have not been proved, but may be present where thicker sequences are preserved, for example in the Sleaford Low.

Ten boreholes within the district have penetrated strata of Dinantian age (Figure 12). Of these, only six have provided definitive biostratigraphical data. It has proved possible to subdivide the Carboniferous Limestone of the Grantham district chronostratigraphically, on the basis of fossils recovered from borehole samples. The Dinantian stage names used are essentially those of George et al. (1976). Riley (1993) has discussed the current usage of the Dinantian stages proposed by these authors, described the various biostratigraphical schemes available, and drawn attention to the problems involved in the recognition and correlation of the seismic sequence stratigraphy proposed by Ebdon et al. (1990), Fraser et al. (1990) and Fraser and Gawthorpe (1990). No lithostratigraphical subdivision has been attempted, although there is likely to be stratigraphical continuity with the outcrop area in Derbyshire, some 80 km to the west.

DETAILS

In Cox's Walk Borehole, limestones referable to the Holkerian Stage were recovered from between 499.75 m and 566.25 m They are predominantly medium- to coarse-grained, pale grey packstones and grainstones; micritised grains and peloids are common. Some of the beds are dolomitised. Ooids were recorded on the lithological log, but were not seen during examination for foraminifera. The uppermost 8 m of the sequence, beneath the basal Silesian unconformity, comprises numerous brecciated and stylolitised horizons with oil and tar bleeds, together with minor sulphide mineralisation (principally galena and pyrite). Brecciated limestone, 0.45 m thick,

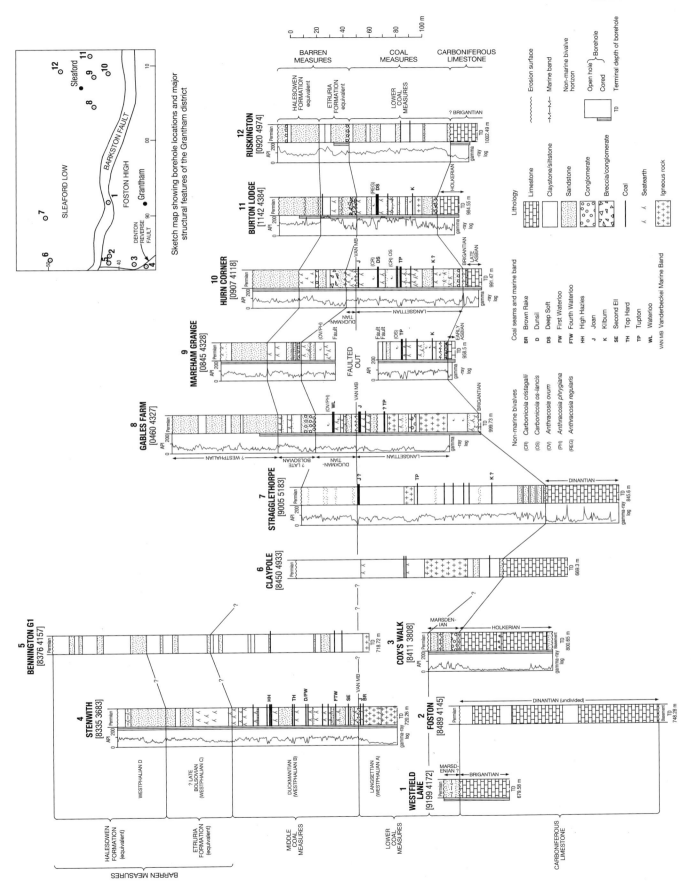

Figure 12 Correlation of Carboniferous rocks in selected boreholes.

also occurs at 530.65 m. The basal bed (3.75 m thick), a medium-grained packstone with sandy and silty laminae, rests on sheared and weathered basement.

The highest sample to yield significant foraminiferal assemblages (528.20 m depth) contains possible *Pojarkovella* and an undescribed species of *Globoendothyra*. Somerville and Strank (1984, fig. 6e) recorded the latter (as *Eblanaia*) from Holkerian strata in North Wales. *Pojarkovella* ranges from the *Pojarkovella nibelis–Koskinotextularia* (Cf5) Zone (Holkerian) to the lower part of the *Neoarchaediscus* (Cf6) Zone (early Asbian). In the absence of other early Asbian guides, the sample is interpreted as Holkerian. Higher samples are not diagnostic, but the paucity of fauna is more characteristic of Holkerian strata than Asbian. Lower in the sequence, at 546.15 m, a good Holkerian assemblage with both *Pojarkovella* and *Holkeria* occurs. The presence of *Pojarkovella* at 565.47 m indicates that this deepest sample is still within the Holkerian. The foraminiferal evidence complements that of the brachiopods; *Davidsonina carbonaria* occurs between 528.15 m and 533.50 m, and there are numerous horizons with *Daviesiella* between 514.00 m and 534.55 m. *Linoprotonia corrugatohemisphaerica* occurs at 559.05 m.

Burton Lodge Borehole [1142 4384] also yields foraminifera of Holkerian age (Cf5 Zone) between 972.50 and 983.00 m; they include *Dainella holkeriana* and *Pojarkovella nibelis*. The macrofauna, of brachiopod debris, is not diagnostic. Minor oil staining is present.

In Mareham Grange Borehole [0845 4328], limestones of early Asbian Stage are present between 952.98 m and terminal depth at 958.50 m, beneath the basal Silesian unconformity. The top 3.58 m are increasingly dolomitised towards the unconformity. Some sulphide mineralisation and rare oil stains were recorded on the lithological log. Two thin sections from 954.5 to 957.5 m are of a medium- to coarse-grained packstone and a medium- to coarse-grained peloidal grainstone, respectively.

The presence of bilaminar palaeotextulariids, together with the dasyclad *Koninckopora*, indicates an age no older than the *Neoarchaediscus* Cf6α Zone (Asbian). The presence of *Groessensella* shows that it is the Cf6 Subzone (early Asbian) that is represented. There are no late Asbian indicators present. Macrofauna is abundant. Biostratigraphically significant components include the corals *Dibunophyllum bourtonense*, *Koninckophyllum vaughani*, *Siphonodendron junceum* and *S. pauciradiale*, and the brachiopod *Gigantoproductus* ex gr. *maximus*.

Hurn Corner Borehole [0907 4118] proved late Asbian strata beneath Brigantian limestones, between 981.6 m and terminal depth at 991.47 m. These are predominantly dark grey, shaly, petroliferous, medium- to very coarse-grained grainstones and packstones, interbedded with a grey to dark reddish brown pyritic siltstone with plant debris. The presence of bilaminar palaeotextulariids, together with the dasyclad *Koninckopora*, indicates an age no older than the *Neoarchaediscus* Cf6 Zone (Asbian). The macrofauna includes the brachiopod *Gigantoproductus* cf. *semiglobosus*, which together with *Koninckopora* suggests a late Asbian age. Also present are the corals *Clisiophyllum rigidum*, *Dibunophyllum bourtonense* and *Siphonodendron junceum*.

In Hurn Corner Borehole, dolomitised and weathered limestones of the Brigantian Stage (977.1 m to 981.6 m depth) underlie the basal Silesian unconformity. Dolomitisation extends to 980.1 m, below which dark grey packstones occur. The coral *Lonsdaleia duplicata* is present at 980.4 m, indicating an earliest Brigantian age.

In Westfield Lane Borehole [9199 4172], an early to mid-Brigantian sequence was proved between 642.65 m and terminal depth at 679.58 m, beneath the basal Silesian unconformity. The uppermost strata comprise a siltstone 0.45 m thick, underlain by 1.15 m of listricated mudstone down to

644.25 m depth. This mudstone contains miospores including *Lycospora pusilla*, ?*Schulzospora* sp. and *Vallatisporites* sp., an assemblage consistent with the Brigantian age indicated by the underlying fauna. Below this mudstone a steeply inclined, fine- to coarse-grained packstone/wackestone, 2.9 m thick, overlies a siltstone 0.35 m thick, which is underlain by a 0.04 m-thick coal on 1.31 m of seatearth extending down to 648.85 m. The rest of the sequence to 679.58 m comprises very fine- to coarse-grained packstone/wackestone with rare mudstones and siltstones. Patchy dolomitisation is common and galena is present in a fracture at 672.50 m.

The presence of the foraminiferan *Janischewskina* at 645.22 m indicates an age no older than the base of the Cf6δ Foraminiferal Subzone (P1c Ammonoid Subzone). There are no late Brigantian markers so a mid-Brigantian (P1c–P2a ammonoid subzones) age is likely. Below this depth no Brigantian foraminiferal markers are present; however, the consistent lack of the dasyclad alga *Koninckopora*, despite the presence of other dasyclads and *Neoarchaediscus*, points to an early Brigantian age in the upper part of the Cf6γ Foraminiferal Subzone (P1a–b ammonoid subzones).

The coral–brachiopod fauna belongs to the *Dibunophyllum* Zone, but from the faunas recorded it is not possible to distinguish between Asbian and Brigantian assemblages. The presence of *Aulophyllum redesdalense* at 653.76 m may indicate an Asbian age for the strata below this depth, but there is no other evidence to corroborate the correlation.

In Gables Farm Borehole [0460 4327], late Brigantian limestones were recovered from between 998.60 m and terminal depth at 999.73 m. They comprise fine- to coarse-grained packstones and wackestones, pale grey in the top 0.7 m but darker below. Thin shaly partings occur. Foraminifera include *Asteroarchaediscus*, indicating an age no older than the Cf6δ Subzone, the base of which lies within the P1c Ammonoid Subzone of the Brigantian Stage. The presence of *Monotaxinoides* ex gr. *subplana* indicates an age no older than the P2b Ammonoid Subzone, which is late Brigantian. *Eosigmoilina* is not recorded, so it is unlikely that the horizon is younger than mid-Pendleian (E1b2 Ammonoid Subzone). No diagnostic macrofauna was recovered.

Silesian

Silesian (Namurian and Westphalian) rocks were penetrated by all the boreholes which proved the Dinantian limestones, apart from that at Foston (Figure 12). Silesian strata rest unconformably on underlying Dinantian rocks. Chronostratigraphical and marine-band classification follows that of Owens et al. (1985) and Ramsbottom et al. (1978). The lithostratigraphical classification into Millstone Grit, Coal Measures and Barren Measures is based on the Stoke-on-Trent nomenclature (Rees and Wilson, 1998).

MILLSTONE GRIT

In this area, the early Namurian was a period of non-deposition, and of local erosion, so that the top Dinantian surface ranges in age from late Brigantian to Holkerian. Deposition resumed in late Namurian (Marsdenian) to early Westphalian times, when the first major encroachment of delta-top sediments occurred. Within the district, the Namurian sequence is very thin and sandy and lacks the well-developed marine bands present in the Pennine outcrop to the north-west. These marine bands, usually identified by their unique ammonoid (goniatite) assemblages, provide the best means of correlation in Namurian sequences; in their absence, dating of the sequence here has relied on miospores obtained from a few sections. Lack of information has made recognition of the Namurian, and identification of its junction with the overlying Westphalian, very difficult.

Cox's Walk Borehole, between 477.5 and 499.7 m depth, proves the only confirmed Namurian sequence in this district. The sequence is predominantly sandy. Significant miospores recovered from 485 m depth include *Dictyotriletes karadenizensis, Mooreisporites fustis, M. trigallerus, Punctatisporites sinuatus, Reticulatisporites reticulatus* and *Spelaeotriletes triangulus*; the assemblage is consistent with a Marsdenian to Yeadonian age. A marine band, from 485.8 to 486.0 m, yielded numerous sponge spicules, conulariid debris, *Lingula* sp., *Orbiculoidea craigii, O.* cf. *nitida* and *Serpuloides stubblefieldi*. This is likely to represent a marginal marine facies of the Bilinguites superbilinguis Marine Band, the Cancelloceras cancellatum Marine Band or the Cancelloceras cumbriense Marine Band. Sandy Namurian strata are probably also present in Westfield Lane Borehole between 628.94 to 642.65 m depth, but there is no biostratigraphical evidence to corroborate this.

COAL MEASURES

Strata of Langsettian and early Duckmantian (Westphalian A and B) age are considerably thinner than those in the Derbyshire/Nottinghamshire Coalfield to the north-west, particularly in the lowest (early Langsettian) part. The majority of boreholes show a basal erosive contact on Dinantian strata (Figure 12). The Coal Measures were deposited mainly in delta-top and river floodplain environments. The sequence is dominated by mudstones, fine-grained sandstones and siltstones deposited as lacustrine, fluviatile or crevasse splay deposits respectively. Thin black shale horizons, representing marine flooding events (marine bands), are poorly developed in this district, as are thin black lacustrine shales with nonmarine bivalves. This is unfortunate because the faunas present in these lithologies provide the fundamental means of correlation in the Coal Measures. Coarse-grained channel sandstones and braided sheet sands occur, as well as seatearths, some of which are overlain by coals of potentially workable thickness. The coals are correlatives of seams in the Derbyshire/Nottinghamshire Coalfield, and the nomenclature used there has been extended provisionally into the Grantham district. This practice is not entirely satisfactory, due to the poor biostratigraphical control noted above, and to the tendency for seams to fail or combine in this district. Correlation is further complicated by the variable presence of lavas and igneous intrusions, and of local oxidation of the coals by late Carboniferous and Permian weathering.

Significant amounts of igneous rocks occur within the Lower Coal Measures. Detailed description is lacking, but these rocks are likely to resemble the Westphalian igneous rocks of the Vale of Belvoir Coalfield to the south-west and the Kelham Hills to the north-west. These were demonstrated by Kirton (1984) to include alkaline and tholeiitic basalts. Burgess (1982) provided a review of Westphalian igneous rocks in the East Midlands. He considered that basement fractures along the northern margin of the London–Brabant Massif acted as a conduit through which the magma was emplaced. Regionally, two phases of sill intrusion can be recognised; one took place during the Langsettian Stage, associated with extrusive volcanism, and the other occurred prior to deposition of the Barren Measures. Despite the lack of detailed description in the borehole logs, it is possible to distinguish between intrusions, which show sharp boundaries on the gamma-ray logs, and extrusive volcanic rocks, which have a less clear gamma-ray signature.

Lower Coal Measures

These beds are of Langsettian age (Westphalian A). The Subcrenatum Marine Band, which marks the base of the Langsettian Stage, has not been positively identified. It may be represented by a *Lingula* band in Mareham Grange Borehole between 949.77 and 951.38 m, which contains *Lingula mytilloides* and *Serpuloides*, and an indeterminate nonmarine bivalve in the base of the band. Higher marine bands are recorded in the overlying 5 m on the borehole log, but no samples have been retained. The nonmarine ostracod *Geisina arcuata* occurs (940.75 to 941.7 m depth) with fish debris overlying the probable Kilburn Coal. Nonmarine bivalves are recorded on the borehole log, but no samples are available. Between 915.52 and 916.45 m, the nonmarine bivalves *Anthracosia* cf. *aquilina* and *Carbonicola* ex gr. *os-lancis* occur, confirming the presence of the Tupton Coal below. Late Langsettian strata are absent due to faulting.

In Hurn Corner Borehole, nonmarine bivalves are recorded from 960.5 m depth, but none have been retained. The Kilburn Coal is thought to occur at 955.64 m. Nonmarine bivalves occur above the Tupton Coal at 924.47 to 924.85 m and include *Carbonicola cristagalli* and *C. os-lancis*. Further assemblages with *C. cristagalli* occur between 911.64 and 911.82 m, above the Deep Soft Coal.

Burton Lodge Borehole preserves the thinnest proved Langsettian sequence. The Kilburn Coal is thought to lie at 948.85 m and is overlain by a nonmarine bivalve fauna. No samples of this were retained. A further nonmarine bivalve horizon occurs between 918.65 and 919.51 m, overlying a coal correlated with the Deep Soft Coal. *Anthraconaia* sp., *Anthracosia* cf. *regularis* and *Naiadites* sp. are present, indicating a late Langsettian age. The youngest part of the Langsettian sequence is absent due to erosion prior to the deposition of the Barren Measures. The presence of Langsettian sequences in Claypole [8450 4933], Ruskington [0920 4974] and Stragglethorpe [9005 5183] boreholes is inferred on general stratigraphical grounds (Figure 12).

Igneous rocks are present in several boreholes, including Burton Lodge (951 to 956 m depth), Bennington G1 [8376 4157] (713.20 to terminal depth at 718.72 m), Claypole (562.05 to 594.66 m), Gables Farm (930.00 to 938.00 m and 954.00 to 974.42 m), Stragglethorpe (682.00 to 690.00 m) and Stenwith [8335 3683] (696.00 to terminal depth at 720.26 m). In Burton Lodge Borehole, the gamma-ray log profile is very serrated, suggesting that this may be an extrusive rock. Similarly in Gables Farm Borehole, between 930 to 938 m, the extrusive nature is further corroborated by the presence of a thin coal and palaeosol within the unit. The lower unit of igneous rocks (954.00 to 974.42 m) in Gables Farm Borehole appears to be a sill, judging from the distinctive trace on the gamma-ray log, as does the igneous rock in Stragglethorpe Borehole. There are no gamma-ray logs available for Bennington G1 or Claypole boreholes, so it is not possible to confirm whether the igneous rocks in these sections are sills or lavas.

Middle Coal Measures

The Middle Coal Measures of Duckmantian age (Westphalian B) rest conformably on the Lower Coal Measures. The Vanderbeckei Marine Band (Clay Cross), which marks the base of the Middle Coal Measures and of the Duckmantian Stage, has been confirmed in Stenwith, Gables Farm and Hurn Corner boreholes. In this district it is developed in a marginal marine *Lingula* faunal phase (Calver, 1968) and lacks the characteristic ammonoid *Anthracoceratites vanderbeckei*. The band is therefore recognised by its position in relation to the nonmarine faunas which bracket it. In Hurn Corner Borehole, a marine fauna is present between 896.25 and 897.20 m depth, comprising *Paraconularia quadrisulcata*, *Lingula mytilloides*, conodont and fish debris. Duckmantian strata persist for a further 8.25 m, up to the unconformity with the Barren Measures. The Vanderbeckei Marine Band in Gables Farm Borehole occurs between 905.82 and 907.04 m, the upper 0.3 m comprising an arenaceous foraminiferan facies, with the remainder of the band containing sponge spicules, *Lingula mytilloides*, *Orbiculoidea cincta* and fish debris. In Stenwith Borehole, the Vanderbeckei Marine Band is recorded between 690.00 and 693.00 m, but no samples are available. In Mareham Grange Borehole, the Vanderbeckei Marine Band is faulted out. In Burton Lodge Borehole, all the Duckmantian strata were removed by erosion prior to deposition of the Barren Measures. This may also be the case in Ruskington Borehole. The horizon of the marine band is probably present, but unrecognised, in the Bennington G1, Claypole and Stragglethorpe boreholes; correlation in the north-west of the district is thus conjectural.

Information on Duckmantian nonmarine faunas is generally poor, but early Duckmantian nonmarine bivalves are present in Mareham Grange Borehole between 892.17 and 892.34 m depth, comprising *Anthracosia* cf. *lateralis*, *A.* cf. *ovum*, *A.* cf. *phrygiana* and *Naiadites* sp., thus placing limits on the extent of faulting. Reddening appears above 884.0 m and the top of the Duckmantian sequence is drawn at the erosive contact with the overlying Barren Measures at 874.70 m. In Gables Farm Borehole, nonmarine faunas consistent with a horizon around the Dunsil/Waterloo group of coals occur between 885.80 and 886.66 m and include *Anthracosia ovum* inter *phrygiana*, *A. lateralis* and *Naiadites* cf. *quadratus*. Stenwith Borehole shows the thickest Duckmantian sequence (96.09 m) that can be recog-

nised with confidence; the youngest Duckmantian strata lies above the High Hazles Coal, a considerable distance below the expected position of the late Duckmantian marine bands.

Barren Measures

In the Grantham district, strata above the productive Coal Measures are inferred to be of late Bolsovian (Westphalian C) to Westphalian D age, though biostratigraphical control is lacking. Deposition took place in a better-drained environment than that of the Coal Measures, in an upper floodplain setting with seasonal variation in rainfall. The sequence resembles the 'barren red' strata that conformably overlie the coal-bearing beds at outcrop to the west, and the informal term 'Barren Measures', used in the Stoke-on-Trent district (Rees and Wilson, 1998) is applied to them. In this district, the base is unconformable, resting mainly on early Duckmantian strata, but in Burton Lodge Borehole they rest on strata of Langsettian age. Intra-Westphalian erosion has thus removed all evidence of any late Duckmantian and early Bolsovian strata that may have been deposited.

The Barren Measures can be divided into two parts, mainly on the basis of the gamma-ray logs. A lower division, with a basal conglomerate/breccia, fines upwards into sandstones, siltstones and seatearths with thin coals. These beds are tentatively correlated with the Etruria Formation of the Stoke-on-Trent district and are thus inferred to be of late Bolsovian age. They are generally 25 to 35 m thick. The upper division is dominated by sandstone, which is micaceous and may represent the Halesowen Formation (Westphalian D age) of the West Midlands (Powell et al., 1992). The base appears to be erosional. The sandstones are generally between 15 and 30 m thick, and show a characteristic 'barrel-shaped' profile on the gamma-ray log. The sandstones are separated by siltstone and mudstone with rare seatearths. Lacustrine 'Spirorbis' limestones, which are a characteristic component of the Halesowen Formation in its type area, have not been recorded.

Erosion prior to deposition of the Permian sequence was extensive, and has removed any younger Carboniferous formations that may have been deposited.

The thickest, well-defined sequences are preserved in Stenwith (84.5 m) and Gables Farm (108 m) boreholes, but Bennington G1 Borehole may contain the thickest sequence (120.09 m).

The Etruria Formation equivalent in Burton Lodge Borehole shows a 13 m-thick basal sandstone resting unconformably on Coal Measures. The unit has several internal erosion surfaces. Quartz pebbles occur, particularly towards the base; the top shows some reddening. An overlying unit, 14 m thick, consists of siltstones and fine-grained sandstones in which two thin dirty coals are present, each underlain by seatearth. The overlying Halesowen Formation equivalent is about 32 m thick and rests with erosive contact on a seatearth. The formation comprises a stacked sequence of cross-bedded sandstones each with an erosional base. Thin shaly horizons occur, and there is some reddening.

In Ruskington Borehole, most of the Barren Measures were uncored apart from the basal sandstone, but the log closely resembles that of Burton Lodge Borehole. The basal sandstone, which is about 13 m thick, is medium to coarse grained, pyritic and bituminous; it is especially coarse grained towards the base. It is overlain by a finer-grained sandstone, about 9 m thick, which contains a thin coal. These strata and the basal sandstone are tentatively correlated with the Etruria Formation. The overlying Halesowen Formation is about 30 m thick and shows some reddening.

In Hurn Corner Borehole, the Etruria Formation equivalent is about 36 m thick; the basal sandstone is about 23 m thick and carries a shaly unit in its middle part. The sandstones are medium to coarse grained, angular clasts of quartz and igneous rock are recorded, and sideritic nodules are common. Some reddening is present. The basal sandstones are overlain by interbedded siltstone and mudstone, 13 m thick, which contains thin dirty coals and seatearths. The Halesowen Formation equivalent is predominantly of medium- to coarse-grained micaceous sandstone and is 34 m thick. Erosion surfaces are present, as are mudflake conglomerates. Some reddening occurs. There are also veins infilled with anhydrite.

In Mareham Grange Borehole, the basal sandstone of the Etruria Formation equivalent is 20 m thick and is relatively shaly, with several seatearths. As in the boreholes described above, the upper part of the formation comprises siltstones and mudstones with thin coals and seatearths. The Halesowen Formation equivalent is 34 m thick, the lower 25 m comprising cross-bedded sandstones with mudflake rip-up clasts. In contrast, the upper 9 m contains only thin sandstones and is predominantly of siltstone and mudstone with stacked seatearths, one of which, 2 m below the top of the formation, contains a calcrete.

Gables Farm Borehole shows 27.5 m of Etruria Formation equivalent. The basal sandstone 11 m thick, contains several quartz conglomerates or breccias and is overlain by 16.5 m of medium- to fine-grained sandstones, siltstones and mudstones with seatearths and a thin coal. The Halesowen Formation equivalent is 80 m thick and is predominantly of coarse- to medium-grained, cross-bedded, micaceous sandstone with mudflake conglomerates and siltstone partings. Some reddening is present.

The Barren Measures sequence in Bennington G1 Borehole is not well recorded, and correlation is conjectural. The Etruria and Halesowen formation equivalents cannot be distinguished.

The Etruria Formation equivalent in Stenwith Borehole is about 50 m thick and lacks a basal sandstone, but comprises a stacked sequence of seatearths with thin coals. The overlying Halesowen Formation equivalent is 35 m thick, the lowest 20 m consisting of medium- to coarse-grained, cross-bedded and laminated, micaceous, reddened sandstones, interbedded towards the top with siltstones. The uppermost 15 m of the formation are dominated by silt-stones, with a pair of seatearths, one of which may contain calcrete nodules.

PERMIAN

Rocks of undoubted Permian age underlie much of the district. These strata were deposited in or close to the Late Permian Zechstein sea and some include biostratigraphically diagnostic marine fossils. Data relating to the Permian part of the succession has been obtained from boreholes drilled in and around the district during exploration of the underlying Carboniferous rocks for coal and hydrocarbons. The Permian sequences in most of the boreholes were not cored and use has been made of chipping samples and geophysical log interpretations to build up the comparative sections and palaeogeographical inferences shown in Figures 13 and 14. The boreholes are concentrated in the west and east of the district, and information about the Permian rocks is lacking for large areas in the centre. Three boreholes which lie just outside the district are included here to allow a fuller discussion of the sequence; these are Woolsthorpe Bridge [8434 3488], Broach Road [9292 5455] and Blankney [0635 5967] (Figure 13). Several seismic profiles are available for the district, but from them it is difficult to recognise subdivisions within the Permian–Sherwood Sandstone succession.

Permian strata in Britain, as in the rest of northern Europe, are divided into Lower and Upper Permian, although those terms are not necessarily used in the same way as in other parts of the world. Apart from this division, no formal biostratigraphical or chronostratigraphical classification has been applied to the Permian strata of the British Isles and surrounding areas.

The Lower Permian strata of the British Isles are wholly of terrestrial origin and comprise mostly siliciclastic 'red-bed' deposits, equivalent to the Rotliegende of northern Germany and the North Sea basin. The strata referred to the Upper Permian include the marine deposits of the Zechstein Sea and those nonmarine Permian rocks which can either be correlated with the Zechstein deposits or are known to postdate the initial Zechstein transgression.

The Zechstein Sea occupied a large part of northern Europe, including north-east England, and four or five depositional cycles (Zechstein 1–5) (Table 4) are recognisable within the full Zechstein succession. The Upper Permian strata in eastern England are assigned to lithostratigraphical groups based on those cycles (Smith et al., 1974), of which three appear to be represented in this district. At its maximum extent the south-western extremity of the Zechstein sea reached the Nottingham area, with the southern shoreline extending eastwards from there and crossing this district, roughly from west to east. The inferred geographical position of the region during the Permian was epicontinental and just north of the equator; the climate was tropical and arid (Glennie, 1986).

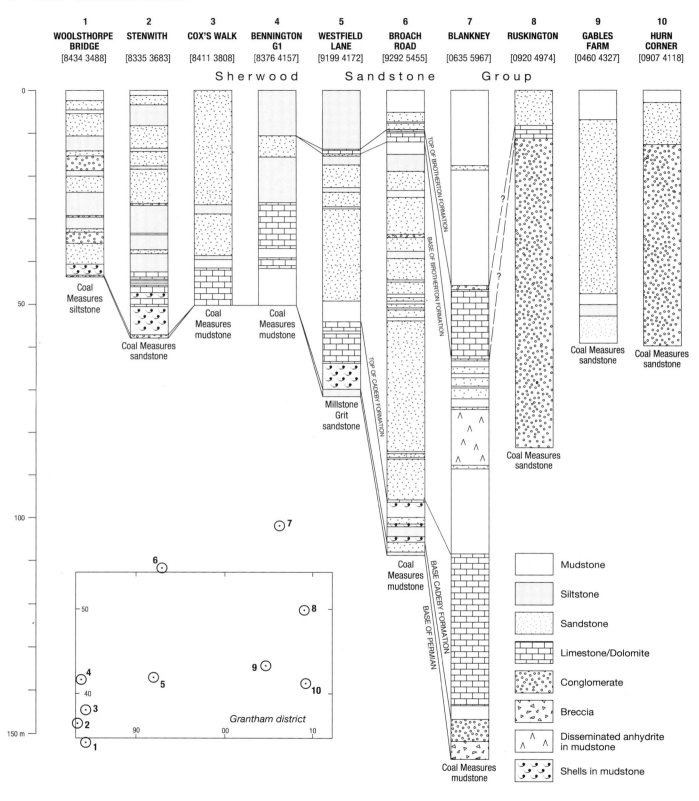

Figure 13 Comparative sections through Permian strata from boreholes in and around the district. (Correlation of strata in boreholes 8 to 10 is uncertain.)

Lower Permian

Basal Permian Sands and Breccias

This imprecise term is applied to all the Permian terrestrial deposits, mostly sandstones and breccias, underlying the marine Zechstein strata in north-east England and the East Midlands. In at least some parts of Yorkshire and the East Midlands, sandstones of this formation are thought to have been completely reworked by the Zechstein transgression (Versey, 1925) and, therefore, have been regarded as belonging to the Upper Permian. However, they are all referred to the Lower Permian here for convenience. It is difficult to distinguish the Basal Permian Sands from Carboniferous Barren Measures in boreholes (as it may be at surface), and where Zechstein strata are absent it is also difficult to differentiate them from overlying Triassic arenaceous rocks. Consequently, estimation of thickness is speculative.

In the western part of the Grantham district, the Basal Permian Sands and Breccias are apparently absent in most boreholes and, where present, do not exceed 2 m in thickness. The unit is not recorded in Stragglethorpe [9005 5183], Foston [8489 4145], Westfield Lane [9199 4172] and Cox's Walk [8141 3808] boreholes. Cores from Stenwith Borehole [8335 3683], close to the western boundary of the district, proved 0.2 m of red-brown, subordinately grey-green breccia with a coarse siltstone matrix. Pebbles are generally less than 10 mm across and consist of 'green grit', quartz or quartzite, and undetermined igneous rocks. A 2 m-thick breccia was also recorded in the chippings log of Three Shire Oak Borehole [8221 4304]. An 18 m-thick succession of red mudstone and sandstone with subordinate pebbly layers recorded in Bennington G1 Borehole [8376 4157] may include, at its top, the Basal Sands and Breccias. Most of these strata, however, almost certainly represent the Halesowen Formation of late Carboniferous age.

In the eastern part of the district, in Gables Farm, Hurn Corner, Mareham Grange, and Burton Lodge boreholes, the Lower Permian may be represented by red sandstones, conglomerates and breccias (Figure 13), but no Zechstein strata are proved. However, farther north, in Ruskington Borehole, about 80 m of red conglomerate may include strata of Early Permian age. The conglomerate is overlain by a carbonate unit, which is likely to be either the Cadeby or Brotherton Formation.

The absence of the Basal Sands and Breccias in most of the western part of the district contrasts with the Nottingham district to the west where equivalent strata, though thin, are widespread and virtually continuous (Howard et al., in preparation). A bare rock pediment with a few localised patches of thin residual gravels

Figure 14 Conjectural Permian palaeogeography of the district.

a. Early Permian land surface before Zechstein transgression.
b. Z1 carbonate phase.
c. Z3 carbonate phase.

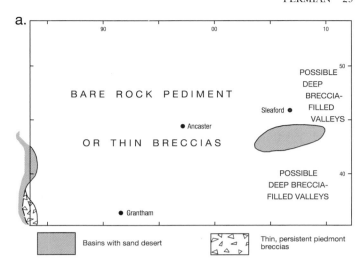

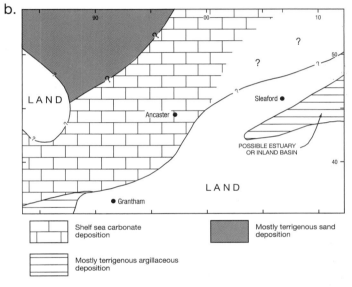

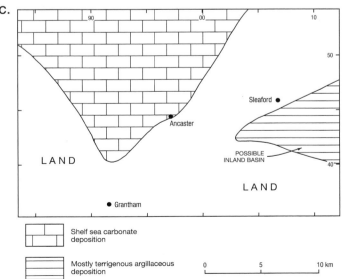

Table 4
Permian
lithostratigraph-
ical divisions
and informal
chronostrati-
graphical
classification.

	Zechstein cycles	Formations (Smith et al., 1986)	Former formation names
UPPER PERMIAN	Z_5 ↑ Z_4	Roxby Formation	Upper Permian Marl
	Z_3	Brotherton (Magnesian Limestone) Formation	Upper Magnesian Limestone
	Z_2	Edlington Formation	Middle Permian Marl
	Z_1	Cadeby (Magnesian Limestone) Formation	Lower Permian Marl / Lower Magnesian Limestone
LOWER PERMIAN		Basal Permian sands and breccias	

probably occupied the western part of the Grantham
district during the Lower Permian (compare with Smith,
1979), perhaps indicating that the area was slightly
elevated topographically compared to adjacent areas.
The thicker series of strata tentatively assigned to the
Lower Permian in the east of the district may include
both fluvial and aeolian intercalations, analogous to part
of the thick, Lower Permian succession of the southern
North Sea (Cameron et al., 1992).

Upper Permian

Upper Permian strata have been proved in the northern
and western parts of the district, where they are at least
100 m thick; they may also occur south-east of Sleaford.
They are probably absent from the southern part of the
district. Wedge-like, northward thickening of the Upper
Permian sequence is attributed to the littoral position of
the district on the southern shore of the Zechstein Sea.
However, the overall northward-thickening wedge is not
simply made up from individual formation wedges.
There are considerable lateral (east–west) variations in
lithology, probably associated with variable sources and
volumes of terrigenous sediments. Correlation of the
borehole sequences is thus mostly tentative, although
four boreholes, Woolsthorpe Bridge, Stenwith, Westfield
Lane and Broach Road (Figure 13) have yielded biostratigraphical evidence. The first three cycles of the
Zechstein succession are represented in this district by
strata variously referred to the Don (Z1), Aislaby (Z2) or
Teesside (Z3) groups. Each cycle was initiated by a
marine transgression and deposition of marine, predominantly carbonate, sediments. The later phases of each
cycle are characterised by evaporites which were precipi-
tated as the water in this epicontinental basin evapo-

rated, and dried out. Within each successive cycle there
was a reduction in the area flooded, so that the Z1 strata
mostly have a wider areal distribution than those of Z2
age and so on (Figure 14). Evaporites are uncommon in
this district, because of its marginal position in relation
to the depositional basin, and the dominance of terrigenous sediments; Smith (1989) postulated that ephemeral
rivers entered the Zechstein Sea in this region. The
nomenclature of Upper Permian strata in eastern
England is based on a revision by Smith et al. (1986)
(Table 4).

CADEBY FORMATION

This term is applied to the predominantly carbonate
deposits of the early part of the first Zechstein cycle (Z1)
in the East Midlands and Yorkshire. It includes the
former Lower Magnesian Limestone of the region
(Table 4) and that part of the Lower Permian Marl
which lacks the distinctive lithology of the Marl Slate,
and is partly older and partly contemporaneous. The
Marl Slate is a thin, carbonaceous, laminated dolomite
thought to have been deposited immediately after the
first Zechstein transgression, under anoxic conditions in
the deeper parts of the basin, and is absent from
marginal areas. The remainder of the Lower Permian
Marl was considered by Smith et al. (1986) to be a facies
variant of the lower subdivision (Wetherby Member) of
the Cadeby Formation. The two subdivisions, the
Wetherby and Sprotbrough members, which are distinguishable at outcrop, are not usually recognised in
boreholes.

The Cadeby Formation is probably confined to the
south-western part of the district, and consists mostly of
carbonate strata. Cox's Walk and Bennington G1 boreholes both proved limestone and/or dolomite at the base

of the Zechstein succession. In Stenwith, Westfield Lane and Woolsthorpe Bridge boreholes (Figure 13), the carbonate unit is underlain by argillaceous strata containing marine macrofossils (equivalent to the 'Lower Permian Marl'; Table 4). In addition, a sample from 544.5 m depth, about 1.2 m above the Basal Permian Sands and Breccia, in Woolsthorpe Bridge Borehole, yielded a characteristic Zechstein miospore assemblage. The Cadeby Formation sequence proved in Westfield Lane Borehole (Figure 13) consists of:

	Thickness m	Depth m
Edlington Formation base at	2.10	612.75
CADEBY FORMATION		
Limestone, dolomitic, multi-coloured (red-maroon-purple-green-ochre-pink); calcite- and pyrite-lined vugs; siltstone bands; *Bakevellia binneyi, Schizodus?*	2.10	614.85
Siltstone, dull maroon, red, brown and grey; with subordinate greyish green silty limestone; *Agathammina pusilla,* gastropods, *Bakevellia binneyi*	0.65	615.50
Limestone, colour-banded including medium grey; mudstone partings; plant fragments, foraminifera, gastropods, *Bakevellia binneyi*	7.10	622.60
Siltstone, grey, pyritic; plant fragments including *Pseudovoltzia liebeana, Bakevellia binneyi, Schizodus obscurus*	6.23	628.83
Limestone, pale greyish green; quartz pebbles; *Pseudomonotis speluncaria, Schizodus?*	0.11	628.94
Siltstone/sandstone, mostly greyish green;	1.49	630.43

MILLSTONE GRIT

In the north-west of the district, the thickest Cadeby Formation sequences are mostly sandy throughout, with only subordinate carbonate beds. Broach Road Borehole, 300 m north of the sheet boundary, proved a sandstone-dominated sequence below a carbonate horizon which is correlated with the Z3, the Brotherton Formation. The lowest 53 m or more of this sequence are inferred to represent the Cadeby Formation on the basis of a *Bakevellia* recorded at the top and further characteristic Zechstein 1 fossils found in the lowest 10 m. The latter include foraminifera, *Lingula* cf. *credneri, Bakevellia binneyi, Permophorus costatus* and palaeoniscoid fish scales. The Cadeby Formation is absent in Foston and Claypole boreholes, suggesting the presence of a local palaeo-high towards the west of the district (Figure 14).

Farther east, identification of the formation is problematical. In Ruskington Borehole, a dolomite could be of Z3 age, but is more likely to be Z1. To the north of the district, in Blankney Borehole [0635 5967], Z1 carbonate unit is approximately 35 m thick and consists of cream and grey limestone. South of Sleaford, in Gables Farm (Figure 13) and Mareham Grange boreholes, the Cadeby Formation may be represented by a thin mudstone/siltstone unit, 5.2 m and 1.4 m thick respectively, near the base of largely arenaceous sequences of inferred Permian age.

EDLINGTON FORMATION

This was formerly the 'Middle Permian Marl' or 'Middle Marls' of the Yorkshire and East Midlands Upper Permian. Like most of the other formation names in both the old and new terminologies, it is based on strata in a largely marine succession where the Zechstein 1 and 3 carbonate formations are present, and consequently can be difficult to apply to the more terrestrial sequences found in this district. It was defined as the siliciclastic strata which lies between the Cadeby and Brotherton formations at and near outcrop in the region (Smith et al., 1986), and consists of mudstones and subordinate siltstones and sandstones, with some dolomites and gypsum. Its age ranges from late Z1 to late Z2 and some of the dolomite beds within it may represent the feather edge of the Z2 carbonate unit, the Kirkham Abbey Formation, which is best developed in east Yorkshire and offshore but probably never reaches outcrop.

The Edlington Formation is, therefore, clearly defined in Westfield Lane Borehole and others to the north of the district, including Newark, Stragglethorpe, Broach Road, Bassingham Fen [9319 5856] and Blankney. In other boreholes where the Cadeby Formation is the only Zechstein carbonate unit present, it is assumed that all siliciclastic strata above it belong to the Edlington Formation, on the general grounds that the older Zechstein formations are more widely distributed than the younger ones.

The thickness of the formation appears to range from about 10 to 40 m in the west and centre of the district. The borehole logs indicate very variable lithologies with dominant mudstone, mostly red but with green mottling in places, and subordinate siltstones, sandstones and breccias/conglomerates which are more likely to be green, yellow or white. Halite pseudomorphs, gypsum, nodular anhydrite and thin dolomite beds are all recorded. In the east of the district, sandstone, described as red-brown and pink-brown, and up to 60 m thick in Gables Farm and Mareham Grange boreholes south of Sleaford, is tentatively assigned to the Edlington Formation. The possible correlative strata in Hurn Corner Borehole consist largely of breccias and conglomerates.

The Edlington Formation is thought to have been deposited in a position marginal to the Zechstein basin after the first cycle marine phase. Smith (1989) considers that the strata are proximal to distal fluviatile and lacustrine deposits, with wind-blown sands, lagoonal carbonates and evaporites occurring locally.

BROTHERTON FORMATION

The Brotherton Formation (Magnesian Limestone) is the Zechstein 3 carbonate unit (formerly the Upper Magnesian Limestone) of Yorkshire and the East Midlands (Smith et al, 1986). It is proved only in the northern part of the district and in Westfield Lane Borehole and consists of cream to buff and grey, thin-bedded dolomite with some wavy (possibly algal) laminae. Thicknesses up to about 3 m are recorded within the district but the formation is about 16 m thick in Blankney Borehole, about 5 km to the north. The formation was deposited in a shallow, hypersaline sea and this district lay across its southern shoreline.

The formation is usually characterised by the presumed alga, *Calcinema permiana*, and the bivalves *Liebea* and *Schizodus*. *Calcinema permiana* and *Schizodus* were recognised only in Westfield Lane Borehole, between the depths 570.40 and 571.25 m. An embayment in the southern shore of the Zechstein Sea (Figure 14c) indicated by the Brotherton Formation in the Westfield Lane Borehole is a recurrence of a feature indicated by the presence of the Cadeby Formation in the same borehole.

A single Zechstein carbonate unit in the Ruskington Borehole, consisting of about 2 m of granular white dolomite and dolomitic limestone, is probably less likely to be of Z3 (Brotherton Formation) age than Z1, but Z3 cannot be ruled out. Mudstone units, up to about 6 m thick, high in the inferred Permian sequences in the four boreholes south of Sleaford (Gables Farm, Mareham Grange, Hurn Corner and Burton Lodge) may correlate with the Brotherton Formation.

ROXBY FORMATION

At and near outcrop in Yorkshire and the East Midlands, including this district, the name Roxby Formation is applied to the siliclastic deposits of inferred Permian age overlying the Brotherton Formation. Basinwards, where higher Zechstein carbonate and evaporite units are present, the use of the name is restricted to strata overlying the highest of such units present. It thus equates with the former terms 'Upper Permian Marl' (Table 4) and 'Upper Marls'. The formation is overlain by the Sherwood Sandstone Group, which is inferred to be largely of Triassic age, but there is no biostratigraphical evidence in the region for dating either the Roxby Formation or the Sherwood Sandstone. The Permian–Triassic boundary is taken, by convention, at the base of the Sherwood Sandstone, although it is likely that the lowest beds of that group in this area are of Permian age.

The Roxby Formation is here regarded as confined to those northern and central parts of the district where the Brotherton Formation has been recognised. The top is taken at the base of the lithologically monotonous sandstone sequences which characterise the Sherwood Sandstone in the region, thus any mudstone in this part of the succession, and consequently any sandstone underlying it, is included with the Roxby Formation. The greatest thickness of beds thus assigned to the formation in the district was recorded in Stragglethorpe Borehole, as about 26 m of interbedded red mudstone, siltstone, sandstone and conglomerate. The formation appears to thin westwards, southwards and eastwards from that area. The lithologies indicate a reversion to the desert basin–alluvial flats environments which prevailed prior to the Z3 marine transgression.

TRIASSIC

Rocks of Triassic age underlie the entire district, but for the most part are concealed beneath younger Jurassic rocks. Upper Triassic strata subcrop beneath thin Quaternary deposits in a small area in the north-west corner of the district. As with the Permian sequence, boreholes provide the main information on the Trias; these are concentrated in the north-west, south-west and east of the district with no data from the centre. Most of the boreholes were drilled to explore for coal and hydrocarbons within the Carboniferous rocks at depth. The Trias was generally not cored, but geophysical logs and chipping samples allow subsurface correlation of the sequence.

Much important data have been provided by the Fulbeck boreholes (Appendix 3), commissioned by UK Nirex Ltd as part of an investigation for a possible site for the disposal of low-level radioactive waste. The cores were presented to BGS by UK Nirex Ltd on termination of the project, and are archived in the National Geosciences Records Centre at BGS Keyworth. Detailed core logging has enabled correlation with the well-known Triassic sequence of the adjacent Nottingham district (Elliott, 1961; Warrington et al., 1980; Howard et al., in preparation). The cores enable precise matching of lithology and lithostratigraphy with geophysical log response, thereby providing an excellent reference for log correlation between other boreholes in the Grantham district.

The British Triassic sequence encompasses three major lithostratigraphical divisions; in upward succession these are the Sherwood Sandstone, Mercia Mudstone and Penarth groups. In this district, the Sherwood Sandstone Group equates precisely with the former 'Bunter' Series, and the last two groups are generally equivalent to the 'Keuper' and 'Rhaetic' units respectively, usage of which has been discontinued due to their mixed lithostratigraphical and chronostratigraphical connotations and passes literally into the Upper Permian units described above (Warrington et al., 1980). Chronostratigraphical evidence for the precise placement of the base of the Trias is lacking in Great Britain. The boundary is conventionally placed at the base of the Sherwood Sandstone Group, although there is strong evidence in parts of Nottinghamshire that the lowermost part of the group is of Permian age and passes laterally into the Upper Permian units described above (Warrington et al., 1980, p.59). The base of the Jurassic is defined as the lowest occurrence of ammonites of the genus *Psiloceras* (Cope et al., 1980a). In many parts of Britain, including the East Midlands, the lowermost beds of the Lias Group (the 'Pre-planorbis Beds') are devoid of ammonites and are therefore, by definition, of Triassic age. These strata are described together with the rest of the Lias Group in Chapter 4.

The Triassic stratigraphy of the district is summarised in Table 5. The chronostratigraphy is tentatively inferred from the limited evidence available for the East Midlands as a whole (Warrington et al., 1980; Howard et al., in preparation); little independent chronostratigraphical evidence is so far available for the Grantham district.

Sherwood Sandstone Group

The southern margin of the Late Permian Zechstein Basin lay across the East Midlands, and the resulting

Table 5 Stratigraphical nomenclature of Triassic rocks in the Grantham and adjacent districts.

Nottingham and Newark district (Lamplugh et al., 1980)	South Nottinghamshire (Elliott, 1961)	South Nottinghamshire (Warrington et al., 1980)	Grantham district (after Charsley et al., 1990; Howard et al., in prep.)	Chronostratigraphy (after Warrington et al., 1980; Howard et al., in prep.)
Lias (pars) — Hydraulic Limestone Series			Lias Group (pars): Scunthorpe Mudstone Formation (pars) / Barnstone Member	Hettangian — Jurassic
Rhaetic — White Lias	Rhaetic Series	Penarth Group: Lilstock Formation	Penarth Group: Lilstock Formation / Cotham Member	Rhaetian — Upper Triassic
Rhaetic — Avicula–Contorta Beds		Penarth Group: Westbury Formation	Penarth Group: Westbury Formation	
Keuper — Tea Green Marl	Keuper Series	Mercia Mudstone Group: Blue Anchor Formation	Mercia Mudstone Group: Blue Anchor Formation	Norian
	Keuper Series: Parva Formation	Mercia Mudstone Group: Glen Parva Formation	Mercia Mudstone Group: Cropwell Bishop Formation	
	Keuper Series: Trent Formation	Mercia Mudstone Group: Trent Formation		Carnian
	Keuper Series: Edwalton Formation	Mercia Mudstone Group: Edwalton Formation	Mercia Mudstone Group: Edwalton Formation / Hollygate Sandstone Member	
	Keuper Series: Harlequin Formation	Mercia Mudstone Group: Harlequin Formation	Mercia Mudstone Group: Gunthorpe Formation / Cotgrave Sandstone Member	Ladinian — Middle Triassic
	Keuper Series: Carlton Formation	Mercia Mudstone Group: Carlton Formation		
	Keuper Series: Radcliffe Formation	Mercia Mudstone Group: Radcliffe Formation	Mercia Mudstone Group: Radcliffe Formation	
Keuper — Keuper Marl	Keuper Series: Waterstones Formation	Mercia Mudstone Group: Colwick Formation	Mercia Mudstone Group: Sneinton Formation	Anisian
Keuper — Waterstones	Keuper Series: Woodthorpe Formation	Mercia Mudstone Group: Woodthorpe Formation		
Bunter — Pebble Beds	Bunter Series	Sherwood Sandstone Group: Nottingham Castle Formation	Sherwood Sandstone Formation	Scythian (Lower Triassic) — Lower Triassic
Bunter — Lower Mottled Sandstone		Sherwood Sandstone Group: Lenton Sandstone Formation		

(System-level label spanning the Chronostratigraphy column: Triassic) lateral attenuation and facies variation within the various lithostratigraphical divisions of the Late Permian led to a complex non-sequence at the base of the overlying Sherwood Sandstone. In the north-west and centre of the Grantham district, (Broach Road and Westfield Lane boreholes, Figures 13 and 15), the Sherwood Sandstone overlies the uppermost Permian, Roxby Formation (Z4 to Z5 cycles), overlapping the Brotherton Formation to rest on the Edlington Formation in the south-west (Cox's Walk, Stenwith and Woolsthorpe Bridge boreholes). In the east of the district, where correlation of the Permian is less certain in Gables Farm and Hurn Corner boreholes, the Sherwood Sandstone may rest on the Brotherton Formation.

Two component formations of the Sherwood Sandstone Group are mappable at outcrop in the Nottingham district to the west (Howard et al., in preparation). The Lenton Sandstone Formation (formerly Lower Mottled Sandstone), passes up into the Nottingham Castle Sandstone Formation (formerly Bunter Pebble Beds) which contains subordinate conglomerate. To the east of Nottingham, borehole chipping samples and gamma-ray logs indicate an overall coarsening-upward sequence within the lower half of the Sherwood Sandstone, but the two formations cannot be differentiated. Similarly, in the Grantham district, the borehole evidence available does not allow separation of these formations.

No single borehole has cored the entire thickness of the Sherwood Sandstone in the Grantham district; Broach Road (Figure 15) and Westfield Lane boreholes cored the lower part of the sequence. The uppermost 21 m was cored in Fulbeck Borehole 1 [8889 5053] (Figure 16). Other lithological evidence is available only from chippings. Thicknesses of the group vary from 170 m in Broach Road Borehole to 90 m in Cox's Walk Borehole, reflecting a regional trend of thickness attenuation towards the south and south-west in the East Midlands as a whole (Taylor, 1968).

The lowermost 6 m of the group in Broach Road Borehole consists of reddish brown conglomerate with a matrix of poorly sorted muddy sandstone. Pebbles are typically 10–50 mm across and are composed of a range of lithologies, including pinkish white limestone, green siltstone, white and brownish red quartzite, and green 'hard rock'. Similar conglomerates occur at the base of the Sherwood Sandstone in the adjacent Nottingham district, and typically display a decidedly lower gamma-ray log response than the rest of the group (Howard et al., in preparation). Gamma-ray logs of the group in Ruskington, Gables Farm and Hurn Corner boreholes (Figure 15) display similar profiles, suggesting the presence of a basal conglomeratic unit. The unit is apparently absent in Cox's Walk, Stenwith and Westfield Lane boreholes, in the south-west of the district.

A further 77 m of strata, overlying the basal conglomerate and representing much of the lower half of the group, were cored in Broach Road Borehole (Figure 15). The borehole proved mainly pale reddish brown sandstone, fine to medium grained, with intraformational mudstone clasts and scattered pebbles. Cross-bedding is common. Reddish brown mudstones with siltstone or very fine sandstone laminae, commonly shrinkage-cracked, are interbedded with the sandstone. The number of mudstone interbeds and clasts decreases upwards through the sequence, accompanied by a slight upward increase in sandstone grain size. This upward-coarsening profile is also evident in the lowermost 35 m of the group cored in Westfield Lane Borehole. In Broach Road Borehole, the profile is matched by a slight upward-decreasing gamma-ray log response; similar log motifs are present in other boreholes in the district (Figure 15).

Chippings from the upper half of the group in the Ruskington Borehole prove red, fine- to medium-grained sandstone with scattered quartz pebbles. In Fulbeck Borehole 1 (Figure 16), the uppermost 21 m of the group consists mainly of pinkish red, medium- to coarse-grained sandstone. Cross-bedding is common throughout, with intraformational mudstone clasts and, less commonly, small quartz and quartzite pebbles aligned along bottomsets. Pebbles are much less common than in comparable levels of the Sherwood Sandstone in the adjacent Nottingham district. Planar lamination is evident at a few levels. A 0.8 m-thick bed of reddish brown mudstone with very thin beds or laminae of pale greenish grey, fine- to medium-grained sandstone lies about 13 m below the top of the group.

The Sherwood Sandstone Group in the East Midlands is interpreted as the deposit of a major braided river complex flowing eastwards or north-eastwards across the region, though with an ultimate southerly (Armorican) provenance (Warrington and Ivimey-Cook, 1992). Semi-arid climates prevailed, with seasonal river discharge. Aeolian sand deposition with redistribution of sediment by fluvial processes has been postulated for the generally finer-grained lower part of the group (Taylor, 1974; Mader, 1992).

Mercia Mudstone Group

The Mercia Mudstone Group (formerly the 'Keuper' Table 5) has been mapped in the adjacent Nottingham district (Charsley et al., 1990; Howard et al., in preparation). This has shown that some of the formational boundaries defined by Elliott (1961), and subsequently adopted by Warrington et al. (1980), are not mappable at surface. Some of their formations have therefore been merged (Table 5) and given new names (Howard et al., in preparation).

In the East Midlands, the Mercia Mudstone consists mainly of reddish brown mudstones and argillaceous siltstones, gypsiferous at many levels, and displaying a variety of laminated, deformed and structureless textures. Numerous beds of greenish grey or grey dolomitic siltstone or sandstone ('skerries') are present, with the more prominent beds marking some of the formational boundaries, notably the Sneinton and Edwalton formations. Other formations, for example the Radcliffe and Blue Anchor formations, are mapped on the basis of distinctive soil colours and textures.

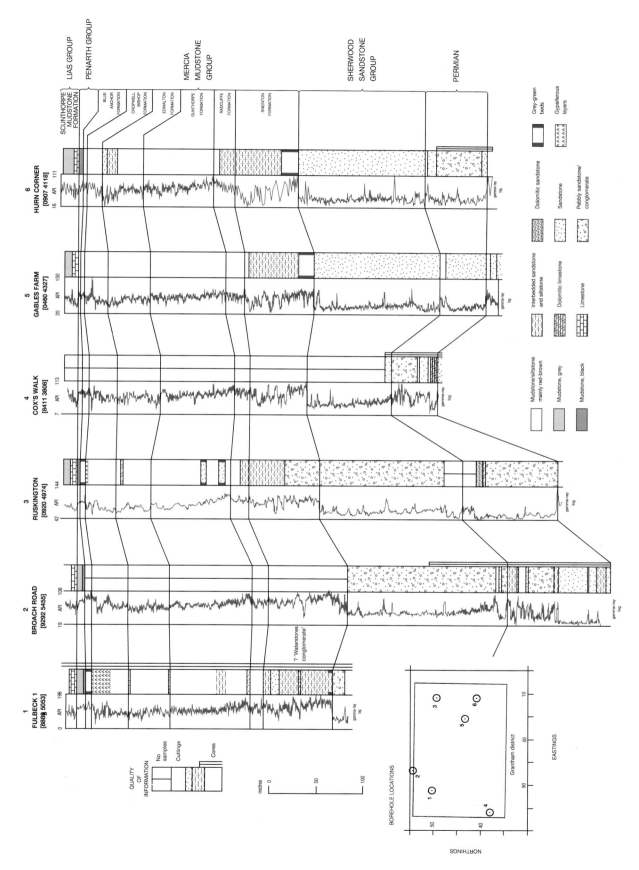

Figure 15   Correlation of Triassic rocks between selected boreholes in the district.

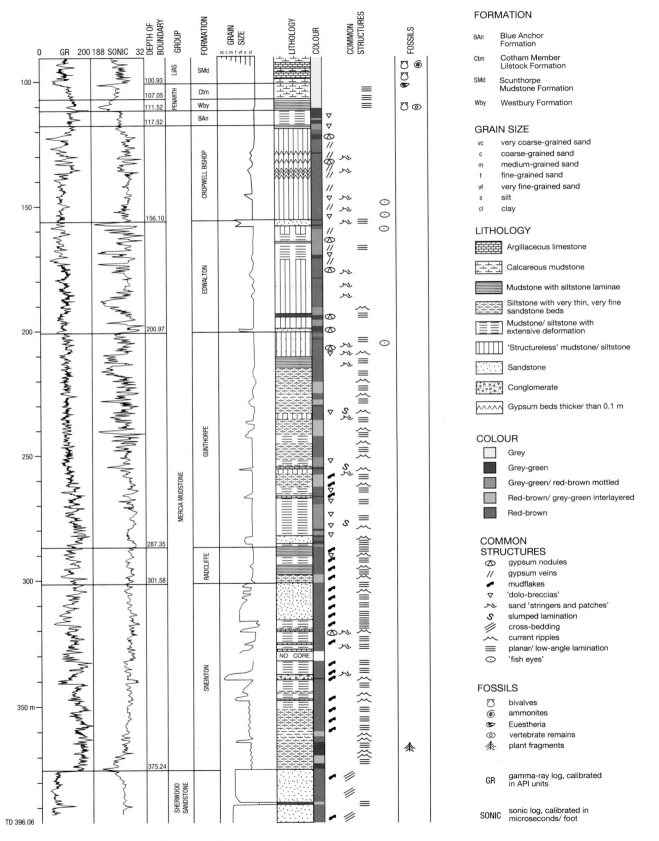

Figure 16 Detailed logs of Fulbeck Borehole 1 [8889 5053].

In the Grantham district, the cored Fulbeck Borehole 1 enables precise definition of formational boundaries and their matching with gamma-ray and sonic log responses (Figure 16). Sonic logs are unavailable for other boreholes in the district, but Balchin and Ridd (1970) demonstrated that correlations can be effected within the group beneath much of Lincolnshire using gamma-ray logs. Although formational boundaries do not always give the strongest gamma-ray log response within the sequence, their correlation across the district is mostly straightforward (Figure 15). The logs indicate that the group thins towards the south-east with 279 m in Broach Road Borehole and 230 m in Hurn Corner Borehole; thinning of the Cropwell Bishop Formation accounts for much of this difference, and other formations show comparatively little variation.

Recent interpretations of Mercia Mudstone palaeoenvironments in the East Midlands suggest deposition in playa mudflats or sabkhas into which distal fluvial systems periodically drained (Warrington and Ivimey-Cook, 1992; Mader, 1992). Shallow hypersaline seas were periodically developed in the Southern North Sea Basin (Fisher, 1986) to the east. Laminated mudstones and siltstones were deposited subaqueously, probably in seasonal lakes; the more structureless mudstones were probably deposited as aeolian dust (Wills, 1970), adhering to damp mudflats on which 'ploughed ground' may have been developed due to evaporite crystal precipitation and solution (Arthurton, 1980). The thicker sandstones of the Sneinton and Edwalton formations are thought to have been deposited by overbank floods from low sinuosity rivers (Warrington and Ivimey-Cook, 1992; Mader, 1992); thinner sandstones may represent sheet floods across the mudflats following rainstorms. Gypsum formed from the evaporation either of interstitial brines or shallow hypersaline water bodies. Brines were of continental origin during some periods, marine during others (Taylor, 1983). The persistent gypsum beds of the upper part of the group (Cropwell Bishop Formation) have been interpreted as marine flooding events from an adjacent hypersaline sea (Taylor, 1983). At the top of the group, the supratidal sabkha environments of the Blue Anchor Formation (Warrington and Ivimey-Cook, 1992) were succeeded by the fully marine environments of the overlying Penarth Group.

SNEINTON FORMATION

The Sneinton Formation (Table 5) corresponds to the Woodthorpe and Colwick formations of the terminology of Warrington et al. (1980). The formation is 73.7 m thick in Fulbeck Borehole 1 and varies from a maximum of 85 m in Broach Road Borehole to only 60 m in Cox's Walk Borehole.

In Fulbeck Borehole 1 (Figure 16), the formation was proved between 301.58 and 375.24 m depth. It consists mainly of reddish brown argillaceous siltstone interbedded with very thin to thin beds of buff-grey sandstone, mainly fine-grained, but grading to coarse in a few beds. A thin conglomeratic sandstone with small subangular to rounded pebbles of quartz and quartzite occurs at 340 m depth, about 39 m below the top of the formation, and corresponds with a marked negative spike on the gamma-ray log. Above this level, thicker sandstone beds (up to 0.20 m) are common, and thinner sandstone beds may amalgamate at the expense of the intervening siltstones. Micaceous planar laminae, normal grading and current ripples are common in the sandstone beds, but many beds are apparently structureless. Stratification is disturbed extensively at some horizons by soft sediment deformation and shrinkage cracks. Nodular gypsum and anhydrite occur in places. The basal 10.7 m have a dominant and distinctive greenish grey or bluish grey colour; carbonaceous plant fragments were noted towards the top of this unit.

The pebbly bed at 340 m may represent the 'Waterstones Conglomerate' of the adjacent Nottingham district (Swinnerton, 1918). A minor unconformity is evident at this horizon, with erosion of underlying strata (the Woodthorpe Formation of Elliott, 1961) becoming more pronounced towards the south and west (Howard et al., in preparation). In Fulbeck Borehole 1, the strata above the conglomerate produce a more strongly serrated gamma-ray log profile than the underlying beds. These divisions are recognisable in other boreholes (Figure 15), and probably correspond to the Woodthorpe and Colwick formations of Warrington et al. (1980) (Table 5). The lower division (Woodthorpe Formation) is substantially thinner, approximately 20 m, in Cox's Walk Borehole than in the others shown in Figure 15 (for example, Ruskington), where 35 to 45 m are recorded. This thinning possibly indicates increasing erosion towards the south-west beneath the conglomerate, as in the adjacent Nottingham district. The lithology of the greenish grey beds at the base of the Sneinton Formation strongly resembles the Retford Formation (formerly 'Keuper Green Beds') of central and north Nottinghamshire (Smith and Warrington, 1971).

RADCLIFFE FORMATION

The Radcliffe Formation, one of Elliott's (1961) original subdivisions, is distinguished from the formations above and below by its distinctive thinly laminated character and pinkish or purplish red colouration (see below). On geophysical logs the top of the formation is marked by a peak in the gamma-ray response, and the formation can be identified within the Mercia Mudstone beneath much of eastern England. The formation is 14.2 m thick in the Fulbeck Borehole 1, thickening eastwards to about 20 m in Hurn Corner Borehole (Figure 15).

In Fulbeck Borehole 1, the formation consists mainly of reddish brown, purplish brown and pinkish red mudstone and argillaceous siltstone, with closely spaced, very thin laminae and very thin beds of pale grey siltstone or very fine- to fine-grained sandstone. Thicker sandstone beds (20–100 mm) are present in the middle and lower parts of the sequence. Structures in the sandstones include micaceous planar laminae, current ripple lamination and normal grading. Small mudstone clasts are abundant at the base of individual sandstone beds. A few halite pseudomorphs occur. Shrinkage cracks and soft sediment deformation structures are common, but disruption of stratification is much less extensive than in the adjacent formations.

GUNTHORPE FORMATION

The Gunthorpe Formation combines the Carlton and Harlequin formations of Elliott (1961). The boundary between Elliott's formations was defined as the top of the Plains Skerry, a thick bed of pale greenish grey dolomitic siltstone or very fine-grained sandstone, with penecontemporaneous slump structures. Recent geological surveys in the Nottingham district (Howard et al., in preparation) indicate that this bed is not consistently mappable, and that the characteristic lithologies of the Plains Skerry can be developed at other levels in the middle part of the formation. On geophysical logs, the base of the Gunthorpe Formation is marked by a maximum in the gamma-ray response, corresponding to the 'Regional Gamma Marker' of Balchin and Ridd (1970). The formation, 86.4 m thick in Fulbeck Borehole 1, shows a slight thickness variation across the area from 88 m in Broach Road Borehole to 75 m in Hurn Corner Borehole (Figure 15).Three main lithologies which occur within the formation in the Fulbeck Borehole 1 are described below.

Interbedded sandstone, siltstone and mudstone   This consists typically of very thin to thin beds of greyish green dolomitic siltstone or very fine sandstone interbedded with greyish green or reddish brown mudstone, usually with very thin siltstone laminae. Sandstones display planar and low-angle lamination, current ripple lamination and common halite pseudomorphs. Individual sandstone beds may amalgamate to form composite beds up to 0.30 m thick. Shrinkage cracks and soft sediment deformation structures are common, but do not extensively disrupt stratification. This lithotype is dominant in the middle part of the formation, tending to occur as 'packages' of strata 0.15–1.5 m thick, separated by similar thicknesses of either of the other two lithotypes.

Deformed argillaceous siltstone and sandy siltstone   This lithology displays a diffuse and irregularly deformed texture with traces of original stratification preserved in places. It is usually dull reddish brown in colour with diffuse greenish grey mottles. A number of processes may have been responsible for the deformation, including desiccation, soft sediment deformation and the growth and solution of interstitial evaporite crystals. This lithology is dominant in the lowest 25 m of the formation, and is also intercalated in the middle part of the formation.

'Structureless' mudstones and siltstones   These are typically reddish brown in colour, commonly with small greenish grey reduction spheroids. Vestigial thin interlamination of mudstone and siltstone, and discontinuous thin 'wafers' of fine- to medium-grained sandstone are visible in places. The uppermost 12 m of the formation are composed of this lithology, and thinner units occur in the middle part of the formation.

Gypsum is fairly common throughout as small nodules and as subhorizontal veins. Alteration to anhydrite is common. A 0.2 m bed of greenish grey, fine-grained, dolomitic sandstone with slumped lamination occurs at 256.0 m depth, resembling the Plains Skerry of Elliott (1961, see above).

EDWALTON FORMATION

One of Elliott's (1961) original divisions, the Edwalton Formation can be mapped in the adjacent Nottingham district by the presence of sandstones at the base and top of the sequence. These sandstones are the Cotgrave Sandstone Member and the Hollygate Sandstone Member, respectively (Elliott, 1961; Warrington et al., 1980), and have been proved in the Fulbeck Borehole 1. They both produce a distinctive negative signature on gamma-ray logs, enabling them to be correlated between boreholes (Figures 15 and 16). The Edwalton Formation is 44.9 m thick in Fulbeck Borehole 1, with remarkably consistent thicknesses of around 45 m in all other boreholes except Ruskington, where the formation appears to thin to about 37 m.

In Fulbeck Borehole 1, the Cotgrave Sandstone Member consists of 1.6 m of pale greenish grey fine- to medium-grained sandstone, apparently structureless. The sandstone is argillaceous in the lower half, but cleaner and strongly cemented by dolomite in the upper half.

Above the Cotgrave Sandstone, core recovery was poor from the lower two thirds of the formation. These strata consist mainly of reddish brown structureless mudstones and siltstones, similar to those of the Gunthorpe Formation (see above), though with more common sandstone 'wafers'. Thin beds of greenish grey siltstone and very fine-grained sandstone occur in places; they show planar and current ripple lamination and are strongly cemented by dolomite. The upper third of the formation, below the Hollygate Sandstone, consists of deformed argillaceous siltstones and mudstones, again similar to those of the Gunthorpe Formation but with more clearly defined greenish grey mottling.

The Hollygate Sandstone Member is 2.7 m thick and consists of pale greenish, grey fine- to coarse-grained, dolomitic sandstone interbedded with reddish brown sandy mudstone. Faint trough cross-bedding is visible in the coarse-grained sandstones, with finer sandstones displaying planar and current ripple lamination. Small gypsum nodules, generally less than 10 mm in diameter, are abundant in the upper part of the formation.

CROPWELL BISHOP FORMATION

This subdivision (Howard et al., in preparation) merges the Trent and Glen Parva formations of Warrington et al. (1980) (Table 5). The formation, 38.6 m thick in the Fulbeck Borehole 1 (Figure 16), shows more marked lateral thickness variation across the district than the other formations of the Mercia Mudstone Group. From Fulbeck, the formation thins southwards to 30 m in the Cox's Walk Borehole and eastwards to only 16 m in Hurn Corner Borehole (Figure 15). It is inconclusive from geophysical logs whether this is due to depositional thinning or whether erosion at the base of the overlying Blue Anchor Formation is responsible.

In Fulbeck Borehole 1, the formation consists almost entirely of reddish brown, structureless, silty mudstones and argillaceous siltstones as described from the Gunthorpe Formation (see above). Greenish grey reduction spheres are common. A 0.45 m-thick bed of dark greenish grey mudstone with very thin siltstone laminae lies about 1 m below the top of the formation. Similar laminated beds at this level elsewhere in the East Midlands have yielded fish scales and bone fragments (Elliott, 1961). At 145.4 m depth, a 0.25 m-thick bed of greenish grey mottled, reddish brown siltstone with lenses of medium- to coarse-grained sandstone may correlate with the Windmill Hill Sandstone of the Nottingham district (Howard et al., in preparation). Gypsum, commonly altered to anhydrite, is abundant throughout, in the form of nodules and veins. Sub-horizontal veins are typically composed of satin spar gypsum, with steeply inclined or vertical veins usually made up of agglomerations of small gypsum nodules. A number of discrete beds of gypsum, up to 0.45 m thick, in the upper part of the formation probably correlate with the commercially important Newark Gypsum seams of the adjacent Nottingham district. The marked negative signature produced by these beds on the gamma-ray logs can be recognised in Broach Road, Ruskington and Cox's Walk boreholes (Figure 15).

BLUE ANCHOR FORMATION

The Blue Anchor Formation (Warrington et al., 1980) (formerly the Tea Green Marl; Table 5) is easily differentiated at outcrop and in borehole samples by its distinctive pale greenish grey colour. The lower boundary is, however, difficult to delineate precisely on gamma-ray logs alone. The formation is 6.0 m thick in Fulbeck Borehole 1 and 3.4 m in Ruskington Borehole, where the base can be identified with fair reliability from chipping samples. A general eastwards thinning to around 2 m or less in Gables Farm and Hurn Corner boreholes is tentatively inferred from geophysical log evidence.

In Fulbeck Borehole 1, the formation consists of pale greenish grey, dolomitic, argillacous siltstone. Fine interlamination of mudstone and siltstone is present in the middle part of the formation, but other parts display a very diffuse disturbed texture with signs of soft sediment deformation and possibly slumping. Strongly dolomitic layers are typically brecciated into small angular clasts. Films, possibly fissure infills, of dark grey mudstone from the overlying Westbury Formation extend down into the uppermost few centimetres of the Blue Anchor Formation.

Penarth Group

Both constituent formations of the Penarth Group, the Westbury and Lilstock formations (Warrington et al., 1980), are mapped in the adjacent Nottingham district (Howard et al., in preparation). In the East Midlands region, only the Cotham Member of the Lilstock Formation is consistently present. The overlying Langport Member (formerly White Lias) is developed locally as a single discontinuous bed of white limestone generally less than 0.2 m thick (Kent, 1953; 1968b; 1970).

The Penarth Group occurs at rockhead in the extreme north-west of the district where it is concealed by Quaternary deposits. Numerous boreholes penetrate the group at depth. The boreholes at Fulbeck Airfield (boreholes 1 and 5 [9061 5178]) both cored a complete section, proving the Westbury Formation and Cotham Member of the overlying Lilstock Formation. Records of chippings collected from Ruskington Borehole enable tentative recognition of the two formations (Figure 15). Although the group as a whole can be identified in other boreholes using geophysical logs, further subdivision is not possible with any confidence.

Fulbeck Borehole 1 (Figure 16), Fulbeck Borehole 5, Stragglethorpe and Broach Road (Figure 15) boreholes, located in or just beyond the north-west of the district, prove Penarth Group thicknesses of 10.6 m, 10.8 m, 11 m and 9 m, respectively. There is considerable thinning of the group towards the south, with only about 4.5 m proved in Cox's Walk (Figure 15) and nearby Stenwith boreholes. Eastwards thinning is even more marked, with thicknesses between 2 and 5 m in Ruskington, Gable's Farm, Hurn Corner (Figure 15), Mareham Grange and Burton Lodge boreholes. No thickness data are available from the centre of the district. Kent (1938) refers to a water borehole [9164 3511] at Grantham which encountered 6.1 m of 'light grey micaceous and sandy clay' overlying 'very hard stone'. Kent assigned these strata to the Penarth Group, but they directly overlie red mudstones (probably Cropwell Bishop Formation of the Mercia Mudstone Group) and may therefore partly represent the Blue Anchor Formation. These thickness variations confirm the isopachyte map of Kent (1968b, p.179), which shows an area of attenuated deposition extending north-eastwards from Leicester towards the Sleaford area. From Fulbeck, the group thickens north-westwards towards the outcrop at Newark (14.1 m at Bantycock Mine, Howard et al., in preparation). Westwards from Cox's Walk Borehole, the group thickens to 8.7 m at Barnstone (Sykes et al., 1970), ultimately reaching a maximum of 17 m at Bunny, in the Nottingham district (Kent, 1953). To the south-east of the district, the group thickens rapidly to around 20 m near Stamford (Kent, 1968b). The group is known to thicken to the north and east of the district (Kent, 1968b; Lott and Warrington, 1988), with up to 75 m developed offshore in the Southern North Sea Basin (Lott and Warrington, 1988).

The Westbury Formation was deposited during and immediately after a widespread late Triassic (mid- to late Rhaetian) marine transgression (Warrington and Ivimey-Cook, 1992). In the Grantham and surrounding districts, sedimentation took place within a generally low-energy, shallow marine environment on the gently subsiding East Midlands Shelf. Lateral passage into a littoral sandstone facies bordering the contemporaneous Anglo-Brabant landmass takes place towards the south (Warrington and Ivimey-Cook, 1992). The overlying Lilstock Formation is believed to have been deposited in a lagoonal environ-ment with fluctuating salinity levels (Mayall, 1983; Warrington and Ivimey-Cook, 1992), before fully marine conditions were re-established, with the deposition of the Lias Group.

WESTBURY FORMATION

In Fulbeck Borehole 1, the Westbury Formation consists of 4.5 m of dark grey silty mudstone, with lenticles and very thin beds of pyritous siltstone and fine-grained micaceous sandstone with load casts. Fulbeck Borehole 5 proved 4.0 m of similar lithologies.

Other boreholes yield little lithological information. The formation is probably represented by approximately 1.2 m of 'dark grey to black splintery shale' in Ruskington Borehole. In the Nottingham district, 5.2 m have been recorded at Bantycock Mine, 9 km to the west of the Fulbeck boreholes (Howard et al., in preparation). Thus, the limited evidence available indicates that the formation thins steadily eastwards across the Grantham district.

The macrofauna collected from Fulbeck Borehole 1 is largely confined to a few bedding planes, which are covered with thin spreads of winnowed, disarticulated and commonly fragmented bivalves, including *Eotra-pezium concentricum*, *E.germari*, *Protocardia rhaetica* and *Rhaetavicula contorta*. Fish remains, including scales of *Gyrolepis alberti*, bone fragments and coprolites are scattered through the mudstones, mainly in the basal few centimetres. No horizons were sufficiently rich in verte-brate remains to be described as 'bone beds'. Such

macrofossil assemblages are typical of the Westbury Formation which, although almost devoid of ammonites, generally contains a more diverse fauna of shallow marine fossils than the lower part of the overlying Lias Group (Warrington and Ivimey-Cook, 1992).

LILSTOCK FORMATION

Only the Cotham Member is represented in Fulbeck boreholes 1 and 5, with no trace of the overlying Langport Member. Fulbeck Borehole 1 proved 6.1 m of pale grey and greenish grey calcareous mudstone with very thin beds and laminae of silt and very fine-grained sand. Brown tints were observed at about the middle of the sequence. The member is 6.8 m thick in Fulbeck Borehole 5, with a similar lithology. Chipping samples proved 0.9 m of 'pale grey clay' in Ruskington Borehole. These thicknesses compare with the 8.8 m proved at Bantycock Mine (Howard et al., in preparation), 9 km to the west of the Fulbeck boreholes. As with the underlying Westbury Formation, the Lilstock Formation thins towards the eastern part of the district.

A sparse and low diversity fauna, typical of the Cotham Member throughout England and Wales, is recorded in both boreholes. A few well-preserved, disarticulated valves of *Eotrapezium concentricum* were recorded from the lowermost 2 m of the member in Fulbeck Borehole 1. The small conchostracan *Euestheria minuta* is present at some levels towards the top of the sequence. Fish remains and scattered foraminifera tests were recorded in Fulbeck Borehole 5.

FOUR

Lower Jurassic: Lias Group

INTRODUCTION TO JURASSIC

Apart from a very small area in the extreme north-west where Triassic rocks crop out beneath drift, Jurassic rocks occur at surface or beneath generally thin Quaternary deposits throughout the entire district. The regional dip is east- to south-eastwards, and averages less than one degree.

The Jurassic succession is divided into four major lithostratigraphical groups, separated by unconformities. The lowest of these is the Lias Group, consisting predominantly of mudstone, with minor limestones, sandstones and ironstones. This is succeeded by the Inferior and Great Oolite groups (Chapter Five), in which limestone predominates, with subordinate mudstone and sandstone. The uppermost Ancholme Group (Chapter Six) is dominated by mudstone. The Lias and Ancholme Group strata contain abundant ammonites, which provide the primary basis for Jurassic zonation. In the Inferior and Great Oolite groups, ammonites are very rare, and other age-diagnostic macrofossils are uncommon, so that the chronostratigraphical subdivision within these groups is less firmly based.

The district formed part of the East Midlands Shelf during the Jurassic Period, and the muds of the Lias and Ancholme groups were deposited in a warm, shallow, open-marine environment. The more varied deposits of the Inferior and Great Oolite groups include distinct rhythmic sequences, reflecting greater terrestrial influence.

In this account, ammonite zones and subzones that are treated as biozones have the nominal taxa printed in italics. In the younger Jurassic (Callovian and Oxfordian stages, the zones and subzones referred to are chronostratigraphical units in which ammonite species give their names to the zones; they are written in Roman type.

The following account of the Lias is based on that by Brandon, Sumbler and Ivimey-Cook (1991) with additional data relating to later developments in the survey of the Grantham district.

LIAS GROUP

The Lias Group (Powell, 1984) is a marine mudstone sequence resting on the Triassic Penarth Group and underlying the Middle Jurassic Inferior Oolite Group. Its outcrop occupies the western third of this district, and it maintains a thickness of about 270 to 280 m. It is composed mainly of grey shaly mudstone with subordinate beds of limestone, sandstone and ironstones. The mudstones also contain layers with limestone (calcite mudstone) nodules, ironstone (siderite mudstone) nodules and smaller phosphatic nodules. Some of the beds are highly fossiliferous. Generally the fauna is dominated by bivalves, of which the oyster *Gryphaea* is particularly conspicuous in the lower part of the sequence. Gastropods, belemnites, crinoids and brachiopods all occur commonly at certain levels, but for biostratigraphical purposes the most important fossils are ammonites. These evolved rapidly throughout the Mesozoic and form the basis of a refined biostratigraphical subdivision (Figures 17, 19, 20). Lithofacies and biofacies suggest that Lias deposition within this district and on the surrounding East Midlands Shelf was in a warm, fairly shallow, open-shelf sea.

Traditionally, the Lias was subdivided into Lower, Middle and Upper Lias. Although these were originally conceived as lithostratigraphical units, they have become inextricably linked to the chronostratigraphical stages and substages. For this reason, the old stratal divisions have been abandoned; the current nomenclature is based on detailed work by the British Geological Survey in the area around Fulbeck Airfield [900 510] (Brandon et al., 1990; Table 6). The lower part of the Lias Group, formerly the 'Lower Lias' and lower part of the 'Middle Lias', is now divided into two formations of roughly equal thickness. The lower formation, the Scunthorpe Mudstone Formation, is characterised by mudstone units with numerous thin limestone beds. The overlying Brant Mudstone Formation is characterised by abundant limestone and sideritic ironstone nodules, but generally lacks limestone beds. The Dyrham Siltstone Formation, recognised in the south-western part of the district, corresponds with the lower part of the former 'Middle Lias', the Marlstone Rock Formation forming the upper part. The 'Upper Lias' corresponds with the Whitby Mudstone Formation.

Exposures in the Lias Group of the district are sparse and, for the lower two formations, the stratigraphical sequence was initially deduced from ditch dredgings and feature mapping. Key boreholes proving the stratigraphy of the Scunthorpe Mudstone Formation are Fulbeck Borehole 5 [9062 5179] and Fulbeck Borehole 1 [8889 5053] on Fulbeck Airfield. Copper Hill Borehole [9787 4265] (Ivimey-Cook et al., in preparation) penetrated the Whitby Mudstone, Marlstone and Brant Mudstone formations and the uppermost 19.51 m of the Scunthorpe Mudstone Formation. In addition, certain parts of the Lias Group were formerly exploited for brick clay or ironstone. Although few sections are now open, many details were recorded in the past. The stratigraphy of the Lias Group in this district and the adjoining Vale of Belvoir has been summarised by Sumbler (1993a).

Scunthorpe Mudstone Formation

The type area for the Scunthorpe Mudstone Formation is in the Kingston upon Hull and Brigg district, to the

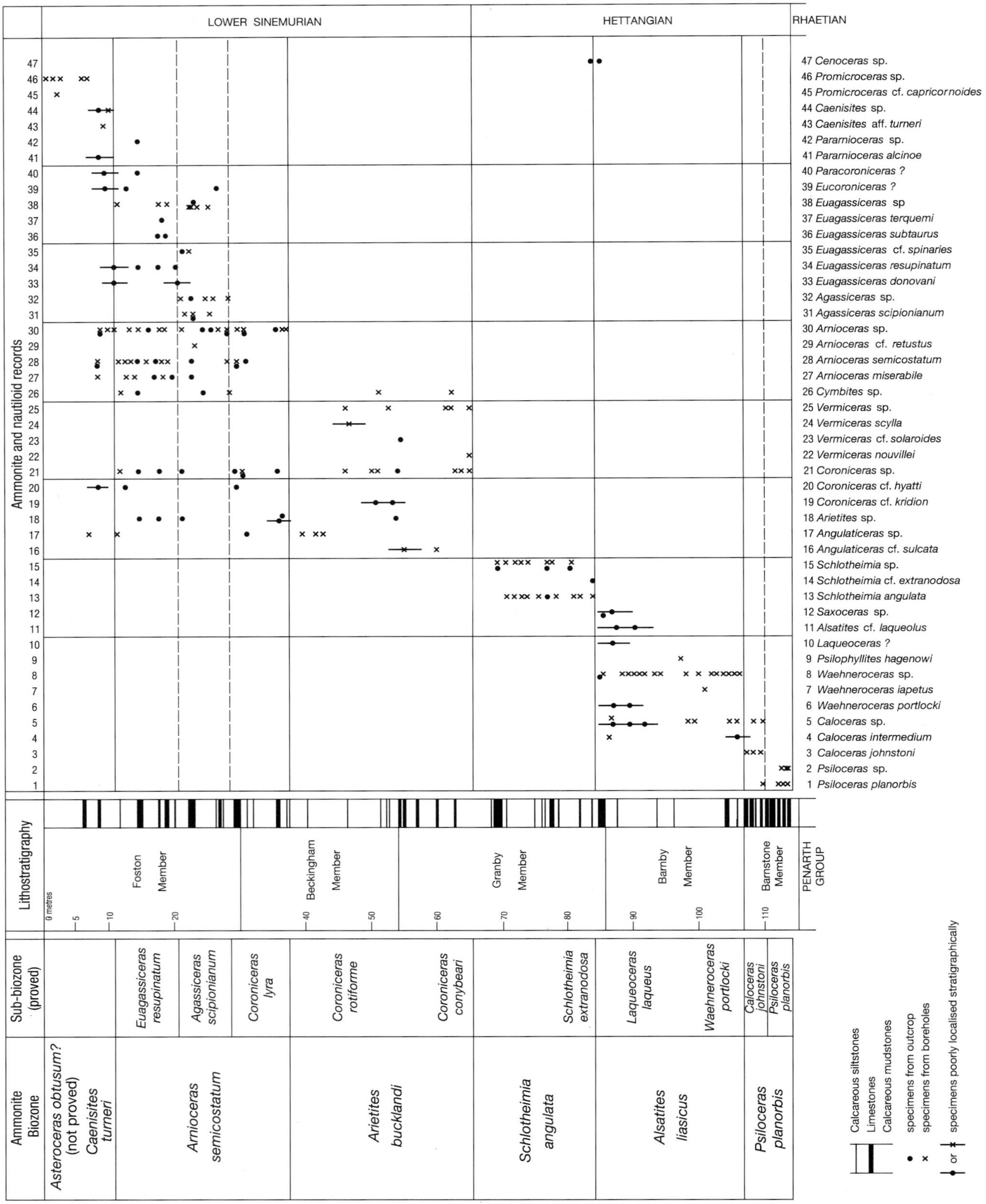

Figure 17 Ammonite biostratigraphy of the Scunthorpe Mudstone Formation (after Brandon et al., 1990). Lithostratigraphical sequence is based principally on Fulbeck Borehole 1, with higher beds (above 20 m) added from Fulbeck Borehole 5.

north, where the formation was defined by Gaunt et al. (1992). Within the Grantham district, reference sections include a complete sequence in Fulbeck Borehole 5, between 4.58 and 117.65 m depth, in which all the constituent members are defined (Brandon et al., 1990; Figure 18), and a partial sequence in Fulbeck Borehole 1, between 0 and 100.93 m depth, which penetrated all but the highest beds of the formation (Ivimey-Cook et al., in preparation). Halved cores from both these boreholes are stored at BGS, Keyworth.

The formation can be recognised throughout much of the East Midlands Shelf (Brandon et al., 1990, fig. 7). More locally, it thins north-eastwards from a maximum thickness of about 128 m in the Vale of Belvoir, and in the Grantham district it probably maintains a thickness of about 113 m. It crops out in the western part of the district and can be recognised by its geophysical signature in deep boreholes penetrating younger rocks in more eastern parts of the district. For example, in Gables Farm Borehole [0460 4327] near Sleaford the thickness is estimated to be 115 m.

The Scunthorpe Mudstone Formation is characterised by grey, variably calcareous, silty mudstone containing numerous thin limestones. In the type area, the formation becomes increasingly ferruginous towards the top with the development of the Frodingham Ironstone Member. In the Grantham district, the greater part of the sequence comprises dark grey, weak, fissile mudstones or claystones, with calcium carbonate content typically varying between 10 and 20 per cent. Most of the remainder of the sequence consists of medium grey, moderately strong, blocky mudstones and silty mudstones, which are generally more calcareous, containing up to 50 per cent carbonate. Limestones, typically 0.1 to 0.3 m thick, form a relatively small, though conspicuous, part of the formation. They generally contain 60 to 70 per cent calcium carbonate. Some are primary bioclastic limestones, indicating episodes of higher energy sedimentation than that which prevailed during deposition of the muds; they include lenticular, wave-reworked or current-winnowed deposits, subsequently indurated by carbonate cement. Other limestone beds are strong, well-cemented, argillaceous calcite mudstones ('cementstones') partly of secondary origin, as are limestone nodules within the mudstones (Hallam, 1964). Many of the limestone beds are laterally very persistent, and form features which can be traced for many kilometres across the district with little change in character. Some can be recognised in boreholes across extensive areas of the East Midlands Shelf.

Throughout south Lincolnshire and the Vale of Belvoir (including the Grantham district), the Scunthorpe Mudstone Formation is divided into five members (Table 6, Figure 17, 18). The Barnstone, Granby and Foston members consist of mudstone with numerous widespread, closely spaced, thin limestone beds. These are separated by the Barnby and Beckingham members, consisting of mudstone with rare limestones. In the Granby and Foston members, the limestones occur typically in groups of several closely spaced beds, these groups are separated by 2 to 5 m of mudstone. Each limestone bed

or group of beds forms a dip and scarp feature, by which it has been mapped. The limestone-rich Barnstone, Granby and Foston members are readily identified on downhole geophysical borehole logs (Figure 18) because the limestone beds show higher sonic velocities and lower natural gamma-ray activity than the intervening mudstones.

The formation ranges in age from latest Rhaetian to earliest Upper Sinemurian. The *obtusum* Biozone of the latter substage is thin and may be locally absent due to a disconformity at the base of the Brant Mudstone Formation. Generally, the macrofossils found in the field are most conspicuous within or adjacent to the limestone beds; this fauna is dominated by bivalves and ammonites, with some belemnites, gastropods, brachiopods, and crinoids. Of the microfauna, foraminifera and ostracods are found throughout the formation (Ivimey-Cook et al., in preparation).

BARNSTONE MEMBER

The type section is Fulbeck Borehole 5 between 109.40 and 117.65 m depth. Fulbeck Borehole 1 proved the member between 92.66 and 100.93 m (Brandon et al., 1990). This member was formerly known as the Hydraulic Limestones, referring to its use for cement manufacture. The Barnstone Member consists of alternating mudstones and limestones and is largely concealed beneath superficial deposits in the north-west of the district. The base, corresponding with the base of the Lias Group, rests sharply, and apparently conformably, on the Cotham Member of the Penarth Group.

It is 8.25 m thick in Fulbeck Borehole 5. Limestone makes up about 30 per cent of the sequence. The limestone beds, mainly uniform argillaceous calcite mudstones, are typically 0.1 to 0.2 m thick, and rarely exceed 0.3 m. Those in the lowest 2 to 3 m are rich in shell debris; others are markedly laminated and bituminous, suggesting deposition in very quiet anaerobic conditions. Kent (1937; 1964) suggested that the individual limestone beds are laterally persistent, and this has since been confirmed by correlation of geophysical borehole logs. The intervening mudstones, typically up to 0.7 m thick, include finely laminated, dark grey, bituminous 'paper shales' and medium grey, calcareous mudstones.

The Barnstone Member ranges in age from latest Rhaetian to early Hettangian. The beds yield a rather sparse fauna, mainly of bivalves, and with ammonites indicative of the *planorbis* Biozone in the higher beds. In Fulbeck boreholes 1 and 5 and at outcrop in adjoining districts, the diagnostic ammonites of the *planorbis* Subbiozone first occur a little above the base of the Barnstone Member. By current definition (Cope et al., 1980a), beds below this level, about 2 m above the base in Fulbeck Borehole 1, are of Triassic age. These basal 'Pre-Planorbis Beds' (Trueman, 1915; Kent, 1937) are characterised by the bivalves *Liostrea hisingeri*, *Modiolus minimus* and *Pleuromya tatei* and echinoid spines. Both subzones of the *planorbis* Biozone are proved in Fulbeck Borehole 1, with *Psiloceras planorbis* between 99.08 and 97.8 m and the overlying *johnstoni* Sub-biozone with

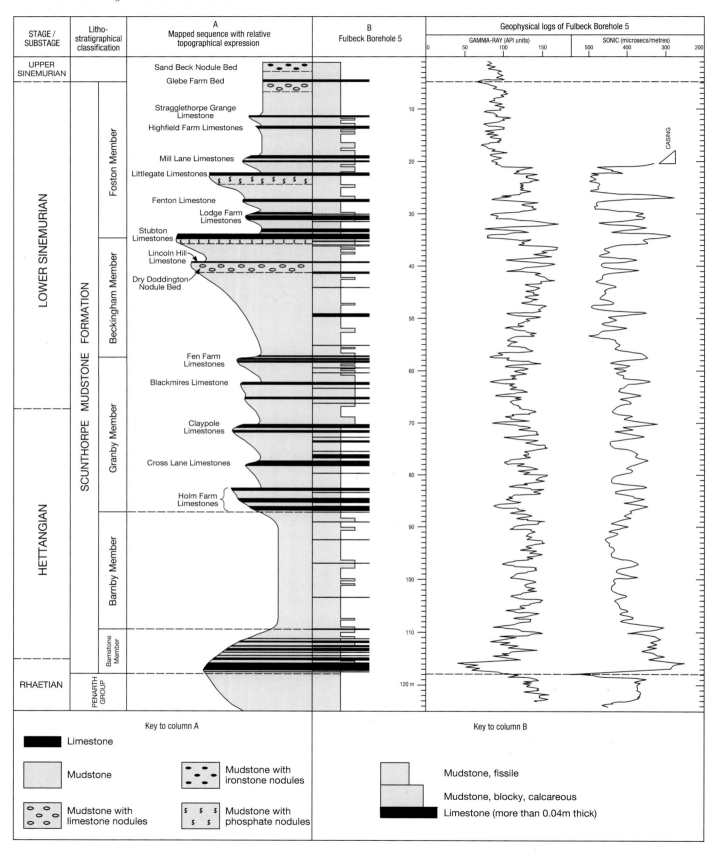

Table 6
Stratigraphical terminology for the lower part of the Lias Group compared with that used by Kent. (Not to scale).

Stage/Substage	Current nomenclature		Swinnerton and Kent, 1949; 1976; Kent, 1930	Traditional subdivisions
	Formation	Member or Bed		
Toarcian	Whitby Mudstone		Upper Lias	Upper Lias
Upper Pliensbachian	Marlstone Rock		Marlstone Ironstone or Marlstone Rock	Middle Lias
	Dyrham Siltstone		Middle Lias mudstones and siltstones or Middle Lias clays	
Lower Pliensbachian	Brant Mudstone 113 m	'Pecten Ironstone'	Upper Clays	Lower Lias
		Jericho Gryphaea Bed		
		Loveden Gryphaea Bed		
Upper Sinemurian		Brandon Sandstone	Sandrock	
		Glebe Farm Bed	Obtusum-Oxynotum Clays	
Lower Sinemurian	Scunthorpe Mudstone 113 m	Foston Member 31 m	Ferruginous Limestone Series	
		Beckingham Member	Bucklandi Clays	
		Granby Member 30 m	Granby Limestones	
Hettangian		Barnby Member 22 m	Barnby or Angulata Clays	
		Barnstone Member 8 m	Hydraulic Limestones	
Rhaetian				

Figure 18 Lithostratigraphy of the Scunthorpe Mudstone Formation (after Brandon et al., 1990).

The lithological core log, natural gamma-ray and sonic logs of Fulbeck Borehole 5 are shown (column B), together with the sequence as mapped (column A), indicating the relative magnitude of the topographical features formed by the beds (no grain size variation implied).

Caloceras johnstoni at 93.21 and 94.92 m. The base of the *liasicus* Biozone in Fulbeck Borehole 1, at 92.40 m, lies 0.26 m above the highest limestone of this member. The microfauna in the lower part of the member is characterised by the inception of a number of foraminifera including *Reinholdella planiconvexa* and *Lingulina collenoti*, together with the ostracod *Ogmoconchella aspinata*. The appearance of *Marginulina prima* within the *planorbis* Biozone is also biostratigraphically important.

BARNBY MEMBER

The type section is in Fulbeck Borehole 5 between 87.35 and 109.40 m depth. The reference section in Fulbeck Borehole 1, between 71.20 and 92.66 m, is described by Ivimey-Cook et al. (in preparation).

The member forms low-lying ground in the north-western part of the district where most of the outcrop is concealed beneath alluvium of the River Witham or other superficial deposits. It is 22.05 m thick in Fulbeck Borehole 5 and maintains this thickness, approximately, throughout the district.

The Barnby Member consists of grey calcareous mudstones with rare thin argillaceous limestones, which make up only about 1 per cent of the sequence in Fulbeck Borehole 5. Similarly, few limestones are recognised in Fulbeck Borehole 1 but two sections [8351 5036 and 8350 5029] along Shire Dyke, which were examined during the survey, each expose a 0.1 m-thick argillaceous limestone in the basal few metres of the member.

The fauna is dominated by the bivalves *Liostrea*, *Cardinia* and *Lucina* and ammonites. Fossils collected by Kent from the Shire Dyke, west of Barnby in the Willows, indicate that the Barnby Member exposed there is probably entirely of *liasicus* Biozone age. The fauna includes *Cardinia listeri*, *Alsatites* cf. *laqueolus*, *Caloceras* sp., *Saxoceras* sp., and *Waehneroceras* sp. Other fossils recorded from the member during the survey are given below. In Fulbeck Borehole 1, the *liasicus* Biozone is proved between 92.40 and 71.90 m. The lower beds yielded *Waehneroceras* cf. *iapetus* at 86.85 m, suggesting the *portlocki* Sub-biozone. Other *Waehneroceras* occur below 75 m depth and *Caloceras* occurs sporadically throughout. The higher *laqueus* Sub-biozone is poorly proved, though *Psilophyllites* cf. *hagenowi* occurs at 82.98 m.

In Fulbeck Borehole 5, a number of ostracod inceptions have been noted, including those of *Polycope cerasia*, *Cytherella concentrica*, *Isobythocypris elongata*, *Kinkelinella translucens* and *Cytherelloidea circumscripta*. The foraminifera *Ophthalmidium liasicum* is common in the upper part of the member.

Fossils from the upper part of the member collected from dredgings [848 519 and 845 517] along Shire Dyke include *Liostrea hisingeri*, *Cardinia ovalis*, *Saxoceras* sp. and *Waehneroceras* cf. *portlocki*. A section [8442 5133] along the River Witham, near Witham Farm, comprised 0.9 m of grey fissile mudstone, with *Cardinia ovalis*, overlying 0.1 m of grey argillaceous shelly limestone probably in the middle part of the member. About 1 km farther south, a section [8480 5034] along the river exposed 1 m of weathered, grey mudstone with limestone nodules containing *Cardinia* cf. *hybrida*, *Cardinia ovalis* and *Lucina* sp. Between the two exposures [from 845 508 to 846 506], loose material yielded *Saxoceras*? and *Waehneroceras portlocki*, again indicating the *liasicus* Biozone.

About 1 m below the top of the member, exposures along a drain [8481 4966 and 8462 4952] north of Claypole showed about 0.5 m of grey mudstone with a basal 0.08 m nodular limestone. The exposures yield *Cardinia ovalis*, *Liostrea* sp., *Saxoceras* sp., *Waehneroceras* sp.

and crinoid ossicles, indicating the upper part of the *liasicus* Biozone. A thin limestone, also in the upper few metres of the member, is exposed in a ditch [8442 4814] south of Claypole. It yields serpulid tubes, gastropods, *Liostrea hisingeri*, *Lucina limbata*, *Mactromya arenacea*, *Plagiostoma* sp., *Pseudolimea* sp., *Laqueoceras*? and echinoid radioles. The ammonite indicates the upper, *laqueus* Sub-biozone, of the *liasicus* Biozone. The lowest record of *Gryphaea* in the local Lias sequence occurs in Fulbeck Borehole 1 at 71.45 m depth.

GRANBY MEMBER

The type section of the member is Fulbeck Borehole 5 between 56.75 and 87.35 m (Figure 18). The reference section, Fulbeck Borehole 1 between 39.85 and 71.20 m, is described in more detail elsewhere (Ivimey-Cook et al., in preparation).

The member forms an outcrop 0.75 to 2 km wide in the north-east of the district, from west of Beckingham [875 537], southwards to Long Bennington [835 450], although from the vicinity [850 515] of Barnby in the Willows northwards all but the highest beds are concealed by superficial deposits. The member extends southwards in a complex, faulted, anticlinal structure to the vicinity [855 410] of Allington. The member is 30.60 m thick in Fulbeck Borehole 5.

The Granby Member consists of grey calcareous mudstones with numerous thin, laterally persistent, limestones comprising about 14 per cent of the sequence in Fulbeck Borehole 5. These typically occur in groups of closely spaced beds which give rise to mappable features, with brash in a brownish grey, clayey soil on the dip slopes. The limestone beds are typically about 0.1 m thick, and consist predominantly of argillaceous calcite mudstone with lenses of harder, grey, well-cemented, relatively clean, shelly and bioclastic limestones; the latter dominates the weathered limestone brash found on the dip slopes. The main groups of limestone beds (Figure 18) are, in ascending order: Holm Farm Limestones, Cross Lane Limestones, Claypole Limestones, Blackmires Limestone and Fen Farm Limestones (Brandon et al., 1990). They can usually be distinguished by a combination of lithology and faunal content.

The Granby Member spans the *angulata* Biozone of the Hettangian and the earliest part of the *bucklandi* Biozone of the Lower Sinemurian. The macrofauna includes bivalves, ammonites (which are locally common in the limestones), nautiloids (in the lowest limestone beds), brachiopods, gastropods, corals and crinoids. Large, conical internal casts of burrows (*Kulindrichnus*, or 'turnip stones') (Hallam, 1960), composed of bioclastic limestone, are common on the dip slopes.

The **Holm Farm Limestones** are approximately 4.5 to 5 m thick (82.76–87.35 m in Fulbeck Borehole 5) and include three units of limestone, each comprising up to four limestone beds. Mapping has shown that limestones 'X' and 'Y' of Brandon et al. (1990), are best included within the Holm Farm Limestones. The lowest unit ('X') marks the base of the Granby Member, and the second ('Y') is 1.5 to 2 m higher. The third limestone unit in the

Holm Farm Limestones (82.76–82.96 m in Fulbeck Borehole 5) caps a strong scarp feature on which all three limestone units crop out, for example southwards from Holm Barn Farm [849 508]. It consists mostly of a hard, pale grey, shelly, bioclastic limestone, weathering pale brown, with abundant coarse shell debris, and *Kulindrichnus*. In Fulbeck Borehole 5, this limestone unit is about 0.20 m thick, and a 0.04 m-thick, possibly nodular, limestone occurs just below.

In Fulbeck Borehole 5, the beds between the 'X' and 'Y' limestone units yield *Schlotheimia angulata* at 86.20 m, this is 1.15 m above the base of the member (Figure 18). Data from the Nottingham district (Howard et al., in preparation) indicate that the *liasicus–angulata* biozonal boundary is probably within the limestones forming 'X'. Units 'X' and 'Y' contain the nautiloid *Cenoceras* sp., a form not found during the surveys of the Grantham or Nottingham districts in any overlying beds of the formation. In Fulbeck Borehole 5, *Planularia inaequistriata* first appears immediately above limestone 'X'.

The fauna from the third limestone unit includes serpulids, gastropods, *Astarte* sp., *Camptonectes* sp., *Cardinia crassiuscula*, *C. hybrida*, *C. listeri?*, *C.* sp. cf. *ovalis*, *Liostrea irregularis*, *Plagiostoma giganteum*, *Pseudolimea* sp., *Pseudopecten* sp., ostracods and echinoid spine fragments.

The mudstones between the Holm Farm and Cross Lane limestones are on average 4 m thick; the logs of many of the Fulbeck Airfield boreholes (including Fulbeck Borehole 5) record a 0.07 m-thick limestone bed, about 2.5 m above the Holm Farm Limestones. These mudstones contain *Gryphaea*.

The **Cross Lane Limestone** (76.34–78.26 m in Fulbeck Borehole 5) forms a moderately strong feature from the vicinity [853 497] of Cross Lane, Claypole southwards to Long Bennington [834 456] and northwards to the River Witham [854 514], beyond which it is hidden under drift. Brash typically consists of pieces of hard, pale grey, weathering pale brown, shelly, bioclastic limestone. The limestone contains abundant small bivalves both entire and as fragments. The Cross Lane Limestone is represented in the Fulbeck Airfield boreholes by several, thin limestones within about 1.5 to 2 m of strata, and seven occur in Fulbeck Borehole 5. The limestones are typically about 0.1 m thick. Sonic logs (Figure 18) suggest that the beds in the lower part of this unit are more indurated, and that they produce the mapped feature.

A fauna includes *Spirillina* and other foraminifera, serpulid tubes, gastropods, *Cardinia hybrida*, *C. hybrida* var. *depressa*, *Liostrea irregularis*, pectinids, *Plagiostoma giganteum*, *Schlotheimia* sp., ostracods (such as *Ogmoconcha hagenowi* and *Nanacythere elegans*) and echinoderm fragments. *Gryphaea* is rare, but was recovered from a comparable horizon in Fulbeck Borehole 1.

The mudstones above the Cross Lane Limestone average 6 m in thickness and include a thin limestone, or a group of several limestones, about 4 m above the base.

The **Claypole Limestone** (70.30–71.78 m in Fulbeck Borehole 5) forms a strong feature, with a broad dip slope. In ditch sections [8588 4938; 8606 4935] near Claypole, a medium grey, argillaceous, bioclastic, shelly limestone up to 0.4 m thick is exposed. The profile of the associated feature suggests that two closely spaced beds are present, as confirmed by the Fulbeck Airfield boreholes; in Fulbeck Borehole 5, the Claypole Limestone comprises two 0.25 m-thick beds separated by 0.98 m of mudstone with nodular limestones in the upper part. This is the lowest limestone unit with common *Gryphaea*.

Fossils from the Claypole Limestone include foraminifera, the compound coral *Septastrea* sp., *Calcirhynchia calcaria*, *Pleurotomaria* sp., *Cardinia* cf. *insignis*, *Gryphaea arcuata*, *G. arcuata incurva*, *G. arcuata* trans. to *G. maccullochii*, *Mactromya arenacea*, *M. subglobosus*, *Pholadomya* sp., *Plagiostoma* sp., *Pleuromya?*, *Pseudolimea* sp., *Schlotheimia* sp., ostracods (including *Nanacythere aequalicostata* and *Paracypris redcarensis*) and crinoid fragments. *Schlotheimia* sp. which indicates the *angulata* Biozone, occurs at 54.56 m in Fulbeck Borehole 1 and *Calcirhynchia* sp. at 54.80 m.

The mudstones between the Claypole and Blackmires limestones are 8 to 9 m in thickness. They include a thin bioclastic limestone (or group of limestones) about 5.5 m above the base. Locally, this forms a subordinate mappable feature on the scarp formed by the Blackmires Limestone, for example west of Claypole. Indeterminate fragments of arietid ammonites, the earliest evidence for the *bucklandi* Biozone, were found at 66.22 m in Fulbeck Borehole 5. This level corresponds with the occurrence in Fulbeck Borehole 1 of *Vermiceras* sp. at 50.85 m and *V.* cf. *rouvillei* at 50.70 m, both indicating the *conybeari* Sub-biozone.

The **Blackmires Limestone** (62.10–62.40 m in Fulbeck Borehole 5) forms a moderate feature, which is well developed near Blackmires Farm [864 504]. Pieces of hard, grey, weathering brown, bioclastic, shelly limestone occur on the dip slope, together with abundant *Gryphaea*. A ditch exposure [8712 5131] shows a total thickness of about 0.2 m of the limestone. Fulbeck Borehole 5 proved a single, 0.3 m-thick, limestone bed, but logs of other Fulbeck Airfield boreholes prove from one to three limestones; the most persistent, corresponding with the mapped bed, is up to 0.4 m thick.

The fauna collected includes foraminifera, colonial serpulids cf. 'Sarcinella', *Pleurotomaria anglica*, *Ptychomphalus solarioides*, *Astarte* sp., *Cardinia* cf. *ovalis*, *Gryphaea arcuata* trans. to *G. maccullochii*, *Pseudolimea* sp., ostracods, crinoid columnals and echinoderm fragments. The Blackmires Limestone is also notable for the presence of well-preserved specimens of the simple coral *Montlivaltia haimei*.

The mudstones between the Blackmires and Fen Farm limestones are 4 to 5 m thick. Many of the Fulbeck Airfield boreholes show one or two thin limestones in this unit. In Fulbeck Borehole 5 both are very shelly, and the lower is rich in crinoid debris. *Isocrinus psilonoti* was also found in Fulbeck Borehole 1 in these beds (at a depth of 45.30 m) which also contain *Lingula*. The extinction of the foraminifera *Lingulina tenera substriata* in the mudstones between the Blackmires and Fen Farm Limestones is biostratigraphically important in Britain.

The **Fen Farm Limestone** (56.75–58.14 m in Fulbeck Borehole 5) marks the top of the Granby Member. It forms a moderately strong feature with a broad dip slope, as near Fen Farm [868 510], on which *Gryphaea* and pentacrinoid columnals are common. Brash consists of medium grey, weathering pale orange-brown, bioclastic, shelly limestone with small thin-shelled bivalves and characteristically abundant crinoids; *Kulindrichnus* is common. In Fulbeck Borehole 5, the Fen Farm Limestone comprises three separate beds, in ascending order 0.32, 0.12 and 0.15 m thick. The middle bed is packed with *Gryphaea*, and probably corresponds with a *Gryphaea*-rich limestone, 0.2 m thick, with lenses of pentacrinoid debris and large *Plagiostoma*, exposed in ditches [8697 4995 and 8702 4973] north of Stubton.

The fauna collected from the Fen Farm Limestone belongs to the *conybeari* Sub-biozone of the *bucklandi* Biozone, and comprises foraminifera, *Montlivaltia haimei*, *Lucina* sp., *Gryphaea arcuata*, *G. arcuata incurva*, *Plagiostoma giganteum*, *Vermiceras* cf. *solaroides*, ostracods, echinoid spines and pentacrinoid columnals.

BECKINGHAM MEMBER

The beds in Fulbeck Borehole 5, between 34.65 and 56.75 m, form the type section of the member (Figure 18; Brandon et al., 1990). A reference section is Fulbeck Borehole 1 between 17.93 and 39.85 m. The member crops out as a 0.5 to 1 km-wide belt across the western side of the district, from Beckingham in the north to west of Allington in the south. Thickness varies from 21 to 24 m within the district.

The Beckingham Member consists predominantly of bluish grey shaly mudstones with rare thin argillaceous limestones. Limestone nodules are common within the Dry Doddington Nodule Bed, near the top of the member.

The member ranges in age from the *bucklandi* Biozone to the *semicostatum* Biozone of the Lower Sinemurian. Typical fossils include the bivalves *Gryphaea* and *Pseudopecten*, ammonites and sporadic pentacrinoid fragments. Fossils from the mudstones within about 1 m of the base of the member, collected from a ditch [8708 4957] near Stubton, include pyritised gastropods and ammonites: *Ptychomphalus* sp., *Coroniceras?* juv., *Arietites?* juv., and crinoid columnals. This fauna indicates a probable *bucklandi* Biozone age, as does *Vermiceras* sp. from Fulbeck Borehole 1, between 31.65 and 50.85 m depth. There are no further ammonites diagnostic of zonal age up to 22.75 m where *Arnioceras* sp. indicates the *semicostatum* Biozone, though *Angulaticeras* spp. are recorded at several intermediate levels.

Although the member consists predominantly of mudstones, the Fulbeck Airfield boreholes proved the presence of a few thin limestone beds, one of which, 7 to 8 m above the base, is rich in pentacrinoid debris. Lenticular slabs of dark grey, very argillaceous, crinoidal limestone up to 0.05 m thick, dredged from the Sutton Dyke [between 8755 5240 and 8735 5330], are probably from this bed. Up to 0.2 m of nodular argillaceous limestone with crinoid debris and *Plagiostoma giganteum* exposed in the dyke [8774 5203] just south of Yew Tree Farm may be the same, or a slightly higher bed. Fossils collected by Kent from approximately this level [probably 8743 5410] at Beckingham suggest a late *rotiforme* Sub-biozone age and include *Cardinia lanceolata*, *Gryphaea arcuata*, ostreids, *Coroniceras* cf. *kridion* and pentacrinoid columnals. Mudstone from about this level has been dug from small pits [8520 4535; 8408 3998 and 8430 3997] south of Dry Doddington and west of Allington, probably for brick-making.

The **Dry Doddington Nodule Bed** (38.62–40.56 m in Fulbeck Borehole 5) typically forms a strong bench-like feature on the slope below the base of the Foston Member. Locally, as at Dry Doddington [853 465], Lincoln Hill [844 457] and Beckingham, it gives rise to a particularly strong feature which is visible from the west for several miles. Roughly 2 m thick, the nodule bed lies about 17 to 18 m above the base of the Beckingham Member. Its outcrop is characterised by numerous ovoid, ochreous-yellow-weathered, grey, argillaceous limestone nodules, typically 0.05 to 0.20 m across, in a brownish grey clay soil. The nodules are generally unfossiliferous, though in some cases they are crowded with small *Modiolus*. A sparse fauna from the nodules comprises gastropods, *Modiolus hillanus?*, *M.* sp. juv., *Pseudolimea* sp. and *Arietites?* (the latter possibly from one of the adjacent limestones).

Being composed mainly of grey mudstone, the Dry Doddington Nodule Bed is difficult to recognise in borehole logs, although many of the Fulbeck Airfield boreholes prove one or two thin beds of limestone, which probably lie at its base. Fulbeck Borehole 5 proved 0.18 m of soft, silty limestone with ferruginous shell fragments at 40.74 m. These limestones have not been traced at outcrop. Kent (1963 MS) recorded a section which exposed these beds during widening of Claypole railway cutting [about 8642 4820] in 1941. It showed 3.1 m of mudstone with sporadic 'ironstone' nodules and scattered *Gryphaea*, between two thin argillaceous, ferruginous, shelly limestones. The lower limestone is described as 0.1 m thick with abundant *Gryphaea* and sporadic *Cardinia* spp.

The **Lincoln Hill Limestone** (38.50–38.62 m in Fulbeck Borehole 5), immediately above the Dry Doddington Nodule Bed, lies 3 to 4 m below the top of the Beckingham Member. Although mappable only in some places (e.g. at Lincoln Hill), it probably extends throughout the district. It is present in many of the Fulbeck Airfield boreholes; it is recorded as 0.30 m and 0.12 m thick in Fulbeck boreholes 1 and 5 respectively, and was recorded as 0.23 m thick in Claypole railway cutting (Kent, 1963 MS). Brash consists of medium grey, silty, shelly, bioclastic limestone impregnated with limonite, associated with abundant *Gryphaea*.

The fauna, from the early part of the *semicostatum* Biozone, includes foraminifera, bryozoan fragments, gastropods, *Cardinia* cf. *hybrida*, *Gryphaea arcuata* trans. *G. maccullochii*, *Pseudopecten* sp., *Arietites?*, *Arietites* or *Coroniceras*, *Arnioceras* sp. and echinoderm fragments.

The mudstones forming the upper few metres of the Beckingham Member were formerly worked for brick-making near Rectory Farm [882 523]. The fauna collected from these beds at several localities is from the early *semicostatum* Biozone. It includes crinoid columnals, *Montlivaltia haimei*, *Angulaticeras* sp., *Arnioceras semicostatum*, *Arnioceras* sp. and *Coroniceras*?. The ammonites are typically phosphatised. The beds are attributed to the *C. lyra* Sub-biozone as redefined by Ivimey-Cook and Donovan (1983). The topmost 1 m contains numerous small, hard, fawn-weathering, elongate ovoid phosphatic nodules, up to 0.03 m long. The upper 0.5 m of this nodule bed were exposed in a ditch [8604 4611], near Hill Farm, Dry Doddington.

FOSTON MEMBER

The Foston Member approximates to the Ferruginous Limestone Series of Swinnerton and Kent (1949). The type section is Fulbeck Borehole 5 between 4.58 and 34.65 m (Brandon et al., 1990). The lower part of the member was proved by Fulbeck Borehole 1 between 0 and 17.93 m, and the uppermost 19.51 m of the member were penetrated by Copper Hill Borehole from 182.60 m to its terminal depth at 202.11 m. The member has an approximately 2 km-wide outcrop in the western part of the district; much of the upper part is concealed by drift deposits, 30.07 m thick in Fulbeck Borehole 5, its thickness is fairly uniform across the district.

The Foston Member is a unit of grey mudstones, characterised by numerous laterally persistent, feature-forming limestone beds, which comprise about 10 per cent of the sequence. The limestones become increasingly silty and sandy upwards, possibly indicating a change of climate or current regime. Moreover, the beds become sandier in the northern part of the outcrop, suggesting a generally northerly source for the sand. Persistent beds of phosphatic nodules occur, commonly beneath limestone beds (for example beneath the Stubton Limestone). Many of the nodules are penetrated by minute borings, and the beds contain well-preserved, phosphatised ammonites, suggesting periods of reworking. Large nodules of argillaceous limestone are present in the upper part of the member.

The member ranges in age from the *semicostatum* Biozone up into the *turneri* Biozone (Lower Sinemurian), and possibly into the *obtusum* Biozone (Upper Sinemurian). The fauna is dominated by bivalves including *Camptonectes*, *Cardinia*, *Gryphaea*, *Lucina*, *Oxytoma*, *Protocardia*, *Pseudolimea*, and *Pseudopecten*, together with ammonites.

Mappable limestone beds and groups of beds were named by Brandon et al. (1990), and are described below, in ascending order.

The **Stubton Limestone** (33.51–34.65 m in Fulbeck Borehole 5) generally forms an extensive dip slope, as at Stubton [875 487]. The limestones are particularly distinctive as they produce a rich, rusty-brown, silty loam, with a copious brash of orange-brown, ferruginous, shelly, bioclastic limestone containing numerous *Gryphaea,* which are commonly abraded and bored. Limonitic ooids are abundant in some pieces and there are common irregular, orange-brown 'limonite' veins and patches.

Exposures in ponds [8838 5213; 8856 5205] at Rectory Farm show up to 0.5 m of rubbly, unevenly bedded

ferruginous limestone, with lenticular clay interbeds. Similar limestones were exposed in a pond [8781 4844] at Stubton and along Foston Beck [8720 4472 to 8724 4451]. Jukes-Browne (1885, p.30) refers to a section in a pit [c.853 400], south-west of Allington Church, which exposed a section in these beds.

In the Fulbeck Airfield boreholes, the Stubton Limestone comprises two to four beds of limestone of varying thickness interbedded with mudstone. These occur over a vertical thickness of 2.4 m of strata, and typically the limestones total about 1.5 m. Generally, they comprise a thin, lower bed of non-ooidal, argillaceous limestone and an upper, thicker, ferruginous, ooidal bed. Seen fresh, the upper bed is a brown and grey mottled, intensely burrowed, *Gryphaea*-rich limestone with polished siderite or goethite ooids. In Fulbeck Borehole 5, the lower and upper beds are 0.14 and 0.61 m thick, respectively, and are separated by 0.41 m of mudstone. In many Fulbeck Airfield boreholes, one or two thinner limestones occur in the underlying mudstone, about 1 m thick; in some boreholes these beds have apparently coalesced to form a thicker bed. The limestones were dug for walling stone at Stonepit Plantation [855 405], Allington (Jukes-Browne, 1885, p.31), and at several places [8325 3876, 8361 3843 and 8384 3835] near Cox's Walk Farm, west of Sedgebrook.

Fossils are abundant and varied, and suggest early *semicostatum* Biozone, *lyra* Sub-biozone. They include foraminifera, serpulid tubes, *Montlivaltia haimei*, *Calcirhynchia calcaria*, *Piarorhynchia*?, *Bourguetia*?, *Procerithium* sp., *Pleurotomaria anglica*, *Zygopleura* sp., *Cardinia crassiuscula*, *C. hybrida*, *C. hybrida* var. *depressa*, *C. listeri*, *Chlamys* sp., *Gryphaea arcuata* trans. to *G. maccullochii*, *G. maccullochii*, *Modiolus* cf. *scalprum*, ostreids, *Oxytoma inequivalve*, *Pleuromya*?, *Pseudolimea* sp., *Pseudopecten* sp., *Arnioceras* cf. *semicostatum*, arietitids, *Coroniceras* sp. and *Coroniceras* sp. cf. *hyatti*.

Above the Stubton Limestone the Fulbeck Airfield boreholes proved one or two thin beds of limestone within the mudstones. In Fulbeck Borehole 5, the upper bed (0.23 m thick at 32.61 m) is very similar to the Lodge Farm Limestones in lithology and fauna. Sporadic, small, phosphatic nodules occur in the mudstones just below the Lodge Farm Limestones, which lie about 2.5 m above the top of the Stubton Limestones. They are exposed up to 1 m in a nearby ditch [8693 4384]. A loose specimen of *Coroniceras* sp. cf. *lyra* from these beds suggests the *lyra* Sub-biozone of the *semicostatum* Biozone.

The **Lodge Farm Limestone** (29.51–30.90 m in Fulbeck Borehole 5) produces a weak to moderate feature, with local limestone brash. Slabs from ditches and small sections consist of hard, grey, weathering pale brown, silty, bioclastic limestone with numerous *Gryphaea* and *Pseudopecten* valves. The *Gryphaea* are commonly abraded and bored and there are local patches of limonite. Up to 0.1 m of limestones are exposed in ditches [8695 4734 and 8681 4712], near Lodge Farm, Stubton. Three similar limestones, between 0.05 and 0.15 m thick, within 1 m of grey mudstone, are well exposed along Foston Beck [8694 4498 to 8702 4495] and further exposures of up to 0.2 m of limestone occur upstream [8725 4436 and 8717 4400]. About 1 m of grey mudstone with several similar rubbly limestones up to 0.2 m thick were also exposed in two ditches [8650 4249 and 8650 4263], east of Foston. In the Fulbeck Airfield boreholes, several thin limestones (six in Fulbeck Borehole 5) with mudstone interbeds, totalling about 1.5 m thick, are assigned to the Lodge Farm Limestone, although individual beds are difficult to correlate and are probably impersistent.

The fauna collected at outcrop consists of gastropods, *Cardinia hybrida*, *C. lanceolata*, *Gryphaea arcuata* trans. to *G. maccullochii*, *G. maccullochii*, pectinid fragments, *Plagiostoma* sp., *Eucoroniceras?*, ostracods and echinoderm fragments. Above the Lodge Farm Limestone, about 2.75 m of grey mudstones with sporadic phosphate nodules yield *Arnioceras* sp. at outcrop. *Agassiceras* sp. and *Euagassiceras?* from about 1 m above the Lodge Farm Limestone in Fulbeck Borehole 14 (at 32.37 m depth) indicate the *scipionianum* Sub-biozone. The inception of the foraminifera *Astacolus semireticulata* in the mudstones between the Lodge Farm and Fenton limestones is an important event in Britain and the North Sea Basin in the *scipionianum* Sub-biozone.

The **Fenton Limestone** (26.76–27.10 m in Fulbeck Borehole 5) lies about 7.5 m above the base of the Foston Member. In the northerly part of the outcrop it forms a moderate to weak feature, for example near Fenton [886 510], with slabby brash scattered locally on the dip slope. Southwards, the limestone typically crops out on the lower part of a scarp slope associated with the overlying Littlegate Limestones, and is readily traced from ditch dredgings. The Fenton Limestone is a distinctive, hard, olive-grey, finely sandy, silty, poorly shelly limestone. The sand, commonly concentrated in lenticles, is most abundant in the northern part of the district. The bed is characterised by common pectinids and numerous small ammonites and, unlike older limestones, generally contains few *Gryphaea*. The limestone, 0.05 to 0.06 m thick, is exposed at two localities in the bed of Foston Beck [8717 4484 and 8721 4347], to the north-north-east and east-north-east of Foston respectively. It is also exposed in the south bank of the River Devon [8319 3753 and 8329 3749], north-west of Stenwith, where it is about 0.25 m thick, with a sharp erosional base.

In the Fulbeck Airfield boreholes, the Fenton Limestone is generally recorded as a single bed, 0.3 to 1.0 m thick or, in a few cases, as a double bed of similar aggregate thickness. It is 0.97 m thick in Fulbeck Borehole 1. In Fulbeck Borehole 5, it is 0.34 m thick, with a 0.26 m bed of highly calcareous mudstone or incipient limestone occurring 0.33 m above it.

Fossils from the Fenton Limestone indicate the *scipionianum* Sub-biozone of the *semicostatum* Biozone. They include foraminifera, serpulids, *Calcirhynchia?*, *Spiriferina* sp., *Camptonectes* sp., *Gryphaea arcuata?* (weakly incurved), *Plagiostoma giganteum*, *Pseudolimea* sp., *Pseudopecten* sp., *Agassiceras scipionianum*, *Arnioceras* cf. *miserabile*, *A.* cf. *semicostatum*, *Arnioceras* or *Coroniceras*, *Euagassiceras* sp., ostracods, echinoderm fragments and palynomorphs.

About 5 m of grey mudstone overlie the Fenton Limestone. The uppermost 1 or 2 m of mudstone, immediately below the Littlegate Limestone, contains common small phosphatic nodules, many with minute borings. This bed normally occupies the crest of the strong feature associated with the Littlegate Limestone and, like the nodule bed immediately below the Stubton Limestones, has been worked locally for brick-making, for example at a small pit [8855 4991] near Fulbeck Airfield.

In Fulbeck Borehole 1, *Agassiceras* sp. has been recovered from 1.2 m above the Fenton Limestone (at 6.75 m), the highest indicator of the *scipionianum* Sub-biozone recorded. An un-named, 0.05 m-thick, calcareous siltstone approximately 1 m above the base yielded *Plagiostoma* sp. and *Euagassiceras resupinatum* from an exposure [8726 4343] along Foston Beck, indicating the *resupinatum* Sub-biozone. *Euagassiceras donovani* was also collected from approximately this level. Ammonites, including *Arnioceras* sp. and *Euagassiceras?*, from the Fulbeck Airfield boreholes, but mainly from Fulbeck Borehole 5, also suggest a *resupinatum* Sub-biozone age; other taxa include *Gryphaea maccullochii*, *Palaeoneilo* sp., *Pseudolimea* sp. and *Pseudopecten* sp..

The **Littlegate Limestone** (21.86–22.07 m in Fulbeck Borehole 5) is generally associated with a very prominent feature, and an extensive dip slope on which brash is patchy. The Fulbeck Airfield boreholes show that two beds of limestone are separated by about 1 m of mudstone; in some of the boreholes the mudstone contains a third thin bed of limestone. In Fulbeck Borehole 1, the lower limestone is a hard, compact, shell-rich rock; the upper one is less shelly and contains a high proportion of fine quartz sand. Other Fulbeck Airfield boreholes show that the lower bed is generally thicker (average 0.25 m) than the upper bed (average 0.20 m), and it seems to be more persistent. In Fulbeck Borehole 5 only the lower bed is present.

In Copper Hill Borehole (between 200.50 and 202.01 m), three limestones are ascribed to the unit, the uppermost being finely sandy. Their thicknesses, in ascending order, are 0.30 m, 0.11 m and 0.18 m. At outcrop in the northern part of the district, the mapped feature is formed by the upper bed; an exposure [8963 5475] showed 0.3 m of unevenly bedded, brown, sandy limestone with ferruginous streaks, containing a sparse fauna of pectinids and *Lucina*. At Green Lane, pieces of ammonite-bearing bioclastic limestone typical of the lower bed were excavated from a ditch [8947 5391], just below a strong feature formed by the sandy limestone.

At Doddington Littlegate, ditch dredgings [about 8730 4708] and field brash [e.g. 8775 4683] yield slabs of hard, grey, shelly, bioclastic, partly silty limestone with irregular, orange-brown, limonite patches. The bed characteristically contains numerous ammonites, and commonly bored *Gryphaea* and *Pseudopecten*. Numerous localities with similar ditch dredgings occur on the long dip-slope outcrop in the south of the district, for example [8455 3760], west of Sedgebrook. Slabs of the rock have been excavated from a pond [8549 3896] at Manor Farm, north of Sedgebrook. The rock was formerly quarried [876 438] at the end of Stonepit Lane, west of Marston.

The fauna of the Littlegate Limestone (mostly from the shelly, lower bed) contains the oldest recorded belemnites from the district and belongs to the *resupinatum* Sub-biozone of the *semicostatum* Biozone. It comprises foraminifera, serpulids, *Spiriferina walcotti*, *Procerithium* sp., *Camptonectes* sp., *Cardinia crassiuscula*, *Gryphaea maccullochii* var. *arcuatiforme*, *Lucina* sp., *Protocardia* sp., *Pseudolimea* sp., *Pseudopecten dentatus*, *Arietites* sp. (very quadrate whole section), *Arnioceras semicostatum*, *Arnioceras miserabile*, *Euagassiceras resupinatum*, *E.* cf. *subtaurus*, *E. terquemi*, belemnites, ostracods, crinoid fragments, echinoderm fragments and *Chondrites* burrows.

The mudstones between the Littlegate and Mill Lane limestones are 2 to 3 m thick and contain scattered large argillaceous limestone nodules in the upper part. In Fulbeck Borehole 5 (between 19.5 and 22.0 m), the mudstones have yielded a fauna consistent with the *resupinatum* Sub-biozone. This includes serpulids, *Antiquilima?*, *Astarte?*, *Bakevellia?*, *Camptonectes subulatus*, *Cuneigervillea?*, *Entolium* sp., *Gryphaea maccullochii*, *Mactromya arenacea*, *Lucina* sp., *Palaeoneilo galatea*, *Plagiostoma giganteum*, *Pleuromya* sp., *Protocardia* sp., *Pseudolimea* sp., *Pseudopecten* sp., *Ryderia doris*, *Arnioceras miserabile* and *A.* cf. *semicostatum*. In Copper Hill Borehole, *Dentalina matutina* was recorded, confirming the upper part of the *A. semicostatum* Biozone. Of the ostracods, the concurrent range of *Kinkelinella triebeli*, *Progonoidea reticulata*, *Ogmoconcha hagenowi* and *Nanacythere elegans* is characteristic of the *semicostatum* Biozone.

The **Mill Lane Limestone** (18.51–19.58 m in Fulbeck Borehole 5) generally forms a weak feature in the southern part of the district, but northwards the feature becomes stronger and has an extensive dip slope, as at Mill Lane [898 547]. The outcrop is characterised by a greyish brown, fine sandy silt soil, generally with little or no brash. Ditches yield debris of grey, weathering fawn to ochreous, silty, finely sandy, shelly limestone grading into highly calcareous siltstone similar to the upper leaf of the Littlegate Limestone. The rock contains numerous pectinids and some *Gryphaea*, and is commonly intensely burrowed. Locally, there is a subdued secondary feature on the dip slope, suggesting that the outcrop is formed by two separate beds. This is confirmed by Fulbeck Airfield boreholes, which typically prove two limestones, up to 0.3 m thick and 1 m apart, within a group of several apparently impersistent limestones spanning a thickness of 2 to 3 m of strata. In Fulbeck Borehole 5, the lower bed is 0.22 m thick and the upper 0.27 m, and they are separated by 0.58 m of mudstone. In Copper Hill Borehole, the Mill Lane Limestone is represented by 0.1 m of sandy limestone at 197.00 m depth overlying 1.0 m of calcareous siltstone. About 0.1 m of sandy bioclastic limestones with *Gryphaea*, *Pseudopecten* and belemnites are exposed in the bed of Foston Beck [8744 4277 and 8757 4267]. About 0.2 m of similar limestone is exposed in the south bank of the River Devon [8351 3729], north of Stenwith.

The fauna collected from the Mill Lane Limestones and associated siltstones and mudstones indicates the upper *semicostatum* Biozone. It includes *Lingula* sp., *Calci-* rhynchia calcaria, *Piarorhynchia juvenis*, *Spiriferina walcotti*, gastropods, *Camptonectes subulatus*, *Cardinia?*, *Chlamys* cf. *textoria*, *Gryphaea maccullochii*, *Modiolus hillanoides*, ostreids, *Plagiostoma* sp., *Protocardia* sp., *Pseudolimea pectinoides*, *Pseudopecten dentatus*, *Pholadomya ambigua*, *Plagiostoma giganteum*, *Protocardia* sp., arietids, *Arnioceras semicostatum*, *Coroniceras* sp., *Cymbites?*, *Euagassiceras* cf. *resupinatum*, *Pararnioceras?*, *Passaloteuthis?*, ostracods, *Pentacrinites* sp., and other echinoderm fragments.

The mudstones above the Mill Lane Limestone are 5 to 6 m thick and one or two thin (about 0.1 m) and evidently impersistent limestones occur in a few of the Fulbeck Airfield boreholes. At outcrop, and especially in ditch dredgings, the uppermost 2 m or so of the unit are characterised by numerous small, commonly bored, phosphatic nodules and ammonites, and sporadic larger argillaceous limestone nodules. These uppermost beds are well exposed along Foston Beck [8734 4007 and 8726 3995], east of Allington, where they contain a rotted ferruginous limestone up to 0.1 m thick near the base.

In Fulbeck Borehole 5 the mudstones, 5.4 m thick, yield an abundant fauna. Fossils from the lower part indicate the *semicostatum* Biozone, *resupinatum* Sub-biozone, but from 3.4 m up (ie. above about 15.1 m depth) are from the *turneri* Biozone. The varied fauna comprises serpulids, an actaeoniniid gastropod, *Antiquilima?*, *Camptonectes subulatus*, *Cardinia* sp., *Gryphaea maccullochii*, *Lucina limbata*, *Meleagrinella?*, *Modiolus* cf. *hillanoides*, ostreids, *Palaeoneilo galatea*, *Plagiostoma giganteum*, *Pleuromya* sp., *Plicatula?*, *Protocardia* sp., *Pseudolimea* sp., *Pseudopecten* sp., *Ryderia* sp., *Tutcheria?*, *Arnioceras semicostatum*, *Caenisites* aff. *turneri* (at 13.45 m), *Caenisites?* (at 15.07 m), coroniceratids, *Cymbites?*, *Euagassiceras?* (at 15.71 m), belemnites and crinoid columnals. The *turneri* Biozone can also be inferred from the inception of the ostracods *Cristacythere crassireticulata* and *Ogmoconchella danica* in the mudstones between the Mill Lane and Highfield Farm limestones in Fulbeck Borehole 5. In Copper Hill Borehole, these mudstones are 6.02 m thick, and the first appearance of *Caenisites*, indicating the *turneri* Biozone, occurs 3.25 m above the base (at 193.75 m depth). The inception of *Kinkelinella intermedia* at 193 m in the same borehole is further confirmation of the *turneri* Biozone. At outcrop, the topmost 2 m of these mudstones yields abundant phosphatised nodules, from ditch dredgings along Foston Beck [8734 4007 and 8726 3995], east of Allington. These also yield ammonites, commonly much bored, including *Arnioceras* sp., *Euagassiceras* cf. *resupinatum*, *Euagassiceras* cf. *donovani*, reworked from beds of the *resupinatum* Sub-biozone.

The **Highfield Farm Limestone** (12.59 to 13.11 m in Fulbeck Borehole 5) forms a weak feature, but its presence can be inferred from ditch dredgings. Slabs, from ditches and an irrigation reservoir [8985 5273] south-east of Highfield Farm House, consist of tough, bluish grey, weathering yellowish brown, silty, slightly sandy, shelly, platy limestone. It characteristically contains large amounts of pyrite, both finely disseminated and in denser masses, which weathers to a brown ochre. *Gryphaea*, some abraded and bored, are abundant; pectinids are common. Reworked phosphatic nodules are also common. Conspicuously pyritous shelly lime-stone, 0.04 m thick, with *Pseudopecten* sp. and phosphatic nodules, is well exposed along Foston Beck [8746 4061], east of Allington. A bed 0.25 m thick, with *Pseudopecten* and *Gryphaea*, is exposed in the bank of the River Devon [8311 3754], north of Stenwith.

Fulbeck Airfield borehole logs show either one or two closely spaced beds of limestone, individually from 0.07 to 0.80 m in thickness. In Fulbeck Borehole 5, a lower 0.15 m-thick bed is separated from an upper 0.02 m bed by 0.35 m of mudstone. Both the limestones and intervening mudstone contain pyritised shells and shell fragments. The bed is represented in Copper Hill Borehole, at 190.85 m depth, by a 0.13 m-thick coarse shell-fragmental limestone, which is sandy in the lower part.

The fauna collected indicates the *turneri* Biozone; it includes foraminifera, *Astarte* sp., *Camptonectes* sp., *Cardinia* sp., *Gryphaea maccullochii*, ostreids, *Plagiostoma gigantum*, *Plicatula* sp., *Pseudolimea* sp., *Pseudopecten* sp., *Arnioceras* sp., *Caenisites* sp., belemnite fragments, ostracods and echinoderm fragments.

The mudstones above the Highfield Farm Limestone are 1.5 to 2 m thick. In Fulbeck Borehole 5, they yield a fauna including *Camptonectes* sp., *Cardinia* sp., *Gryphaea maccullochii*, *Lucina* sp., *Mactromya* sp., *Modiolus* sp., ostreids, *Plagiostoma* sp., *Plicatula?*, *Pseudopecten* sp. and *Angulaticeras?*. In Copper Hill Borehole, 2.19 m of mud-stone above 189.35 m depth yields *Promicroceras* sp. probably from the *turneri* Biozone.

The **Stragglethorpe Grange Limestone** (10.72 to 10.91 m in Fulbeck Borehole 5) forms a poorly defined feature, for example near Stragglethorpe Grange [8995 5270] and in many places it is concealed by drift. The dip slope is covered with a finely sandy loam, but brash is very rare. Slabs from ditches consist of a grey, weathering pale brown, finely sandy, silty, shelly, compact limestone with numerous *Gryphaea* and *Pseudopecten*. The rock is very similar to both the Mill Lane Limestone and the upper leaf of the Littlegate Limestone. About 0.2 m of grey, silty, finely sandy limestone with *Gryphaea* and *Pseudopecten* is exposed [e.g. 8750 4075] along Foston Beck, east of Allington. In the Fulbeck Airfield bore-holes, the Stragglethorpe Grange Limestone is repre-sented by either one bed (as in Fulbeck Borehole 5) or two closely spaced beds of limestone, ranging from 0.1 to 0.3 m thick. The bed was proved in Copper Hill Borehole at 188.31 m depth and comprises 0.35 m of sandy bioturbated limestone which is shell-detrital and finely ironshot in the upper part.

Fossils comprise foraminifera, serpulids, rhynchonel-lid, gastropods, *Gryphaea maccullochii*, *Hippopodium pon-derosum* (poorly inflated type), *Lucina* sp., *Mactromya?*, ostreids, *Modiolus* sp., *Oxytoma?*, *Plagiostoma* sp., *Pseudolimea* sp., *Pseudopecten* sp., *Arnioceras* sp., belemnite fragments, ostracods, fish fragments and palynomorphs.

The mudstones between the Stragglethorpe Grange Limestone and the base of the Brant Mudstone Forma-tion average 5.8 m thick. Though commonly concealed beneath thin drift, they are known from ditch dredgings and the Fulbeck Airfield and Copper Hill boreholes. They were formerly dug near Stenwith [837 368],

probably for brick-making. The uppermost 2 m or so of the mudstone contains grey, argillaceous limestone nodules up to 0.2 m diameter which weather to a yellowish brown colour, like those of the Dry Dod-dington Nodule Bed of the Beckingham Member, and they likewise contain common *Modiolus* sp. Several Fulbeck Airfield boreholes proved a thin pyritised shell layer roughly 0.3 m below the top.

In Fulbeck Borehole 5, the mudstones yield a fauna of *Bakevellia?*, *Camptonectes* sp., *Gryphaea* sp., *Lucina limbata*, *Modiolus* sp., ostreids, *Protocardia* sp., belemnite frag-ments, fish debris and *Chondrites* burrows. In the Copper Hill Borehole these beds, 5.71 m thick, yield bivalves, including *Cardinia* sp., *Gryphaea* sp., *Homomya* sp., *Lucina* sp., *Modiolus hillanoides*, a passaloteuthid belemnite, and the ammonite *Promicroceras* sp., with *Promicroceras* cf. *capri-cornoides* at 2.50 m below the top of the formation. The latter ammonite suggests the presence of the *birchi* Sub-biozone of the *turneri* Biozone. The base of the succeed-ing Brant Mudstone Formation lies within the *oxynotum* Biozone, and therefore the *obtusum* Biozone is either very thin or locally absent, probably due to erosion associated with the base of the Brant Mudstone. In the Copper Hill Borehole, in the upper 4 m of the formation, the inception of *Dentalina varians hauesleri* is indicative of the latest *turneri* or earliest *obtusum* biozones. The ostracod *Kinkelinella vitiosa*, also found at this level, is a good marker of the *obtusum* Biozone elsewhere in Britain.

Brant Mudstone Formation

The Brant Mudstone Formation (Table 6) comprises the poorly defined Obtusum–Oxynotum Clays, Sandrock and 'Upper Clays' of Swinnerton and Kent (1949; 1976), together with the overlying 'Middle Lias mudstones and siltstones' of earlier editions of 1:50 000 Series geological Sheets 114 and 127. The name derives from the River Brant, which flows across the outcrop of the formation between Gelston and west of Waddington [905 452 to 952 637]. The formation is very poorly exposed, and the sequence was originally inferred from mapping and ditch dredgings in the Fulbeck type-area (Brandon et al., 1990).

In order to clarify the stratigraphy of the Brant Mudstone Formation, in 1991, BGS drilled Copper Hill Borehole, near Ancaster. This proved the full thickness of the formation (67.30 m to 182.60 m depth) between the base of the Marlstone Rock Formation and the top of the Scunthorpe Mudstone Formation (Figure 19). Although some problems remain in relating certain mapped beds to the cored succession, this borehole is here proposed as the type-section of the Brant Mudstone Formation. The stratigraphy of the borehole is detailed by Ivimey-Cook et al. (in preparation).

The formation crops out in a 5 to 6 km-wide belt across the western part of the district and forms the rising slopes of the prominent scarp associated with the Marlstone Rock. The formation is 115.30 m thick in Copper Hill Borehole, but thins to about 103 m thick in Gables Farm Borehole, near Sleaford. The formation has a wide distribution on the East Midlands Shelf.

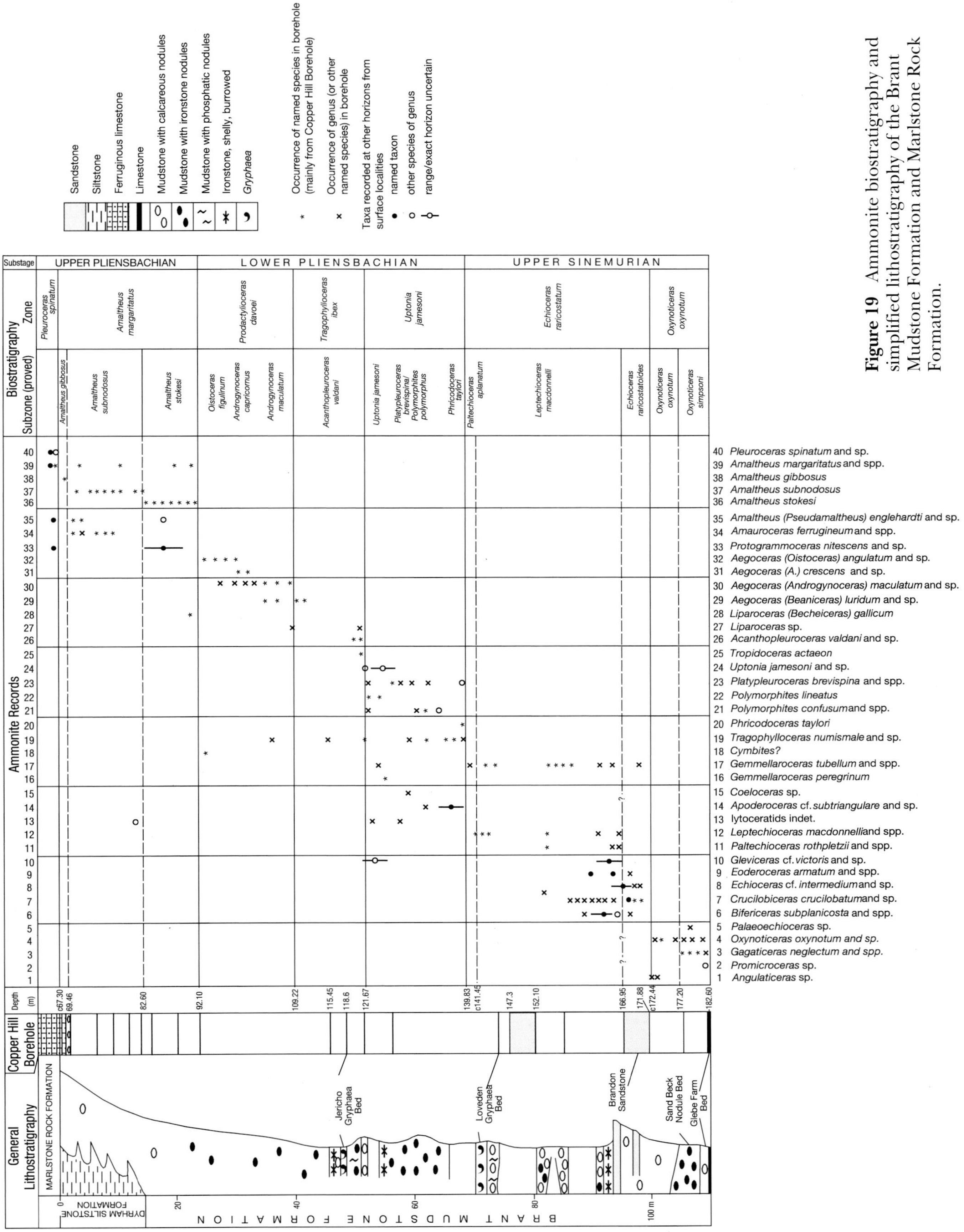

Figure 19 Ammonite biostratigraphy and simplified lithostratigraphy of the Brant Mudstone Formation and Marlstone Rock Formation.

The Brant Mudstone Formation comprises mainly grey, shaly mudstone and silty mudstone, with abundant phosphatic, ironstone (siderite mudstone) and argillaceous limestone nodules at certain horizons (Figure 19). Limestone beds, such as those which characterise the Scunthorpe Mudstone Formation, are very rare. The lower part of the formation includes finely sandy mudstones, and the Brandon Sandstone, which forms a strong feature, lies at about 16 m above the base. These sandy beds are best developed to the north of the district (Brandon et al., 1990, fig. 7), and become increasingly dominant in north Lincolnshire. The sand was probably derived from the north, as with the sandy beds in the upper part of the underlying Foston Member.

The base of the formation is marked by a thin pebbly ferruginous oolite (Glebe Farm Bed). The top is defined by the base of the Marlstone Rock, which rests on grey silty mudstones.

The Brant Mudstone includes the 'Middle Lias mudstones and siltstones' shown on the previous (1972) edition of 1:50 000 Series Geological Sheet 127. These beds are not differentiated in the north of the district, or in Copper Hill Borehole, since there appears to be no lithological distinction by which a boundary line can be mapped. However, beds of 'Middle Lias age' below the Marlstone Rock (i.e. of the *margaritatus* Biozone) have been proved in boreholes and are probably about 25 m thick (Sumbler and Ivimey-Cook, 1996). In the south of the district, around Grantham, the upper part of the *margaritatus* Biozone is more silty and has been differentiated as the Dyrham Siltstone Formation.

The Brant Mudstone formation ranges from the *oxynotum* Biozone of the Upper Sinemurian to the *margaritatus* Biozone of the Upper Pliensbachian. The main faunal elements are bivalves including *Cardinia, Gryphaea, Hippopodium, Pholadomya, Pseudolimea, Pseudopecten*, ammonites and belemnites.

The **Glebe Farm Bed** (4.39–4.58 m in Fulbeck Borehole 5, and 182.40–182.60 m in Copper Hill Borehole) is commonly concealed beneath drift, but is known from a ditch section [8869 4511 to 8874 4493] at Glebe Farm, Hougham, a trench [9029 5097] on Fulbeck Airfield, Fulbeck Borehole 5 and other boreholes, and from numerous ditch dredgings. It rests erosively on the underlying mudstones; the contact may indicate a considerable hiatus in sedimentation.

At Glebe Farm, and in Copper Hill Borehole, the bed consists of two distinct units. The lower unit, up to 0.1 m thick, is a grey, weathering yellowish brown, bioclastic limestone, with abundant bivalve fragments and bored argillaceous limestone pebbles up to 0.08 m diameter. The pebbles, commonly with *Modiolus* cf. *hillanoides*, are reworked nodules from the mudstone below. Fossils, not diagnostic of zonal age, include gastropods, *Camptonectes* sp., *Cardinia* sp., *Gryphaea* sp., *Hippopodium* sp., *Oxytoma inequivalve, Pseudopecten* sp., belemnite fragments and crinoid columnals. A reworked, much bored ammonite identified as aff. *Promicroceras* sp., with adherent ostreids, was recovered from ditch dredgings at Glebe Farm.

The upper unit, typically about 0.3 m thick, but 0.12 m in Copper Hill Borehole, is a ferruginous ooidal limestone, brownish grey where fresh, weathering to deep orange-brown. It contains goethite ooids in a patchily cemented, argillaceous limestone matrix, and varies in texture from a wackestone to a packstone. The goethite of the ooids replaces original iron-manganese silicate (possibly berthierine); locally the ooids are calcitised. It commonly contains scattered small, brown, polished, ovoid phosphatic pebbles (probably reworked nodules), up to 30 mm in diameter. Some contain minute borings. The rock contains a few shells, commonly abraded and bored, and burrows are present. The fauna indicates the *simpsoni* Sub-biozone of the *oxynotum* Biozone. It includes foraminifera, gastropods, *Camptonectes* sp., *Cardinia* sp., *Gryphaea maccullochii, Hippopodium ponderosum, Pachymya* (*Homomya*)?, *Pseudolimea* sp., *Pseudopecten* sp., *Gagaticeras* cf. *gagateum, G.* cf. *neglectum, Oxynoticeras* sp., *Promicroceras*?, and belemnite fragments.

The Glebe Farm Bed is overlain by 1 to 2 m of grey mudstone with sparse argillaceous limestone nodules.

The **Sand Beck Nodule Bed**, though commonly concealed by drift, is exposed in places along Sand Beck [8974 4851 to 9055 5015]. It is also exposed on the north side of the Great North Road along Foston Beck and an adjoining ditch [8770 4169], and has been identified from ditch dredgings at many localities across the district. It is the highest bed proved in the Fulbeck Airfield boreholes, and occurs in Copper Hill Borehole between about 177.2 and 181.5 m.

It consists of 3 to 5 m of grey mudstone with numerous, ovoid, ironstone nodules, which are typically 0.05 to 0.1 m across. They weather orange-brown to red in colour and are commonly veined with calcite and pyrite. Many contain the ammonite *Gagaticeras*. The fauna in the nodules and surrounding mudstones indicates the *simpsoni* Sub-biozone and possibly also the *oxynotum* Sub-biozone of the *oxynotum* Biozone: gastropods, *Gryphaea maccullochii* (wide form), *Gagaticeras exortum, G. gagateum, G. neglectum, Oxynoticeras oxynotum* and belemnite fragments.

The overlying beds form the gentle slope below the Brandon Sandstone scarp and are largely concealed by a fine sandy wash originating from the sandstone. Dredgings and auger samples suggest that they comprise mainly grey mudstone with sporadic argillaceous limestone nodules. Southwards from Stragglethorpe [912 526], a thin, impersistent sandstone lies 2 to 3 m below the Brandon Sandstone and is lithologically similar; locally, it forms a subdued feature. Some of the outcrops interpreted as faulted Brandon Sandstone, south of Brandon [about 898 470], could in fact be this lower bed. The silty mudstone beds immediately below the Brandon Sandstone were formerly worked for brick-making near Hougham [893 450], and south of Brant Broughton [914 531] (Trueman, 1917). The section at the latter pit is reported to have shown 3 m of finely textured sandy clay, with fossils indicating the *oxynotum* Biozone (Trueman, 1918, p.73).

The **Brandon Sandstone** (the Sandrock of Swinnerton and Kent, 1949; 1976) lies 15 to 17 m above the base of the Brant Mudstone. In Copper Hill Borehole it was proved between 167.45 and 171.88 m, with the top lying 15.50 m above the formation base. Estimated to be about

1 or 2 m thick at outcrop, it forms a strong and persistent feature, repeatedly offset by faults, from Brant Broughton in the north, through Stragglethorpe, Brandon, Hougham and Marston, to west of Stenwith [832 364] in the south. The dip slope is characterised by a brown, silty, finely sandy soil with little or no brash. The Brandon Sandstone is a pale grey, weathering buff, silty, shelly, fine-grained calcareous sandstone with scattered specks of mica and abundant burrows. Numerous blocks have been dredged from the River Brant between Brandon and Brant Broughton, and there are small sections [9101 4912, 9106 4922 and 9136 5110] in the river banks near Brandon and at Fulbeck Grange. Fossils tend to be concentrated in lenses, though near the top there are frequent large *Pholadomya* in life position, and also *Modiolus*.

The fauna collected from ditch dredgings and the sparse dip slope field brash mainly indicate the *raricostatum* Biozone, and a specimen each of *Gagaticeras* sp. and *Promicroceras*?, suggesting the *oxynotum* Biozone, may have been reworked. The fossils include: *Cardinia*?, *Gryphaea maccullochii* (wide form), *Modiolus scalprum*, ostreids, *Pholadomya ambigua*, *Pinna* sp., *Plagiostoma* sp., *Plicatula* sp., *Pseudolimea* sp., *Pseudopecten* sp., *Crucilobiceras crucilobatum*, *Echioceras*?, *Gagaticeras* sp., *Gleviceras* cf. *victoris*, *Gleviceras* sp., *Promicroceras*?, belemnites, echinoderm fragments, *Chondrites* and *Gyrolites* burrows and palynomorphs. The ammonites *Bifericeras*?, *Crucilobiceras* sp., a deroceratid tubercule, *Echioceras* sp. and *Gemmellaroceras*? collected from Copper Hill Borehole suggest that the major part of the unit belongs to the *raricostatoides* Sub-biozone (Ivimey-Cook et al., in preparation). The wider age range quoted by Brandon et al. (1990) (including both sub-biozones of the *oxynotum* Biozone) was based on fossils which included specimens from the beds below the sandstone. The foraminifera *Nodosaria issleri* was recorded at 171 m in Copper Hill Borehole, in the lower part of the Brandon Sandstone. This species is confined to the *raricostatum* Biozone in England.

The roughly 20 m-thickness of mudstones, between the Brandon Sandstone and the Loveden Gryphaea Bed, contain large, ovoid, argillaceous limestone nodules. Ditch dredgings reveal that the nodules occur most abundantly at four levels. The lowest nodule bed is about 1.5 m above the Brant Sandstone; nodules from it, dredged from the Brant at many localities, are up to 0.2 m diameter and are pale brownish grey in colour, commonly with a very pale grey or whitish coating. About 7 m above the Brandon Sandstone, similar nodules occur in a bed about 1 to 2 m thick. Locally, for example [9130 4896 and 8862 4005] north-east of Brandon and on Gonerby Moor, a thin bed of grey, bioclastic limestone, up to 0.03 m thick, yielding numerous *Pseudopecten* and *Gryphaea*, also occurs at this horizon; it commonly contains reworked limestone and phosphatic nodules. Roughly 2 to 4 m higher in the sequence, that is, about 10 m above the Brandon Sandstone, similar nodules occur in a third bed 1.5 to 2.5 m thick. Mudstones at about the horizon of this bed were formerly worked at Leadenham Mills (or Broughton Mills) Brickyard [921 531], which closed about 1896 (Trueman 1918). At a number of places, shell-

detrital, commonly pyritous limestone has been found associated with the nodules, for example, in a section [8907 4100] along a drain west of Cliff Farm, underlying a bed with large nodules coalesced into irregular masses. The limestone bed is up to 0.05 m thick, and commonly contains reworked limestone nodules up to 0.2 m across, and smaller phosphatic nodules. At one locality [9261 5430], east of Brant Broughton, the limestone is associated with pyritous argillaceous limestone with a cone-in-cone structure.

About 19 m above the Brandon Sandstone, a fourth nodule bed, 1.5 to 2 m thick, was exposed in a ditch [9135 4675], north-north-east of Loveden Hill. The lower part contains pale grey, spherical, phosphatic nodules, up to about 0.04 m diameter, and the upper part contains brown-skinned, silty, argillaceous limestone nodules, up to 0.3 m diameter. South of Stenwith, only the phosphatic nodules are present. The fourth nodule bed is locally separated from the Loveden Gryphaea Bed by about 1 m of mudstone without nodules.

A varied fauna comprising mainly ammonites and bivalves (Brandon et al., 1990) was collected from the first, second and third nodule beds. It indicates the *raricostatum* Biozone, and, from the second and third beds, the *macdonnelli* Sub-biozone. Specimens collected by Kent from the River Brant [9197 5374], probably from the mudstones overlying the first nodule bed, include *Leptechioceras* cf. *nodotianum* and *Paltechioceras* cf. *rothpletzii*, also suggesting the *macdonnelli* Sub-biozone. The fourth nodule bed yields belemnites but is otherwise poorly fossiliferous.

In Copper Hill Borehole, individual nodule beds could not be recognised in the strata between the Brandon Sandstone and the base of the Loveden Gryphaea Bed (167.45–147.30 m depth). The lowest 15.45 m consists mostly of grey mudstone with scattered limestone nodules and sporadic shell-detrital layers. A 0.07 m-thick *Gryphaea*-rich limestone 10.4 m above the Brandon Sandstone may be that associated with the third nodule bed. A fauna collected from these mudstones, including the ammonites *Bifericeras*, *Crucilobiceras*, *Eoderoceras*, *Gemmellaroceras*, *Leptechioceras* and *Paltechioceras*, confirms that these beds belong to the *macdonnelli* Sub-biozone of the *raricostatum* Biozone. The highest 4.70 m of strata are mostly poorly fossiliferous, fine-grained sandstones, with subordinate siltstones and mudstones; they include a 1.93 m-thick, fine-grained, silty sandstone, with abundant *Chondrites* burrows at 147.37–149.30 m depth. These sandy beds are not recognised at outcrop, although nodules at the equivalent horizon are somewhat silty. The inception of the foraminifera *Marginulina prima interrupta* at 150 m and the disappearance of common to abundant *Dentalina matutina* at 152 m confirms the late *raricostatum* zone. The inception of the ostracods *Kinkelinella foveolata*, *Gammacythere ubiquita* and *Pleurifera harpa* takes place between 150 and 142 m in Copper Hill borehole. These species are generally considered to be indicators of the *jamesoni* Biozone, but are here shown to occur in the upper part of the subjacent biozone.

The **Loveden Gryphaea Bed**, about 22 m above the Brandon Sandstone, does not form a feature but is nevertheless a useful marker; it probably correlates with the

'70 Marker' of the south Midlands (Horton and Poole, 1977). Conspicuous *Gryphaea* in ditch dredgings and field brash have enabled the bed to be mapped across the whole outcrop. In a ditch [9142 4674] near Loveden Hill, it consists of 1.5 to 2 m of bluish grey, shaly, calcareous mudstone yielding abundant large *Gryphaea maccullochii*. It locally includes a 0.08 m bed of grey, platy, shelly limestone in the middle. In Copper Hill Borehole, the Loveden Gryphaea Bed (145.08–147.30 m depth) includes a 0.04 m calcareous mudstone full of *Gryphaea* and belemnites in the upper part. These strata are both underlain and overlain by beds with *Leptechioceras*, indicating the *macdonnelli* Sub-biozone. The extinction of *Nodosaria issleri* at 142 m in Copper Hill Borehole confirms the latest *raricostatum* Biozone. Fossils collected from the many ditch dredgings include *Oppelismilia mucronata*, *Zeilleria* sp., *Camptonectes?*, *Gryphaea maccullochii*, *Gryphaea maccullochii arcuatiforme*, *Gryphaea maccullochii maccullochii*, *Mactromya arenacea*, ostreids, *Pholadomya ambigua*, *Plicatula calloptycus*, *P. spinosa?*, *Pseudolimea* sp., *Pseudopecten* sp. and *Passaloteuthis* spp. A specimen of *Platypleuroceras* sp., quoted by Brandon et al. (1990) as evidence of an early to middle *jamesoni* biozone age, is now thought to have been derived from a higher bed.

Overlying the Loveden Gryphaea Bed, about 4 m of grey mudstone are recognised at outcrop. In Copper Hill Borehole, these mudstones contain thin limestone beds, and have yielded *Leptechioceras* and *Chondrites* burrows.

The grey mudstones occurring between about 4 and 16 m above the Loveden Gryphaea Bed contain abundant ironstone nodules, and form a mappable bed which locally gives rise to a subdued, poorly defined feature. The bed correlates approximately with mudstones containing ironstone nodules and thin limestones in Copper Hill Borehole, between 128.38 m and 140.31 m. The nodules, up to 0.2 m diameter, are composed of smooth, grey, sideritic mudstone, which weathers to brown, red, orange and yellow. Some of the larger nodules are septarian and veined with calcite, and the smaller ones commonly weather into concentric, varicoloured 'skins'. In the upper part of the bed, slabs of burrowed ironstone (similar to that just above the Brandon Sandstone), together with pieces of richly shelly ironstone, have been found at several localities. The mudstones and nodules are generally poorly fossiliferous; however, a few ammonites from the upper part of the bed indicate the middle part of the *jamesoni* Biozone. The fauna includes *Camptonectes* sp., *Pholadomya?*, *Platypleuroceras* cf. *brevispina*, *Polymorphites* cf. *quadratus* and crinoid columnals. *Tragophylloceras* sp. and *Chondrites* burrows are recorded from the lower part of these beds in Copper Hill Borehole. The presence of very rare specimens of the foraminifera *Vaginulinopsis denticulatacarinata*, at 136 m, in Copper Hill Borehole confirms the *jamesoni* Biozone (its inception being at the base of that biozone). The extinction of *Lingulina tenera subprismatica* at 134 m is further support for the presence of the *jamesoni* Biozone.

The overlying 8 m or so of strata are poorly known at outcrop; they comprise a sequence of mudstones with nodules. Some 2 m above the base, a mudstone bed, probably about 1 m thick, contains both large (up to 0.2 m), sometimes septarian, brown-skinned, argillaceous limestone nodules, and small (about 0.05 m), pale grey, phosphatic nodules. About 3.5 m of mudstone with common sideritic nodules overlie this bed; the upper part contains both small (about 0.05 m) phosphatic nodules and large (up to 0.15 m) argillaceous limestone nodules. Limestone nodules from the lower part of this unit have yielded *Modiolus?*, ostreids, *Pholadomya ambigua* and *Platypleuroceras?*. Approximate equivalents to the unit in Copper Hill Borehole yielded ammonites of the *jamesoni* Biozone at depths of about 122 m and below. They include *Platypleuroceras brevispina* at 127.00 m, *Polymorphites* cf. *confusus* at 132.65 m and *P. lineatus* at 122.90 m, as well as *Tragophylloceras* sp. and *Apoderoceras* sp. This sequence also contains a diverse bivalve fauna, including *Gryphaea*. The base of the *ibex* Biozone is drawn at the first occurrence of *Tropidoceras* cf. *acteon* at 121.67 m, closely followed by *Acanthopleuroceras* cf. *valdani* between 121.65 m and 120.31 m.

A pit [9172 3886] dug on the site of the golf course south-west of Belton exposed 2.65 m of mainly mudstone with sideritic ironstone nodules just below the Jericho Gryphaea Bed. The fauna collected included serpulids, *Piarorhynchia* sp., *Tetrarhynchia* cf. *dunrobinensis*, *Gryphaea gigantea*, *Mactromya arenacea*, *Plicatula spinosa*, *Pseudolimea acuticostata*, *Platypleuroceras brevispina*, *Uptonia* sp., *Pseudohastites?*, belemnites and *Isocrinus* columnals. The ammonites were all collected in situ from near the base of the section and indicate the middle subzones of the *jamesoni* Biozone. A loose specimen of *Uptonia jamesoni* indicates the presence of the *jamesoni* Sub-biozone at a higher level in the section.

The **Jericho Gryphaea Bed** occurs approximately 24 m above the Loveden Gryphaea Bed and 46 m above the Brandon Sandstone. It is similar to the Loveden Gryphaea Bed, and comprises about 1 to 2 m of grey mudstone with numerous *Gryphaea* and a thin, platy, bioclastic limestone and sporadic argillaceous limestone nodules. Locally, it forms a slight feature, and is also known from a small exposure [9017 4041] of about 40 mm of bioclastic limestone, west-north-west of Gonerby Grange, and from numerous ditch dredgings, for example [9056 4093] near Jericho Farm, from north-west of Caythorpe [9285 4973, 9272 4946 and 9278 4845] and north of Great Gonerby [8993 4005]. A 0.3 m-thick grey, platy limestone with abundant bivalves exposed in a pit [9208 3884] on the golf course, south-west of Belton, is probably part of the Jericho Gryphaea Bed. In Copper Hill Borehole, approximately correlative strata, between the depths of 118.60 and 121.45 m, comprise calcareous mudstone with nodules and shell fragmental limestone.

Fossils from the Jericho Gryphaea Bed and adjacent beds at outcrop include serpulid tubes, *Gryphaea* cf. *gigantea*, *Pseudopecten* sp., ostreids, *Gleviceras* sp. and belemnite fragments. Brandon et al. (1990) assigned the bed to the *jamesoni* Biozone, but it is now known to lie within the *valdani* Sub-biozone of the *ibex* Biozone. This is established by faunas from Copper Hill Borehole; at 121.67 m, just below the Jericho Gryphaea Bed, the presence of *Tropidoceras* cf. *actaeon* suggests the *masseanum*

Sub-biozone, or the base of the *valdani* Sub-biozone, and *Acanthopleuroceras valdani*, between 121.65 and 120.31 m depth, proves the *valdani* Sub-biozone. The *ibex* Biozone extends over some 12.45 m of beds between 121.67 m and about 109.22 m (Ivimey-Cook et al., in preparation). The thin development of these beds compared with that in the south Midlands implies a relatively condensed sequence.

Fragments of a heavily burrowed, shelly, sideritic ironstone have been found at a few localities [e.g. 9290 4972], from an horizon just above the Jericho Gryphaea Bed. They are thought to have come from strata broadly equivalent to the Pecten Ironstone, of north Lincolnshire (Gaunt et al., 1992). The group of strata including the Jericho Gryphaea Bed and the ironstone bed form the so-called '85 Marker' (Horton and Poole, 1977) which occurs in strata of the late *valdani* to early *luridum* Sub-biozone. In Copper Hill Borehole, these beds were proved between 115.45 m and 118.60 m depth, and comprise silty mudstone containing ironstone nodules, with a 0.3 m-thick silty limestone at the base and a 0.13 m-thick sandy shell-detrital limestone with possible berthierinic grains and ironstone clasts at the top. *Tragophylloceras* sp. was recovered from the upper limestone bed. Evidence for a non-sequence is found at 118.20 m, where rounded pebbles, up to 20 mm in diameter, occur in silty bioturbated mudstones.

The beds above the Pecten Ironstone form a steep slope capped by the Marlstone Rock Formation, but they are generally masked by thin slope deposits. These beds are now known from Copper Hill Borehole (Ivimey-Cook et al., in preparation), in which they are 48.15 m thick. They consist predominantly of pale to medium grey, finely silty mudstones with scattered, commonly septarian, limestone and sideritic ironstone nodules and thin limestone beds.

The fauna of the *ibex* Biozone in Copper Hill Borehole is diverse, with numerous taxa of brachiopods, gastropods, bivalves, cephalopods and some crinoids. The foraminifera fauna includes at 112 m, *Haplophragmoides lincolnensis*, the inception of which forms an excellent marker for the base of the *luridum* Sub-biozone. Mudstones of the *luridum* Sub-biozone continue up to 109.22 m, where the base of the succeeding *maculatum* Sub-biozone (of the *davoei* Biozone) is placed at the first occurrence of *Androgynoceras maculatum*. A pit [9135 3909] on the golf course south-west of Belton, exposed 3.1 m of mainly grey mudstones with silty horizons and sideritic ironstone nodules, probably within the *ibex* Biozone. The fauna included *Camptonectes* sp., *Goniomya*?, *Modiolus* sp., *Palaeoneilo galatea*, *Pseudolimea* sp., *Pseudopecten equivalvis*, *Tutcheria richardsoni*, *Beaniceras*?, belemnites, ostracods and fish scales.

In Copper Hill Borehole, the top of the *davoei* Biozone is taken immediately below an *Amaltheus* at 92.10 m depth. Ammonites show that the *maculatum*, *capricornus* and early part of the *figulinum* Sub-biozones are present. The upper parts of the *figulinum* Sub-biozone may be missing, as *Oistoceras* cf. *angulatum* occurs within 2 m of the top of the zone. The fauna is still diverse, but fossils are less abundant than in the underlying zone. Samples from a borehole [9459 5128], north of Fulbeck, yield a fauna, including *Aegoceras* sp., indicating the *davoei* Biozone (?*capricornus* Sub-biozone), from strata an estimated 32 m below the Marlstone Rock.

The ostracod *Ogmoconcha contractula* is a marker for the *margaritatus* Biozone elsewhere in Britain. Its occurrence at 93 m in Copper Hill Borehole is slightly lower than the first *Amaltheus* at 92.10 m. The presence of *Wicherella semiora kirtonensis* and *Gramannella apostolescui* is significant as these species are characteristic of the *margaritatus* Biozone in Britain.

The base of the *margaritatus* Biozone, defined by the first appearance of *Amaltheus*, is taken at 92.10 m in Copper Hill Borehole; the ostracod *Ogmoconchella contractula*, a marker for the *margaritatus* Biozone, also occurs at approximately this level. The top of the zone is taken arbitrarily at the base of the Marlstone Rock, giving a total thickness of 24.8 m. Ammonites proving the *stokesi* Sub-biozone were found between 92.10 and 82.60 m, and *subnodosus* Sub-biozone between 82.60 m and 69.46 m, at which level *Amaltheus gibbosus* indicates the succeeding *gibbosus* Sub-biozone. Other macrofauna is dominated by 'myid' bivalves such as *Gresslya* and *Homomya*. The uppermost 11 m of the *margaritatus* Biozone were exposed during construction of the Leadenham Bypass [950 510] in 1994, and additional information was gleaned from nearby site investigation boreholes (Sumbler and Ivimey-Cook, 1996). The succession is closely comparable, on a bed-for-bed basis, to that at Copper Hill, although the erosion surface beneath the Marlstone Rock has cut down to a slightly lower level. The strata are dominated by grey mudstones, similar to those lower in the Brant Mudstone Formation, but become somewhat silty with sandy lenticles in the uppermost part. A unit of fine-grained sandstone and siltstone occurs in the topmost 2 m. This unit, belonging to the *gibbosus* Sub-biozone, is also present at Copper Hill; it represents the feather-edge of the Dyrham Siltstone Formation. Several bands of sideritic ironstone nodules in the succession produce abundant fragments of limonite in the soil on the outcrop. Three primary beds of argillaceous sideritic ironstone also occur; these contain scattered rounded grains of green berthierine, probably diagenetically altered faecal pellets. In the highest bed, overlain by the erosive base of the Marlstone Rock, the berthierine is largely altered to whitish kaolinite. These berthierine-bearing beds, also present in Copper Hill Borehole, probably relate to minor transgressive events.

Dyrham Siltstone Formation

In the south Midlands, a unit of siltstone and silty mudstone, the Dyrham Siltstone Formation, occurs beneath the Marlstone Rock, its base occurring in the *davoei* Biozone in its Gloucestershire type area. Traced northwards, the silty beds become less well developed and merge progressively, from the base, into mudstones by lateral passage and interdigitation. The boundary of the Dyrham Siltstone Formation as shown on geological maps is thus both diachronous and somewhat arbitrary. In the northern part of the Grantham district, the Dyrham Siltstone has not been distinguished (although the uppermost 2 m of Brant Mudstone, of the *gibbosus*

Sub-biozone, may alternatively be assigned to this formation; see above). However, in the southern part of the district, between the prominent hill [905 402] west of Gonerby Grange and the Barrowby area [890 356], the uppermost 15 m of strata are considered to be sufficiently silty to be distinguished as the Dyrham Siltstone Formation.

The formation is composed predominantly of grey silty mudstone interbedded with fine-grained, flaggy, ferruginous sandstone and nodular ironstone. The base is generally gradational. However, a sandstone, which locally forms a slight feature, defines the base of the unit from Barrowby eastwards to Mill Hill and Stubbock Hill [877 366 to 888 375], on the slopes east of Great Gonerby [about 907 378] and on a hill [around 916 383], north of Manthorpe. The lowest 0.4 m of this sandstone are exposed in a small section [9043 3591] north of Barrowby Stream, and slabs also occur along a stream [9034 3844], near Manor Farm. This bed may correspond with a thin bed of calcareous sandstone in the lower part of the *subnodosus* Sub-biozone, proved 12.48 m below the Marlstone Rock in Copper Hill Borehole. A second bed of sandstone slightly higher in the succession, crops out east of Rectory Farm [8940 3745 to 8987 3667], between Great Gonerby and Barrowby. A third ferruginous sandstone about 2.5 to 3 m below the Marlstone Rock, which forms a feature along the north side of the hill [about 905 399], southwest of Gonerby Grange, may equate with the sandstone in the *gibbosus* Sub-biozone at Leadenham and Copper Hill.

The Dryham Siltstone was formerly well exposed in brick clay pits [around 905 376] at Gonerby Hill Foot and in a pit [around 905 355] at Earlsfield (Jukes-Browne, 1885, p.36; Trueman, 1918, p.107). These pits, known as Rawdon's, Challan's, and Hempsted's pit respectively, provided an aggregate section through 19 m of strata below the Marlstone Rock. Rawdon's Pit [905 376] still provides a degraded and discontinuous section through 16.2 m of grey mudstone with sideritic ironstone nodules. The mudstone coarsens upwards to become silty and sandy, and is capped by a 0.4 m-thick, flaggy, ferruginous, shelly sandstone. A cutting [9008 3778 to 9012 3770] on the west side of the Grantham Road, Gonerby, exposes 7.3 m of grey, silty, micaceous mudstones reaching to within 2 m of the top of the Dryham Siltstone. There are common laminae of fine-grained sandstone, and a 0.6 m-thick bed 5 m above the base of the section. Fossils collected include *Dacryomya gaveyi*, *Grammatodon insons*, *Meleagrinella* sp., *Palaeoneilo galatea*, *Protocardia truncata*, *Pseudolimea acuticostata*, cf. *Amaltheus wertheri* and *Amaltheus margaritatus*; the last suggests the *subnodosus* Sub-biozone of the *margaritatus* Biozone.

Marlstone Rock Formation

The Marlstone Rock Formation (formerly Marlstone Rock Bed) is a hard, variably ferruginous, calcareous, arenaceous unit that represents a regressive, high-energy episode in the East Midlands Shelf sea, between the deeper water, more quiescent, depositional phases of the underlying and overlying mudstone formations. It is relatively resistant to erosion and forms a prominent scarp across the district. Much of the outcrop was worked for iron ore during the nineteenth century and the early part of this century, and there is considerable information on its thickness and composition, which is summarised by Lamplugh et al. (1920) and Whitehead et al. (1952).

The outcrop of the Marlstone Rock produces a step in the scarp slope of Lincoln Edge, and broader dip slopes on outliers, especially in the south of the district around Gonerby and Barrowby. The recorded thickness varies from about 2.5 to 7.3 m along the outcrop; a typical thickness is 4 to 5 m. The formation is particularly thin near the northern edge of the district, being about 2 m thick north of Leadenham; it disappears completely at Welbourn, about 1 km beyond the district boundary, and is absent northwards to beyond Lincoln. Boreholes south of Sleaford, in the east of the district, also indicate thicknesses of 4 to 5 m. Over much of the outcrop, especially on the dip slopes of the outliers, decalcification and erosion have reduced the Marlstone Rock to a rubble cover on the underlying mudstones, and in some areas, notably around Caythorpe, iron ore workings have removed the formation completely or left only a basal sandstone. Cambering of the Marlstone Rock is common, especially on the eastern, down-dip, side of the Gonerby and Barrowby outliers.

In the southern part of the district, the Marlstone Rock consists of two subdivisions (Plate 3). The basal part is a massive calcareous, more or less ferruginous sandstone, the 'sandrock' of the iron ore workers. This rests with apparent conformity on the underlying strata, and sedimentologically could be regarded as part of the Dyrham Siltstone Formation. The upper part of the Marlstone Rock is a ferruginous, commonly ooidal limestone, which constitutes the iron ore. It rests erosively on the sandrock, or on a thin bed of mudstone which may separate these units; its base is commonly marked by a thin bed of conglomerate, containing pebbles of material reworked from the underlying beds. Northwards, the sandrock dies out, probably because of overstep by the upper unit, such that the latter comes to rest directly on the Brant Mudstone Formation. In Copper Hill Borehole and Leadenham Road cutting (Sumbler and Ivimey-Cook, 1996), the ooidal ironstone unit of the Marlstone Rock, with its basal conglomerate, rests on thin concretionary ironstone beds at the top of the Brant Mudstone Formation; like the sandrock, these may be mapped with the Marlstone Rock.

The upper part of the formation, where unoxidised at depth, is a dark greenish grey fine-grained ooidal packstone to grainstone, composed of berthierine ooids in darker green berthierine-rich mud matrix, or blackish crystalline siderite cement. Oxidation produces a rich reddish brown limonitic rock, the effect being to increase the relative proportion of iron so that the formation has a greater potential as an iron ore at or near the surface. For this reason, quarrying usually ceased where overburden was more than a few metres in thickness (Chapter Eight).

The sandrock facies in the lower part of the Marlstone Rock yields little fauna, but the likelihood is that it belongs to the *margaritatus* Biozone. By contrast, the ooidal ironstone facies is commonly fossiliferous. The most

Plate 3

Marlstone Rock overlying Brant Mudstone Formation in a roadside cutting [871 357] west of Barrowby.

The hard ferruginous limestone, which forms the basal bed of the Marlstone Rock, features liesegang rings of iron oxide, and stands out above the softer Brant Mudstone. It is overlain successively by a thin mudstone bed and a slabby conglomerate of fine-grained ironstone clasts in a sandstone matrix. (A15412)

abundant macrofossils are brachiopods, notably the terebratulid *Lobothyris punctata* and the rhynchonellid *Tetrarhynchia tetrahedra* which which can occur profusely, in clusters. Bivalves notably *Pseudopecten*, are also fairly common. Ammonites are generally scarce, but *Pleuroceras* cf. *spinatum*, indicating the *spinatum* Biozone was recorded in debris from a pit [9001 3625] near Barrowby Road, Grantham. The topmost part of the formation in Lincolnshire belongs to the earliest Toarcian *tenuicostatum* Biozone (Howarth, 1980), as confirmed by a specimen of *Dactylioceras* from Leadenham cutting [9505 5112] (Sumbler and Ivimey-Cook, 1996). Foraminifera from the Marlstone Rock of Copper Hill Borehole also support this subdivision; the inception of *Reinholdella macfadyeni* suggests a late *spinatum* age (*hawskerense* Sub-biozone) for the lower part of the formation and *Lenticulina varians* (subspecies D) suggests the *tenuicostatum* Biozone near the top (Ivimey-Cook et al., in preparation).

Despite the number of old quarries in the formation, sections of the Marlstone Rock in the district are now uncommon. One of the most extensive exposures was at Frieston Ironstone Quarries [938 475 to 929 466]. Whitehead et al. (1952) recorded a composite section there:

	Thickness m
Soil, sandy loam and ferruginous limestone rubble	1.2
Limestone, brownish, shelly, ferruginous; and ironstone, calcareous; upper part flaggy and fissile; bluish green patches, especially towards base	2.4
Limestone, grey, hard, crystalline, shelly, sandy; or sandstone, calcareous; with pale bluish grey and pale brownish patches	0.5

The best sequences recorded more recently have been in Copper Hill Borehole (Figure 20; Ivimey-Cook et al., in preparation), and in two road cuttings near Barrowby. The section in one of the cuttings, on the Grantham A1 bypass [8939 3506], was recorded by Mr R J Wyatt when the road was under construction:

	Thickness m
Rusty brown sandy loam with abundant ironstone fragments	1.22
Limestone, rusty brown, ferruginous, ooidal, very fine-grained, flaggy; abundant rhynchonellids in basal 0.9	1.52
Limestone, rust brown (greyish green where unweathered), ferruginous, sandy, slightly ooidal, fine-grained, massive; abundant rhynchonellids and terebratulids, some bivalves; some lenses of grey, shelly, crystalline limestone	0.38
Sandstone, rusty brown, ferruginous, calcareous, fine-grained, fairly compact; in basal 0.3 becoming a more compact, very fine-grained, slightly shelly limestone which is greyish green where unweathered	1.22

Figure 20 Sections and biostratigraphical classification of the Whitby Mudstone Formation in, and adjacent to, the district. The south Grantham area section is based on brickpit exposures, notably Rudd's Brick Yard [SK 913 345] (see Trueman, 1918; Howarth, 1992).

	Thickness m
Limestone, rusty brown to greyish green, ferruginous, sandy, conglomeritic, massive; abundant small mudstone pebbles which are variously calcareous and ferruginous seen to	0.53

The other road cutting [8712 3570], west of Barrowby, shows a massive ferruginous limestone at the base of the formation, overlain by ironstone conglomerate, and resting on silty mudstone of the Brant Mudstone Formation (Plate 3). More recently, a section of the Marlstone Rock at Leadenham has been described by Sumbler and Ivimey-Cook (1996).

Whitby Mudstone Formation

The term 'Whitby Mudstone Formation', defined by Powell (1984) in the Cleveland Basin, replaces the 'Upper Lias' of former use. It consists largely of grey mudstone with subordinate nodular limestone, and platy calcareous siltstone beds especially near the base. The junction between the Whitby Mudstone and the Marlstone Rock is sharp and uneven, and is probably an erosional non-sequence. The basal beds of the formation belong to the *Harpoceras falciferum* Biozone; there seems to be no evidence to support Truman's (1918) inclusion of these beds in the *Dactylioceras tenuicostatum* Biozone (Howarth, 1992). The upper part of the formation belongs to the *Hildoceras bifrons* Biozone; the younger beds that occur in the type Whitby Mudstone of Yorkshire are absent beneath the unconformity at the base of the succeeding Inferior Oolite Group. The outcrop crosses the district from north to south, comprising most of the slope of the Lincolnshire Limestone scarp. Landslips and associated mudflows down the scarp face have obscured much of the outcrop, especially in the north of the district, and exposures are uncommon. The best section within the district is provided by Copper Hill Borehole (Figure 20; Ivimey-Cook et al., in preparation), and some information from the Leadenham area is given by Sumbler and Ivimey-Cook (1996). Brickclay workings immediately south of Grantham, just beyond the district boundary, were described by Trueman (1918). The ammonites cited have been re-evaluated by Howarth (1992) (Figure 20).

Recorded thicknesses of the formation in the district are mostly between 40 and 50 m. The changes in thickness are irregular and can be considerable over a short distance. In the northernmost part of the outcrop, the formation may be as little as 38 m thick, but in a borehole [9618 4818] at Kesteven Agricultural College, only 6 km farther south, 63.6 m of Whitby Mudstone was

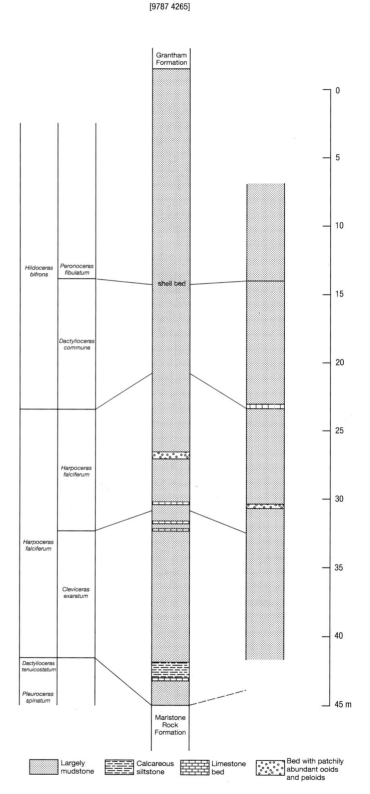

recorded. Thicknesses of about 42 m are typical around Grantham, but the formation is approximately 60 m thick at Great Ponton, 4.5 km to the south. Deep boreholes in the east of the district show a range from 47 to 54 m. Much of the thickness variation is likely to be due to differential erosion prior to deposition of the overlying formations.

The Whitby Mudstone Formation is 46.39 m thick in Copper Hill Borehole (Figure 20). The basal 1.8 m consists of mostly fissile, olive-grey mudstones with fish fragments. Fish fragments are even more abundant in the overlying 80 mm-thick laminated limestone, which is overlain by 1.27 m of muddy, calcareous siltstone with the ammonite, *Cleviceras elegans,* which is diagnostic of the topmost one-third of the *exaratum* Sub-biozone. Above the siltstone is a further 9 m of grey mudstones, with some fish debris, and also *Cleviceras* and *Dactylioceras.* This basal part of the formation in the borehole probably equates with the 'Fish Beds Member' of Horton et al., (1980). Foraminifera are very rare within this thickness of approximately 12 m. This is probably due to the reduced oxygenation at the sea bed during the *exaratum* Subzone. The agglutinating species *Ammodiscus siliceus* is the most common. Above 51 m however, foraminifera become more abundant and calcareous benthonic species appear, including *Citharina collietzi* and common to abundant *Reinholdella macfadyeni*, indicating a return to more oxygenated waters of the *falciferum* Sub-Biozone.

Above the grey mudstones in the borehole are three thin limestone beds, within 2.1 m of stratal depth, which consist largely of pale to medium grey, mostly calcareous, very fossiliferous mudstone with calcareous nodules. Ammonites collected include both *Cleviceras exaratum* and *Harpoceras falciferum*, indicating that these beds span this subzonal boundary. The lower part of the sequence is probably broadly equivalent to the 1.55 m of interbedded calcareous siltstone and mudstone with limestone nodules seen in a ditch [9462 3811] east of Belton Park, where it is only some 7 m above the Marlstone Rock. These beds form a discontinuous topographical feature along the lower slopes of the Lincoln Edge scarp between Grantham and Ancaster, in places bearing grey, hard argillaceous limestone brash. A slightly higher topographical feature, east of Belton Park, may mark the position of the highest of the three thin limestones in Copper Hill Borehole although landslip strongly affects topography in this area. Overlying that highest limestone in the borehole, above 49 m depth, is a further 3.36 m of grey, calcareous mudstone with abundant *Dactylioceras* and *Harpoceras*, capped by a 0.38 m mudstone bed containing many dark brown ooids and peloids. The probable equivalent in the south Grantham sections (Figure 20) was described by Trueman (1918) as 'rubbly ferruginous limestone and clay with scattered oolite grains', 0.15 m thick. This bed is a local representative of the beds with phosphatic ooids which were recorded by Horton et al., (1980) from the *falciferum* Biozone at many localities in the English Midlands.

The ooid-bearing bed in Copper Hill Borehole is overlain by a further 16.5 m of grey, calcareous, shelly, commonly bioturbated mudstones with abundant *Dactylioceras* throughout, and particularly abundant ammonites and bivalves about 3 to 4 m below the top. *Harpoceras* occurs in the lowest 5 m, suggesting that the boundary between the *Harpoceras falciferum* and *Hildoceras bifrons* biozones lies at approximately 40 m depth. The base of the *H. bifrons* Biozone in the south Grantham sections was drawn by Howarth (1992) at the bottom of a 0.3 m-thick 'earthy' limestone recorded there by Trueman (1918). The inception of the ostracods *Kinkelinella persica, K. sermoisensis* and *K. intrepida* at 45 m permits correlation with the Rutland sequences described by Bate and Coleman (1975). Their concurrent range is *commune* Sub-biozone (? and upper *falciferum* Sub-biozone), according to Bate and Coleman, although Copper Hill Borehole shows that the ranges of *K. sermoisensis* and *K. intrepida* should be extended. The disappearance of *Praeschuleridea pseudokinkelinella* at or near the top of the *commune* Sub-biozone is at 33 m depth in Copper Hill Borehole.The highest 11.5 m of the formation in Copper Hill Borehole consists of interbedded massive and fissile, finely micaceous, grey mudstones. They are less calcareous than the underlying beds and yield fewer ammonites. Apart from the top few metres, the beds yield an abundant bivalve fauna including *Nuculana ovum*. Foraminifera are common, but of low diversity. The disappearance of *Dentalina terquemi*, at 29 m, is indicative of the lower part of the *bifrons* Biozone; Copestake and Johnson (1989) place the extinction at approximately the base of the *fibulatum* Sub-biozone. At 23 m, there is a major faunal change to one dominated by agglutinating taxa, including abundant *Ammodiscus siliceus* and common *Trochammina canningensis*. *Ammodiscus yonsnabensis*, a good marker in the North Sea and Yorkshire for the late Toarcian to early Bajocian, occurs rarely. This sequence is equated with the 'Leda ovum Beds' at the top of the formation in Northamptonshire and north Oxfordshire (Horton et al., 1980). Probable equivalent strata, comprising about 10 m of pale grey clay, poorly exposed immediately below the Northampton Sand, were seen in a ditch section [958 433] near High Field House, West Willoughby.

The Whitby Mudstone in this district was deposited in a relatively deep sea, with bottom conditions varying from anoxic, with a limited benthos, to better oxygenated, coarser-grained substrates with a more diverse fauna. The thin limestones between 12 and 14 m above the base in Copper Hill Borehole probably indicate a slight shallowing of the sea, coeval with the more pronounced shallowing and higher energy environments in which the Cephalopod Limestones Member was deposited farther south (Horton et al., 1980).

Within the district, the formation is limited to the early Toarcian *Harpoceras falciferum* and *Hildoceras bifrons* ammonite biozones; younger Toarcian zones and probably the earliest part of the Aalenian are absent.

FIVE
Middle Jurassic: Inferior and Great Oolite groups

The Inferior Oolite Group and Great Oolite Group are a variable sequence of limestones and siliciclastic rocks, which lies between the mudstones of the Lias Group below and the Ancholme Group above. A similar sequence on Humberside was described under the term Redbourne Group (Gaunt et al., 1992). The base of the Inferior Oolite Group is generally at the base of the Northampton Sand. A minor unconformity at the top of the Lincolnshire Limestone separates the Inferior and Great Oolite groups. The top of the Great Oolite Group is taken at the junction of the Cornbrash with the Kellaways Clay. Tentative biostratigraphical and chronostratigraphical correlation is shown in Table 7. Correlation is made difficult by the scarcity of age-diagnostic fossils throughout much of the sequence.

INFERIOR OOLITE GROUP

Northampton Sand Formation

The Northampton Sand, of Aalenian age, unconformably overlies the Whitby Mudstone. It is composed of fine-grained ferruginous sand or sandstone with segregations of iron ore that locally dominate the sequence. Boreholes prove that the formation reaches a maximum thickness of 4.6 m in the south near its outcrop, but is thinner throughout most of the district, and is absent locally. The formation was formerly exploited for iron ore at Leadenham.

The formation is fairly continuous along the upper slopes of the Lincoln Edge escarpment. Breaks in the outcrop were identified adjacent to a fault beside The Beck, south of West Willoughby, and near Sudbrook Hill Farm [9643 4520] on the opposite side of the Ancaster Gap; the formation is also absent in the neighbourhood of Welbourn [968 528 to 974 540], in the north of the district. Establishing the geographical limits of the formation at depth is complicated by confusion with the overlying Grantham Formation in some borehole records. A 3 km-wide strip along the southern edge of the district, which was investigated in 1959 for commercial potential, provides the only integrated data concerning concealed distribution. The data show that the formation is absent around Welby village and in the area east of Welby Lodge and Roman Cafe, which are approximately 4 km down dip, near the A52 Grantham–Boston road.

The Northampton Sand is generally obscured at the surface by wash from the overlying Lincolnshire Limestone, but debris forms a brash at a few localities. Such debris typically comprises soft, sandy limonitic ironstone, rarely with sparse shell fragments. The limonite is typically developed in concentric layers around cores of less weathered material ('boxstone' structure) and ranges from yellow through shades of brown to lustrous purple and black where more massive. Examination with a lens commonly reveals tiny subspherical voids presumably left by the solution of ooids. A large block of brecciated oxidised ooidal ironstone in a rust-brown limonitic ironsand matrix was seen [9586 52290] near Dove's Quarry, Leadenham. Where unweathered, the Northampton Sand of this northern part of the district is a greenish, more or less ooidal and sandy sideritic or berthierine-bearing ironstone. A large block of dark bluish grey ferruginous sandstone at the Welbourn covered reservoir [9742 5403] may be such material from the reservoir excavation. At the time of survey there were a few chance minor exposures provided by tree roots uplifted by a gale. At Belton Ashes [9505 3988] a metre of fine-grained ferruginous sandstone was exposed, with downward gradation into pale blue-grey, shaly mudstone of the Whitby Mudstone. The basal 0.2 m of sandstone are rich in small rounded (25 mm diameter) phosphatic concretions. The formation was also exposed during construction of the Leadenham by-pass (Sumbler and Ivimey-Cook, 1996). Details of the Northampton Sand are otherwise restricted to those from historical records of boreholes and exposures, including sections in a fractured anticline along the railway west of Ancaster Station (Jukes-Browne, 1885) and the ironstone prospect boreholes in the south of the district (Berridge, 1993).

The Northampton Sand was formerly worked at Dove's Quarry [961 524] (immediately west of the present Leadenham Quarry) between 1920 and 1925, where it averaged 2.1 m in thickness. The quarry is now entirely restored and there are no sections visible, but Wedd (in Lamplugh et al., 1920, p.165) gave a generalised section showing from 1.8 to 2.3 m of brown 'boxy' ooidal ironstone with some blue cores. A more detailed section was recorded by W D Evans in 1941; as given by Hollingworth and Taylor (1951, p.87) and Evans (1952, p.324) it lacks part of Evans' original, which is therefore reproduced below. Between the Grantham Formation and the blue clays of the Whitby Mudstone, it showed 2.65 m of brown sandy, partly ooidal ironstone with boxstone structure, and with a bed of plant-rich clay in the upper part:

	Thickness m
8. Rich brown sandy boxstone ironstone.	0.61
7. Blue-green clays with numerous plant fragments	0.05 to 0.10
6. Sandy boxstone ironstone	0.56
5. Ferruginous marl with boxstone	0.05
4. Rich brown ooidal boxstone ironstone; uneven base	0.25

Table 7 Stratigraphy of the Inferior and Great Oolite groups in the Grantham district (partly after Cope et al., 1980b, and Ashton, 1980).

Stage	Zone	Formation		Group
Callovian (in part)	Herveyi	Upper	Cornbrash	Great Oolite Group
Bathonian	*Clydoniceras discus*	Lower	Cornbrash	Great Oolite Group
Bathonian	*Clydoniceras discus*		Blisworth Clay	Great Oolite Group
Bathonian	*Oxycerites orbis*		Blisworth Clay	Great Oolite Group
Bathonian	*Procerites hodsoni*		Blisworth Limestone	Great Oolite Group
Bathonian	*Morrisiceras morrisi*		Blisworth Limestone	Great Oolite Group
Bathonian	*Tulites subcontractus*		Blisworth Limestone	Great Oolite Group
Bathonian	*Procerites progracilis*		Rutland Formation	Great Oolite Group
Bathonian	*Asphinctites tenuiplicatus*		Rutland Formation	Great Oolite Group
Bathonian	*Zigzagiceras zigzag*			Great Oolite Group
Bajocian	*Parkinsonia parkinsoni*			
Bajocian	*Strenoceras garantiana*			
Bajocian	*Strenoceras subfurcatum*			
Bajocian	*Stephanoceras humphriesianum*			
Bajocian	*Emileia sauzei*			
Bajocian	*Witchellia laeviuscula*	Upper	Lincolnshire Limestone	Inferior Oolite Group
Bajocian	*Hyperlioceras discites*	Lower	Lincolnshire Limestone	Inferior Oolite Group
Aalenian	*Graphoceras concavum*		Lincolnshire Limestone	Inferior Oolite Group
Aalenian	*Ludwigia murchisonae*		Grantham Formation	Inferior Oolite Group
Aalenian	*Leioceras opalinum*		Northampton Sand Formation	Inferior Oolite Group

Not to scale. Vertical ruling indicates 'missing' strata.

	Thickness
	m
3. Dull greyish brown ironstone with rolled fragments of quartz, pale grey mudstone and pale yellow fine-grained ferruginous limestone. Sandy texture, but ooidal with large amounts of chamosite and occasional developments of pyrite	0.28 to 0.36
2. Sandy clay ironstone with boxstone structure	0.18
1. Soft clay ironstone. Seen to 0.46 and proved by augering to	0.61

Grantham Formation

The Grantham Formation (formerly Lower Estuarine Series) succeeds the Northampton Sand and is unconformably overlain by the Lincolnshire Limestone. It is dominated by thinly bedded sandstones, siltstones and mudstones, rich in plant material, with traces of coal and sideritic ironstone. Debris from trial pits near Fulbeck [9592 5084; 9586 5088] comprise hard grey massive sandstone, soft brown laminated sandstone, and rubbly, greyish brown sandstone with bivalve shell fragments and clay wisps. A characteristic lithology found as brash in several localities is a coffee-brown, rubbly, calcareous sandstone with abundant serpulid fragments. Material from burrows [9568 5130] south of Stonepit Plantation, comprises white, unconsolidated sand, and soft, white to orange, well-bedded sandstone with clay laminae and lignite fragments. Differentiating this formation from the Northampton Sand is difficult, particularly in old borehole records, as both formations include ferruginous, plant-rich and arenaceous lithologies. Despite this, it is inferred that the formation is more widespread at depth than is the Northampton Sand. However, its outcrop is more restricted: between Fulbeck in the north and Londonthorpe in the south there are only two records at crop. These are near Bleak House, Fulbeck [958 491] and Heath Farm, Sudbrook [969 451]. Former sections near Ancaster Station were described by Jukes-Browne (1885).

The formation is probably of the order of 1 to 3 m thick for much of the subcrop, but Copper Hill Borehole [9787 4265] (Ivimey-Cook et al., in preparation) proved 13.6 m, the thickest succession in the district. Burton Lodge Borehole [1142 4384], Burton Pedwardine, proved 5.2 m of Grantham Formation, and the formation also reaches about 5 m in thickness near Welbourn [974 540], in the north of the district. In the area prospected for iron in the south of the district, thicknesses of over 2 m, with a maximum of 3.51 m [0400 3600], are confined to a 4 km area west and north-west of Newton, but in the west of the prospected area the thickness is generally less than 0.5 m. It is absent between Welby and Londonthorpe and locally elsewhere. In general, there is no reciprocal relationship in thickness between the Grantham Formation and the Northampton Sand, although, locally, the former cuts into or through the latter in channel structures (e.g. at Copper Hill, and near Welbourn).

In Copper Hill Borehole the Grantham Formation is anomalously thick, being proved between from 3.76 to 17.31 m depth. But the lithology is probably typical of the formation. Here, the lower 4.84 m consists predominantly of siltstone and sandstone, and in the upper 8.71 m carbonaceous mudstone is interbedded with sandstone and siltstone, in units up to 0.75 m thick. At the base, 0.34 m of detrital, dominantly rudaceous coal is recorded; this, and fragmental coal occurring in higher beds, were derived from contemporary deposits. Overlying thinly interbedded mudstone and sandstone with fine-grained sandstone pebbles, passes up into sandstone, interlaminated with mudstones and including pebbles and thin lenses of coal. A 2 mm-thick continuous layer of coal at 5.73 m is underlain by 0.28 m of greenish black to olive-black shaly mudstone thought to be a seatearth.

Rare, possibly reworked, foraminifera are present, at 15 m depth, near the base of the formation in Copper Hill Borehole. They comprise common *Ammodiscus siliceus* and *Trochammina canningensis*. At 6 m, very rare moulds of ostracods are present, apparently freshwater forms such as *Darwinula* and *Klieana*?

Natural exposures are now absent but recorded details of former sections are available from the same sites as quoted for the Northampton Sand: Dove's Quarry at Leadenham, Ancaster Station, and the ironstone prospecting strip at the southern edge of the district (see references above). In addition, Sumbler (1993b) quotes two further sections reported in the Leadenham area, including reference to shelly, sandy limestone.

Lincolnshire Limestone Formation

The outcrop of the Lincolnshire Limestone runs north to south through the centre of the district, forming the prominent escarpment of the Lincoln Edge. It rests with local non-sequence on the Grantham Formation and older rocks, and is unconformably overlain by the Rutland Formation. It is the major limestone unit in the Jurassic succession of the north Midlands and has some economic importance.

The formation was subdivided into members and beds by Ashton (1980) (Table 8), based on quarry sections. His classification has recently been supported by down-dip borehole analysis (Emery and Dickson, 1991). Generally, individual quarry sections can be classified in terms of Ashton's scheme (Figure 21), although in most instances the units cannot be mapped between sections, and so the correlations cannot be confirmed. The formation is divided into two parts, the Lower and Upper Lincolnshire Limestone (Kent, 1966), with further local lithological subdivision where possible.

The base of the limestone commonly lies only a few metres below the crest of the west-facing scarp slope of the Lincoln Edge. The outcrop varies in width from 0.5 km on the southern outskirts of Ancaster to 8 km elsewhere. The typically long dip slopes of shallow stony soil on bedrock are locally known as heaths, reflecting their poor natural fertility. The recent practice of using such land for grain production has now been curtailed due to concern over nitrate pollution of groundwater;

Table 8 Stratigraphy of the Lincolnshire Limestone.

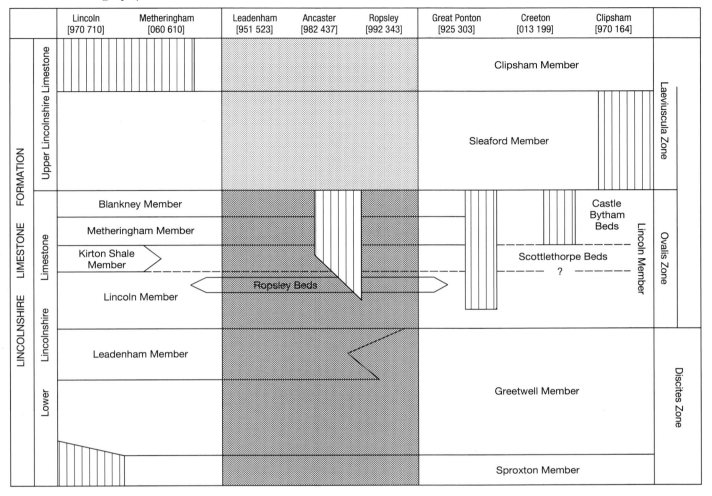

the Lincolnshire Limestone is the major aquifer for large areas of the county.

The formation is generally about 30 m thick, ranging from a minimum of around 25 m near Leadenham, up to 33.5 m near Ancaster. A maximum thickness of over 40 m occurs in south Lincolnshire. There are considerable variations in the thicknesses of individual beds and members. Thus, the Lower Lincolnshire Limestone ranges in thickness from 15 m to 21 m and the Upper Lincolnshire Limestone ranges from 10 m to 16 m (see also Figure 21).

The formation is dominated by limestones and, with the exception of a few thin beds, terrigenous content is sparse. Rocks are typically cream coloured, and more rarely grey or brown, with localised cores of unoxidised bluish grey stone. The assemblage of facies types is typical of marine barrier bar–lagoonal complexes (Ashton, 1977). The mapped lithological subdivisions represent contrasting mixes of the various components, produced by the prevailing conditions of sedimentation and local clast availability. In general, there is a progressive increase in the energy of the sedimentary environment. Thus, the Lower Lincolnshire Limestone is dominated by carbonate mudstones, wackestones and packstones, and the Upper Lincolnshire Limestone by cross-bedded, ooidal grainstones. Within the Upper Lincolnshire Limestone, the exceptionally coarse-grained 'Rag' facies tends to succeed the even-grained ooidal freestones.

Thin sections (Plate 1) show that all rocks have undergone some degree of metasomatic alteration, including partial recrystallisation of matrix, and partial to complete micritisation of ooids and fossil debris. At least some of the micritisation is related to algal growth. Most rocks, especially grainstones, show a degree of recrystallisation associated with compaction, followed by the partial to complete infilling of any remaining voids, first by crusts of non-ferroan calcite and later by spar mosaics of either ferroan or non-ferroan calcite; spar may also selectively replace the cores of fossil clasts. Rocks rich in terrigenous clastics tend to be cemented by more strongly ferroan calcite. A proportion of rocks later suffered selective leaching, leading to a secondary porosity, notably by the dissolution of the cores of ooids.

Fossil remains in the Lincolnshire Limestone are sporadically abundant; they include a wide range of bivalves, together with corals, bryozoans, brachiopods, gastropods, crinoids, echinoids and ostracods. Ammonites are very rare; their occurrence in the formation is

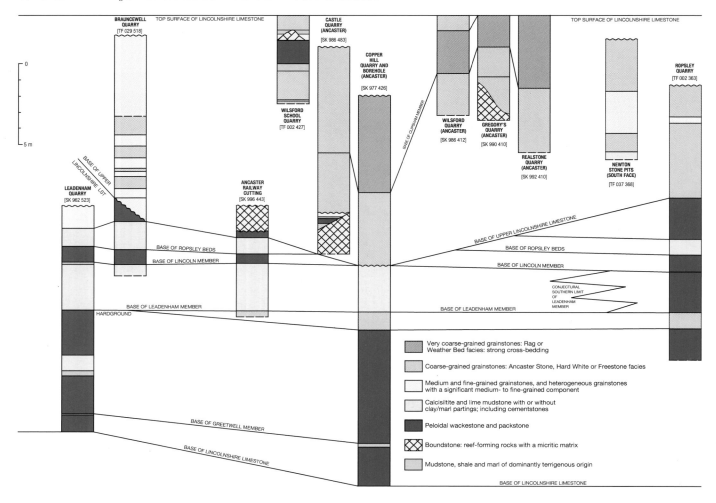

Figure 21 Correlation of the main sections through the Lincolnshire Limestone in the district, based partly on Ashton (1980, figs 6 and 9).

reviewed by Ashton (1977). The basal 2.74 m of the formation (part of Ashton's (1980) Sproxton Member) in the Copper Hill Borehole is assigned to the Bajocian *discites* Biozone on ostracod evidence (the occurrence of *Praeschuleridea decorata*, *Cytherelloidea eastfieldensis*, *Systenocythere exilofasciata*, *Progonocythere reticulata*, and others). The fauna from the top 3.76 m of the formation proved at the base of Walks Farm Borehole [1534 4635] was sparse and poorly preserved, but ostracods and foraminifera together suggest the *discites* to *laeviuscula* biozones.

LOWER LINCOLNSHIRE LIMESTONE

In this district, the Lower Lincolnshire Limestone commonly comprises a rhythmic sequence of thin, graded beds of fine-grained rocks, deposited in a low-energy environment. Compositional range includes carbonate mudstones to calcarenites with terrigenous clay-rich partings, and wackestones to packstones with peloids and ooids set in a finer-grained matrix. Figure 21 summarises the lithological sequences in the major Lincolnshire Limestone sections.

The best 'marker' within the limestone (Unit L4) (Bed 30) at Leadenham Quarry (Sumbler et al, 1991; Sumbler, 1993b) or Bed 13 of Ropsley Quarry (Berridge, 1993) is correlated with the basal bed of Ashton's Lincoln Member (Table 8). The bed (Plate 4) is a characteristically hard and tough heterogeneous shelly ooidal packstone to wackestone, about 1 m thick. It contains a faintly marked median parting, separating a more resistant lower part from a weaker upper part. The bed rests upon a shaly mudstone parting and is overlain by the Ropsley Beds (Plate 4), which comprise a distinctive unit of thinly bedded, pale grey, carbonate mudstone alternating with dark, shaly, mudstone partings. The basal Lincoln Member marker stands out on weathered sections at Ropsley Quarry, Ancaster railway cutting and Leadenham Quarry but has been cut out locally by intraformational erosion at Copper Hill Quarry, Ancaster (Sumbler et al., 1991). Identification of the marker permits correlation of an underlying sequence of dominantly calcisiltite beds northwards from Ancaster. These Leadenham Beds (of Ashton) are thought to be absent at Ropsley Quarry, but the preponderance of fine-grained carbonate rock with

Plate 4 Minor fold structure, Ropsley Quarry, [about 0020 3639].

Viewed looking approximately north-east, along the fold axis. The anticlinal arch is a local structure seen here affecting the Ropsley Beds, thin-bedded limestone alternating with thin, shaly, mudstone partings. They rest on the imperfectly exposed bed which defines the base of the Lincoln Member of the Lower Lincolnshire Limestone. (A15411)

sparse ooids in the Lower Lincolnshire Limestone at outcrop between Ropsley and Ancaster suggests that the Leadenham Beds facies persists through much of this district.

For the most part, the available borehole records are of little help in solving stratigraphical problems in the Lincolnshire Limestone, because the lithological descriptions lack sufficient detail. However, many of the logs record an argillaceous bed marking the top of the Sproxton Member, which is the lowest member of the Lincolnshire Limestone in the district (Table 8). This clay or shale band is generally about 0.5 m thick, but ranges from 0.15 m to 1.37 m. It occurs about 3 m from the base of the formation, but may be found between 1.5 m and 6.5 m from the base. The correlation line on Figure 21 between Copper Hill and Leadenham quarries is uncertain; the lower thinner mudstone band shown on the Leadenham section may be the Sproxton top marker, rather than the thicker bed chosen in the figure (Sumbler et al., 1991; Sumbler, 1993b). However, this correlation is supported by the occurrence of calcareous sandstone, proved by petrographical analysis, immediately overlying the specified mudstone at both Copper Hill and Leadenham quarries. Despite its prominence in borehole sections, the mudstone has not proved mappable at surface in the district, probably due to cambering of the overlying limestone beds.

The best sections through parts of the Lower Lincolnshire Limestone, none of them complete, are provided by Leadenham Quarry (which is currently in use as a landfill site), Copper Hill Quarry and Ropsley Quarry; it is also exposed in Brauncewell Quarry and Ancaster railway cutting. Summary graphical sections with grid references of these exposures are shown in Figure 21 and

detailed descriptions are provided in Sumbler et al. (1991), Samuel (1992a); Berridge (1993), and Sumbler (1993b).

Ostracoda in the Leadenham Quarry can be placed in the *Kinkelinella triangulata* Ostracod Zone (*sensu* Bate, 1978). The zonal and subzonal indices are, unfortunately, absent, but an age determination can be given based on the concurrent range of *Pneumatocythere bajociana*, *Micropneumatocythere convexa*, *Praeschuleridea decorata*, *Cytherelloidea eastfieldensis Systenocythere exilofasciata* and *Protoacanthocythere faveolata*. Foraminifera are sparse, but the presence of *Conicospirillina trochoides* partly confirms this age as it disappears from the record in the early *laeviuscula* Biozone (at the top of the *ovalis* Sub-biozone) according to Morris and Coleman (1989). The age of the fauna therefore, falls within the *discites* Biozone.

The North Ropsley Quarry yields a sparse microfauna, but the presence of the foraminifer *Conicospirillina trochoides* indicates an age similar to that at Leadenham Quarry. Additionally, *Kinkelinella triangulata*, the ostracod zonal index, which equates with the *discites–laeviuscula* biozones, was recorded in the sample from 2.4 m above the floor of the quarry, although ostracod subzonal indices were not found. The quarry yields very rare specimens of *Glyptocythere sp.* and although preservation is poor, it appears to be the unnamed species recorded by Bate (1978, pl. 11, figs. 15–16). He considered that the inception of the genus was biostratigraphically important. Other species that were recorded include *Micropneumatocythere globosa*, *Progonocythere sp. cf. acuminata* and *Eocytheridea carinata*. The fauna found in the North Ropsley Quarry is thus very high stratigraphically and is probably of *laeviuscula* age, and indeed an earliest *sauzei* biozonal age cannot be ruled out entirely, although ostracods characteristic of the later part of that zone, for example, *Fuhrbergiella horrida horrida*, *Flyptocythere polita*, *Malzia unicarinata*, were not found and the palynomorphs preclude the *sauzei* age.

Upper Lincolnshire Limestone

The Upper Lincolnshire Limestone is dominated by grainstone lithologies, particularly of coarse- to very coarse-grained types such as the Ancaster Stone and Ancaster Rag respectively. Lime mud-dominated beds, reef boundstones and limestones of lagoonal origin are also present locally. The base of the Upper Lincolnshire Limestone is taken at the lower limit of consistently developed grainstones. This level is easily recognised where the base of the Upper Lincolnshire Limestone cuts deeply into the underlying succession in much of the centre of the district, but it is less obvious in the north and south where there is less discordance at the boundary, and where bimodal grainstones in the upper division are superficially similar to supposed packstones and wackestones below. Around Wilsford, east of Ancaster, a further complication arises with the local development of truly lagoonal facies in the Upper Lincolnshire Limestone, associated with abundant boundstone bioherms. Here it has been necessary to interpolate a presumed base of the Upper Lincolnshire Limestone at the lowest level of occurrence of the reef mounds.

Subdivision of the Upper Lincolnshire Limestone into the Sleaford Member (Ashton, 1980) (Table 8) and overlying Clipsham Member is not sustainable. The part of Figure 21 which features Copper Hill and Gregory's Quarry may be compared with fig. 12 of Ashton, illustrating an alternative interpretation of the correlation of beds in neighbouring sections near the centre of the district, where such correlation seems feasible.

In the Grantham district, it would seem that the Upper Lincolnshire Limestone was deposited in an environment in which vigorous marine currents were active, causing localised channelling into both the lower part of the Upper Lincolnshire Limestone and the Lower Lincolnshire Limestone.

In the Upper Lincolnshire Limestone, the restricted area of reef boundstones and associated wackestones is noteworthy, and the outlier patterns, around Caythorpe, Normanton and Barkston Heaths, are largely a product of channel infill at the base of the Upper Lincolnshire Limestone. The boundstone-reef/wackestone complex at Wilsford spans the complete thickness of the division but apart from a south-west extension to Syston Park, is rare elsewhere. Much of the outcrop area immediately south-west, south and south-east of Barkston Heath essentially corresponds with the top surface of the formation, as shown by the numerous thin outliers of the overlying Rutland Formation.

The distribution of lithological variants in the Upper Lincolnshire Limestone at depth is as uncertain as that of the Lower Lincolnshire Limestone. Many old borehole records, particularly ironstone prospecting holes in the south, identified a thin, fine-grained 'Crossi' marker bed which various authors have attributed either to the top of the Lower Lincolnshire Limestone or to the base of the Upper Lincolnshire Limestone. Ashton (1979) detailed reasons for abandoning the use of the rhynchonellid brachiopod *Acanthothiris crossi* as a marker bed but states that the span of the fossil nevertheless equates approximately with his 'Middle Lincolnshire Limestone', that is, the upper part of the Lower Lincolnshire Limestone of this account. However, the fossil also occurs in the boundstone facies of the Upper Lincolnshire Limestone, for example at Gregory's Quarry [989 410] and in a trench excavation [034 445] near Rauceby Station (Berridge, 1993); its distribution is probably related more to sedimentary facies than stratigraphical level.

The Upper Lincolnshire Limestone includes three facies types that are absent from the lower part of the formation.

The 'Rag' facies is an exceptionally coarse-grained grainstone with much bioclastic debris accompanying the ooids dominant in the commoner 'Freestone' facies (Plate 1). The Rag facies is very commonly associated with steeply angled cross-bedding (Plate 5), and also commonly shows rapid transition to the 'Freestone' facies within a single cross-bedded unit. At Gregory's Quarry, Ancaster, where it is termed the 'Weather Bed', individual cross-bedded units are commonly 'bluehearted' (Cover photograph) and the rock is, in part, cemented by coarsely crystalline gypsum rather than the more usual calcite spar.

The boundstone facies is variable in composition, locally resembling carbonate mudstone, wackestone or packstone. However, it differs from these lagoonal sediments in the extremely hard and tough nature of the rock, and in a tendency for the rocks to be partially shattered and re-bound by veins of calcite spar. Typically it occurs in lenticular 'reefs', perhaps individual bioherms. The hardness and toughness of the rock is reflected by a topographical expression in places. The rocks commonly contain a range of fossils (Plate 6), including corals which, however, rarely seem to be the main binding influence in the rock fabric, except in the small bioherm at Wilsford School quarry (Sample E67306 from [0026 4272]). In a sample from Gregory's Quarry (E67303 [9893 4104], Plate 6), a network of serpulid tubes appears to provide structural support, but in Castle Quarry (samples E67304 and E67305, [9865 4338] and [9865 4336] respectively) the rocks show no obvious skeletal support.

The third facies, an oncolith-bearing grainstone, is unique to the Upper Lincolnshire Limestone and has been mapped over an area covering less than 0.25 km^2 [000 485], adjacent to the A17 road, at the southern edge of Cranwell airfield. Rounded particles with an ill-defined annular structure, commonly 20 to 30 mm in diameter, are scattered in a matrix of rather ferruginous, poorly sorted grainstone. Traces of similar lithology occur elsewhere, for example north of the airfield near Brauncewell [from 0133 5158 to 0160 5161 and at 0085 5178] and also near the southern edge of the district, in a 1.76 m-thick bed, in the Haceby Lodge Quarry section [0265 3693]. The last-named site lies about 5 m from the top of the formation, and other localities could well be at about this level in the sequence.

The Upper Lincolnshire Limestone was formerly widely exploited for building stone, and Gregory's (plate 10) and Realstone quarries still fulfil a demand for high-quality material. Much of the quarrying work has been

Plate 5 Upper Lincolnshire Limestone, Copper Hill Quarry, Ancaster [9785 4270], looking north-west.

Three major divisions are clearly visible. At the top, about 6 m of north-easterly dipping cross-beds of coarse-grained grainstone, 'Ragstone', correspond with the Clipsham Member Ashton (1980). This rests on 6 m of cream grainstone showing shallower-angle imbricate cross-bedding and includes a dominantly well-sorted coarse oolite ('Freestone' or 'Ancaster Stone') overlying both 'Freestone' and 'Ragstone' facies: together these comprise the Sleaford Member of Ashton (1980). The observer's hammer rests on the unconformity at the base of the Upper Lincolnshire Limestone. About 0.5 m of flaggy, paler coloured Lower Lincolnshire Limestone (Leadenham Member) is exposed. At this locality, the whole of the Lincoln Member, including the Ropsley Beds, is cut out by this unconformity. (A15099)

abandoned through failure of demand or exhaustion of suitable quality or permitted reserves; many abandoned quarries still provide reasonably good sections. A summary of the best of these is shown in Figure 21 and complete details are available for these and other sections in the relevant Technical Reports. Quarries at Braceby and along the A52 inlier west of Newton, in the south of the district, show beds of fine- to medium-grained grainstone that do not readily correlate from section to section and also do not crop out at the surface. Farther north, several extensive quarries in the Ancaster area have been almost entirely backfilled, though others retain partial sections where the infill is incomplete; with the exception of those shown in Figure 21, only Ragstone and Freestone facies are exposed. North of the Ancaster area, few quarry sections remain within the district. One pit [022 473] at Heath Farm, North Rauceby, shows thin- and flat-bedded, mixed, fine-grained beds of lagoonal origin, interbedded with the cross-bedded, coarse- to very coarse-grained grainstones that dominate the Upper Lincolnshire Limestone.

GREAT OOLITE GROUP

Rutland Formation

The term Rutland Formation was introduced by Bradshaw (1978) to supersede the 'Upper Estuarine Series' of earlier usage. The base of the Rutland Formation is sharply unconformable on the Lincolnshire Limestone.

Plate 6 Boundstone, Gregory's Quarry [9893 4104], Wilsford Heath, Ancaster.

Thin-section of a sample (NB39, E67303) from a biohermal reef that locally replaces the lower 'Freestone' and 'Hard White' oolite grainstones in this quarry. Staining shows that most of the rock components are formed of ferroan calcite with variable iron content. This specimen shows a particularly wide range of biogenic components, but is quite typical of the Upper Lincolnshire Limestone boundstones of this district in showing a micritic matrix and large patches of calcite spar which appear as or vuggy infills veins in the field.

5 mm

Photography and key by G K Lott.

Key

a. sponge spicules
b. bivalve
c. ooid
d. serpulid
e. bryozoan

f. lime mud
g. ferroan spar
h. gypsum?
i. geopetal texture
j. borings

For practical mapping purposes, the top of the formation is here placed at the base of the lowest limestone bed of the overlying Blisworth Limestone Formation.

The Rutland Formation of the district is divisible into six shallowing-upwards rhythms. In each, a rapid relative rise in sea level was followed by the accumulation of marine mudstones, passing locally to limestones. Gradual shallowing is indicated by succeeding nonmarine mud-

stones, silts and sands, and culminated in emergence and plant growth, marked by a rootlet bed (seatearth), before a new cycle commenced.

In the Grantham district, the Rutland Formation commonly forms the greater part of a minor slope below the crop of the Blisworth Limestone, making a narrow, sinuous outcrop along the eastern limit of the Lincolnshire Limestone dip slope. It gives a heavy clay soil, usually tinted

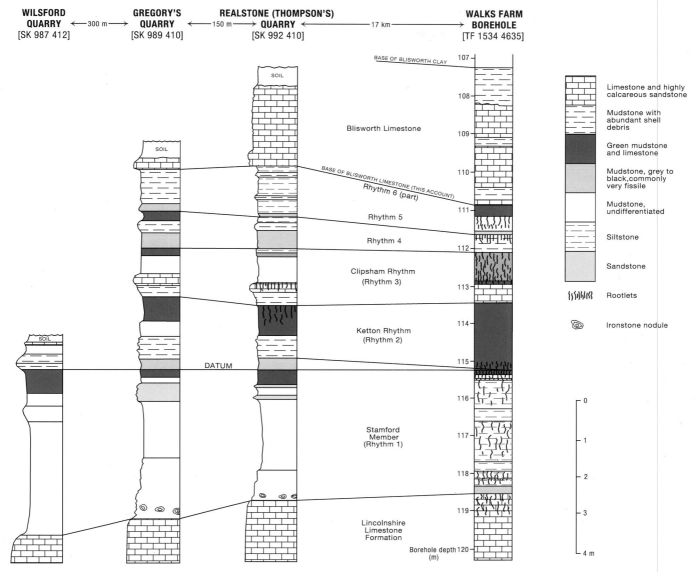

WILSFORD
QUARRY
[SK 987 412]

←— 300 m —→

GREGORY'S
QUARRY
[SK 989 410]

←— 150 m —→

REALSTONE (THOMPSON'S)
QUARRY
[SK 992 410]

←—————— 17 km ——————→

WALKS FARM
BOREHOLE
[TF 1534 4635]

BASE OF BLISWORTH CLAY

Blisworth Limestone

BASE OF BLISWORTH LIMESTONE (THIS ACCOUNT)
Rhythm 6 (part)

Rhythm 5

Rhythm 4

Clipsham Rhythm
(Rhythm 3)

Ketton Rhythm
(Rhythm 2)

DATUM

Stamford
Member
(Rhythm 1)

Lincolnshire
Limestone
Formation

Borehole depth
(m)

SOIL

SOIL

SOIL

Limestone and highly
calcareous sandstone

Mudstone with
abundant shell
debris

Green mudstone
and limestone

Mudstone, grey to
black, commonly
very fissile

Mudstone,
undifferentiated

Siltstone

Sandstone

Rootlets

Ironstone nodule

Figure 22 Correlation of the Rutland Formation of Walks Farm Borehole with the main sections in the district.

reddish brown at the base due to ironstone segregations. Lithological subdivisions are not mappable, except where limestone development is locally thick and persistent, for example, in the extreme north and south of the district. Walks Farm Borehole was drilled by BGS to the east of the district to prove the stratigraphy above the Lincolnshire Limestone. It clearly shows a soil profile at the top of the underlying Lincolnshire Limestone (Figure 22), with partially decomposed limestone penetrated by carbonaceous roots and rhizomes from the limestone surface at 118.53 m depth, down to at least 119.19 m; carbonaceous staining of the limestone gradually peters out downwards.

The Rutland Formation, within the district, is commonly 8 to 10 m thick, ranging between 5 and 11 m. This range is probably due, in part, to the variable development of the overlying Blisworth Limestone, and the boundary between the two may be locally diachronous.

Three quarries to the south of Ancaster, Wilsford, Gregory's (Plate 10) and Realstone quarries, provide sections through the formation where it has been excavated as overburden above Lincolnshire Limestone (Figure 22). The basal Stamford Member is 3.5 to 4.0 m thick, between a third and a half of the total thickness of the formation. A composite section is given below:

	Thickness m
Mudstone, (seatearth) greenish grey, rootlet-bearing	0.2 to 1.0
Mudstone, soft, purplish grey, blocky, interbedded with siltstone and fine-grained sandstone near the top	1.5 to 2.5
Mudstone, hard, purplish grey, hard, ferruginous with ironstone nodules in basal 0.6 m	1.0 to 1.5

Seatearths, which commonly occur at the top of each of the rhythmic units, have been used for correlation between the cycles in the Ancaster quarry sections (Figure 22), and in the Stamford Member the seatearth forms a conspicuous bed of green or greenish grey mudstone. The mudstone is mostly blocky but locally slightly fissile and generally penetrated by vertical carbonaceous rootlets. Commonly, the seatearth is overlain by a thin layer of highly bituminous, dark grey, paper-shale which grades upwards into paler and less fissile mudstone. Bradshaw (1978) equates this shale with the start of a new rhythm but it seems probable that the black paper-shale could be a relict of humic soil, which formed contemporaneously with the seatearth. Overlying mudstone of the succeeding rhythm contains oyster shells, especially in the lower part, and locally has the composition of a muddy limestone. This passes up through mudstone or siltstone to the green seatearth at the top of the unit. Any particular rhythmic unit may be locally or generally incomplete, due to variations in sedimentation and erosion. For example, black shale is apparently missing from the base of the Ketton Rhythm at Wilsford Quarry and green mudstone from the top of 'Rhythm 3' at Realstone Quarry.

The considerable variation between the three closely adjacent sections near Ancaster (Figure 22), inevitably makes correlation with Walks Farm Borehole, some 17 km to the east, somewhat tentative. Nevertheless, the occurrence of layers of green rootlet-bearing seatearth and/or black bituminous shale divides Walks Farm sequence into cycles of comparable thickness to those seen near Ancaster. The Stamford Member is proved between 114.62 and 118.53 m in the borehole; it consists mainly of siltstone with varying proportions of plant fragments, including pyritous and carbonaceous roots. At the base is 0.38 m of dark greenish grey to olive-black fissile mudstone, with partings of white shell debris. The overlying siltstone, 2.83 m thick, and containing sporadic coal fragments, is separated by a 0.03 m sandstone parting from the interlaminated mudstone and fine-grained sandstone above, which includes two coal partings. A mudstone conglomerate bed, 0.13 m thick, overlies this, with a shelly lamina at the base, and showing an upwards reduction in size of the component mudstone pellets, which average about 1 mm thick and several millimetres across. The uppermost bed of the member, between 114.62 and 115.26 m in the borehole, is a greenish grey mudstone showing bioturbation, with sandy burrowfills. In Walks Farm Borehole, the presence of the ostracods *Darwinula incurva* and *Bisulcocypris ancasterensis* at 115.31 to 115.34 m depth is indicative of oligohaline conditions.

The remainder of the formation in Walks Farm Borehole lies between 110.87 and 114.62 m depth, and consists mainly of mudstone, with some fine-grained sandstone and siltstone mostly in the uppermost 1.23 m. The mudstone shows variations in colour, fissility and shell content. One bed of limestone is recorded, a quartzose and muddy medium-grained calcarenite lying 1.93 m below the top of the formation; it is moderately shelly and shows discontinuous laminae, with bioturbation, and roots penetrating at least 0.29 m from the

upper surface. The total thickness of the limestone is about 0.67 m, including the basal 0.09 m in which it is interbedded with sandy, muddy siltstone. At the top of the Ketton Rhythm in Walks Farm Borehole (113.56 m to 113.58 m depth) a number of brackish to marine ostracods were present, including common *Progonocythere laevigata*, *P. triguetra*, *Lophocythere batei*, *Glyptocythere guembeliana* together with less-common *Micropneumatocythere quadrata*, *Fastigatocythere juglandica* and *Marslatourella bullata*. This fauna is characteristic of the *hodsoni* Biozone (Bate, 1978; Sheppard, 1978, 1981). The Clipsham Rhythm, at a depth of 112.12 to 112.14 m, yields several species of *Progonocythere*, including *P. polonica*, *Praeschuleridea confossa* and *Micropneumatocythere brendae*. The *polonica* ostracod zone of Sheppard (1981) is shown to equate with the *hodsoni* Biozone. A sample from 111.15–111.19 m (in Rhythm 5) yielded common ostracods including *Progonocythere triquetra*, *Micropneumatocythere postrotunda* and *M. quadrata* together with *Galliaecytheridea kingscliffensis*, *Fastigatocythere juglandica* and *Glypocythere guembeliana*. This euryhaline fauna is of *hodsoni* Biozone age (Bate 1978; Sheppard, 1978, 1981). These zonal assignments do not agree with that shown in Table 7, and clearly there are problems of correlation still to be resolved.

Palynological analysis of three well-spaced samples from the Rutland Formation of Walks Farm Borehole core indicate a transition from a swampy lacustrine depositional setting to an open marine one. The evidence from the youngest sample suggests that the Rutland Formation is early or mid Bathonian in age, and referable to subzones a and b of the Cse dinoflagellate cyst zone of Riding and Thomas (1992). This is an older date than that indicated by the ostracods (see above), but is compatible with that shown in Table 7.

The general conclusion from the evidence of available sections is that in the Grantham district the formation as defined herein comprises five full sedimentary rhythms with part of a sixth at the top. The rhythms tend to decrease successively in thickness. The first, the Stamford Member, lacks both limestones and calcareous macrofauna, and was probably deposited as a nonmarine facies. All subsequent rhythms include marine units at the base and locally include shelly limestones at this level. These are most common in the Clipsham Rhythm (third rhythm).

There are no natural sections through the Rutland Formation in the district, but during this survey, a pipeline excavation provided temporary sections of up to 2 m depth between Wilsford and Oasby (Plate 7). One [993 392] showed a 1 m-thick bed of shelly limestone in grey clay; another, nearby, but separated from the former by a fault, showed:

	Thickness m
Clay, yellowish brown	0.8
Silt, pale grey	0.2
Clay, purplish grey	1.0
	seen

A trench [993 392] further north showed about 3 m of pale bluish grey clay, mottled purplish to reddish grey at the base of the formation, resting on the Upper Lincoln-shire Limestone. Freshly cleared drainage dykes, west and north-west of Nightingale Farm, showed in all about 3 m of grey to pale grey clay including some laminations of yellowish grey silt and fine-grained sand; the sand also occurred as burrow-infill.

Spoil from a pond [0460 5345] excavated through limestone of the Rutland Formation near Mount Farm, west of Bloxholm, contained limestone slabs up to 0.11 m thick. The limestone was siliceous, shell-fragmen-tal and fissile, splitting into thin flaggy fragments. It was grey, weathering to buff, with scattered specks of dark carbonaceous material, bivalves of various sizes, mostly fragmentary, and the remains of several ophiuroids. This horizon may correlate with the abundant *Ophiohybris griesbachii* recorded by Dawn (1993) in fallen blocks of thin sandy limestone from the base of the Blisworth Limestone in Gregory's Quarry. 'Coal', of sufficient quality to be used as a fuel locally, was reputedly dug from below a sand pit [001 390] at Oasby, although no

workable coal·is otherwise noted in records of the formation elsewhere in the district.

Fossil assemblages collected from the formation during the re-survey of the district show a range of bivalves, brachiopods and echinoids, together suggesting a mid to late Bathonian age. Taxa include *Kallirhynchia vagans*, *Kallirhynchia* sp., *Gervillella?*, *Inoperna?*, *Liostrea* cf. *undosa*, *Modiolus imbricatus*, *Modiolus* sp., *Pholadomya deltoidea*, *Placunopsis socialis*, *Pleuromya calceiformis*, *Praeexogyra hebridica*, *P.hebridica* var. '*subrugulosa*', *Vaugonia moretoni*, ostreid fragments, *Clypeus* sp., ophiuroids cf. *Dermocoma*, and trace fossils of *Thalassinoides* type burrow-fills. Oyster species are the dominant fossil type throughout.

Blisworth Limestone Formation

The Blisworth Limestone Formation (Horton, Shephard-Thorn and Thurrell, 1974), formerly the Great Oolite Limestone of various authors, is also termed the Snitterby Limestone by Gaunt et al. (1992). It comprises

Plate 7 The Barkstone (Foston–Syston–Dembleby) Fault, temporarily exposed in trench section [9928 3919] beside the Roman road west of Oasby, in 1990.

A 0.5 m fault crush zone, composed of mixed clay and limestone from the Rutland Formation and Lincolnshire Limestone respectively, dips 70° north away from the camera. The fault crush is flanked by broken limestone and disturbed clay. The pipe is 25 cm in diameter. (A15414)

Plate 8   Blisworth Limestone and Cornbrash.

Photomicrographs showing some typical lithologies. Scale bar represents 1 mm. Plane-polarised light. Note how these 'Great Oolite' limestones characteristically are rich in siliciclastic debris, in contrast to the Lincolnshire Limestone where quartz sand and silt are rare except near the base.

Petrography and photography by G K Lott.

a. BKD 8554. Blisworth Limestone, quartzose facies. Walks Farm Borehole [1534 4635] at a depth of 110.80 m. E66858. Bioclastic, coarse-grained siltstone to very fine-grained sandstone. The carbonate in this rock is dominantly ferroan calcite with minor non-ferroan calcite, and is restricted mainly to bioclastic debris. Note the presence of fungal or algal threads (dark) penetrating larger bioclasts.

b. BKD 8513. Blisworth Limestone, coquinoid facies, Walks Farm Borehole at a depth of 108.21 m. E66856. Sandy biomicrite (Folk, 1959) or sandy bioclastic packstone (Dunham, 1962). Ferroan spar has replaced most bioclasts and perhaps some of the matrix, but iron-stained, non-ferroan calcite bioclasts are also present. Most colourless material is clastic quartz, opaque material (black) is mostly pyrite and the matrix is micritic calcite. Traces of early non-ferroan calcite dog-tooth spar cement fringe some clasts.

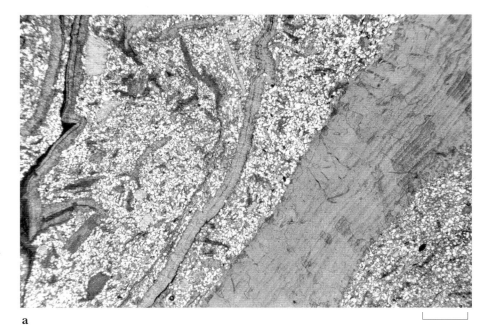

a

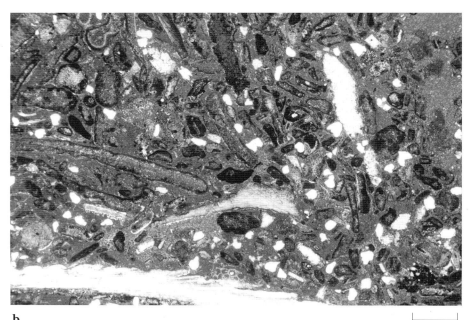

b

a sequence of dominantly limestone beds between the clay-dominant Rutland Formation below and Blisworth Clay above. It probably represents a continuation of the rhythmic sedimentation of the Rutland Formation, but with enhancement of limestone facies.

In the Grantham district, the formation tends to form a minor escarpment, with brash covering an extensive planar dip slope. On gentle valley sides, the formation may form bench features unless cambering has occurred, as seems to be the case east of Oasby. On steep slopes, such as the north-facing hillside running between North Rauceby and Leasingham, the outcrop may not form a clearly visible feature. In general the

brash closely resembles that of limestone in the Rutland Formation and is similar to that of the Cornbrash higher in the sequence, but the Blisworth Limestone is somewhat softer and more clay-rich. Furthermore, the typical lithology is more consistently shell-rich (Plate 8), giving a granular brash with abundant bivalves and brachiopods.

Full details of Walks Farm Borehole, which is the only complete record of the formation in the vicinity of the district, will be published elsewhere (Ivimey-Cook et al., in preparation). In the borehole, the formation is present between 107.23 and 110.87 m depth, and the sequence is shelly and bioturbated throughout. It consists of alternate

Plate 8

c. BKD 8398. Cornbrash, Walks Farm Borehole at a depth of 100.0 m. E66855. Muddy biosparite (Folk, 1959) or muddy bioclastic grainstone (Dunham, 1962). Partially orientated, well-sorted, bioclastic debris (dominantly from bivalves) composed of variably iron-stained, non-ferroan calcite, accompanied by minor silt- to sand-grade quartz grains (colourless), are apparently set in a cement of ferroan calcite spar; some of the 'cement', however, may be replaced bioclasts.

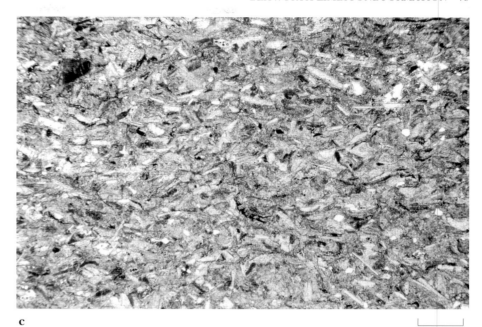

c

beds of shelly mudstone and limestone (mainly medium-grained, calcarenitic) grading to fine-grained, calcareous sandstone. The basal limestone, from 110.72 to 110.87 m depth, is a finer-grained, more strongly cemented calcisiltite. In the Digby Test/Production Borehole [0776 5484], the basal 1 m of the Blisworth Limestone is also recorded as being harder than the overlying 5.6 m. Large fragments of hard, purplish grey to greyish brown, shell-fragmental limestone, believed also to come from the basal part of the formation, occur as brash at locations [045 521 and 050 513] south of Brauncewell.

Natural exposures are absent in the district but the formation can be seen in temporary sections such as trenches and longer-lasting artificial excavations. At the time of survey, a pipeline excavation showed up to 2 m of shelly limestone with clay interbeds in a run of 2 km north to south, crossing Heath Lane, Wilsford [9930 4190]. This section included both the 'common' shelly limestone and the more sandy variant mapped around Wilsford. A degraded section totalling 2 m of rubbly, shelly limestone, interlayered with clay in the basal metre, was seen in the railway cutting on the south side of the Slea valley [056 455] at Sleaford. Shelly, grey calcarenite is exposed along the water line at the northern shore of the artificial lake [020 400] in Culverthorpe Park and along the shores of the artificial lake in Rauceby Park [030 458], where there is also some development of the calcareous sandstone facies. The best available exposure was probably that seen at the top of the overburden face at Realstone Quarry, summarised in Figure 22. There, 1.7 m of rusty-coated, rubbly, shelly, muddy, shaly limestone overlay a basal couplet of thin beds of pure, hard, fossiliferous, fine-grained limestone, 0.4 m thick in all. The base of this unit is taken as the base of the Blisworth Limestone at this locality.

Lithological variation, in the form of intercalations of clay-rich or quartzose sand-rich lithologies (Plate 8), is recorded in many boreholes and is probably widespread, but at outcrop its effects are comparatively rarely seen. The best example occurs on either side of the Ancaster Gap, south-west and north-east of Wilsford. There, the greater part of the formation is so rich in quartz sand that the derived soil is a sandy loam although the parent rock, as seen in trench sections and commonly ploughed from the subsoil, resembles the typical shelly limestone. A tendency towards sandiness was also noted at South Rauceby. In the Brauncewell area, a median clay occurs locally; such intercalations may be related to cyclicity which is better developed in the underlying Rutland Formation.

Borehole records indicate that the formation has an average thickness of about 4 m, with a range of 2.0 to 7.6 m. It seems likely that the main cause of this thickness variation is inconstancy in the development of limestone in sedimentary cycles at the top and bottom of the formation.

The formation is very highly fossiliferous and shells commonly weather out whole in the brash. In particular, whole *Pholadomya* are locally very abundant. The dominant groups are bivalves, showing a high diversity, and brachiopods such as *Digonella digonoides*. Serpulids, bryozoans, gastropods and echinoids are all common: ammonites, however, were not recovered during this survey. The calcareous microfauna in Walks Farm Borehole is similar to that at the top of the Rutland Formation. *Glyptocythere oscillum* occurs at 110.51–110.57 m and *Fossaterquemula blakeana* was recovered at a depth of 109.20–109.28 m. The latter ostracod is the index for the *blakeana* Zone of Sheppard (1981) which equates with the upper part of the *hodsoni* Biozone and the *orbis* Biozone of the ammonite zonation. Foraminifera are mainly long ranging but include late Bathonian *Vaginulina legumen* and *V. harpa*.

Blisworth Clay Formation

The Blisworth Clay Formation, formerly known as the Great Oolite Clay, forms a steep, usually convex, slope of heavy clay soil between the shelf features produced by the Blisworth Limestone and Cornbrash formations. The formation is dominated by mudstone; as seen in Walks Farm Borehole, both its lower and upper boundaries are gradational and conformable. The range of thickness proved by boreholes in this district is from 6.1 to 10 m. Walks Farm Borehole drilled by BGS at Howell, near Heckington, proved Blisworth Clay from 100.25 to 107.23 m depth. The formation is much thicker in the Grantham district than at the type locality, near Blisworth, Northamptonshire (Sharp, 1870).

The mudstone is commonly greenish grey to olive-grey; in places it is blue- or purple-tinged in colour, with olive to black beds associated with more shaly lithologies. It weathers to yellowish or greyish brown clay which is generally smooth and plastic. It is locally silty; medium grey to greenish grey clayey silt was augered in a ditch [0577 5204] north of Cottage Farm, Brauncewell. The texture, as seen in Walks Farm Borehole core, is most commonly homogeneous and blocky. Some fine laminations of mud and fine-grained sand were seen 1 to 2 m above the base, with rare traces of fissility.

Thin sandstone or limestone beds are recorded from the middle of the formation in boreholes; these developments are probably indicative of a weak continuation of the rhythmic sedimentation which is present in the underlying succession. Concretions, probably sideritic, occur sporadically towards the base.

Kaolinite and illite (each between 20 and 50 per cent) are the dominant clay minerals, but relatively high percentages of smectite (each between 7 and 20 per cent) and mixed-layer illite-smectite are also present; the former is believed to be an alteration product of air-fall volcanic ash, and the latter to be either detrital or derived from the alteration of illite. Faunal evidence suggests that deposition took place in a lagoonal environment, possibly with partial and rare marine incursions.

The base and top of the formation, in contact with limestones, are well defined at outcrop, although the upper boundary is obscured by downhill movement of debris from the Cornbrash. The topmost 0.4 m of the mudstone in Walks Farm Borehole, and a similar thickness immediately below the Cornbrash in a ditch section [0574 4396 to 0546 4392] south of Quarrington, are calcareous. Freshly cleared drainage ditches and temporary trenches normally provide the only exposures of the clay. A trench [0452 5017] for pipe-laying near Roxholm showed about 2 m of pale greyish green clay. Other trenches [c.0590 4535] on the west side of Sleaford exposed up to 1.5 m of stiff green clay with subordinate purplish grey clay. Below the topmost weathered zone, small selenite crystals are common; they are mentioned in the log of a borehole [0592 4720] at Holdingham, and were seen in exposures and auger samples during the latest survey.

No brash from sandstone or limestone beds has been seen at outcrop, but during this survey a thin limestone temporarily exposed in a pit [0148 3885] at Aisby, and minor sand lenses at a pond excavation [020 386] about 0.5 km east of Aisby were recorded. The rock fabric at the pond excavation appeared to be fragmental or possibly pelletal. Two units of siltstone and fine-grained sandstone beds occur at about the middle of the formation in Walks Farm Borehole; the upper one, from 104.07 to 104.79 m depth, shows a sharp upper and lower boundary, and the lower, from 105.12 to 105.83 m depth, shows gradational boundaries. Small inclusions or pellets of mudstone are present in each of these units, and fragments of fine-grained sandstone occur in the mudstone of this middle part of the formation.

Walks Farm Borehole proved very hard, probably sideritic, pale brown concretionary layers, 0.4 m thick, between 106.34 and 106.54 m depth. Similar concretions are mentioned by Jukes-Browne (1885, p.62) and are reported from near the base of the Blisworth Clay in the logs of boreholes at Asgarby [1490 4692] and at Bicker [247 385]. The mudstone adjacent to the concretions in the Asgarby bore is described as black shale, including layers of white, thin-shelled bivalves and some pyrite below the concretions. At Bicker, the lower part of the formation featured siltstone and mudstone with some kaolinite and pyritisation.

Parts of the Blisworth Clay from Walks Farm Borehole core, mainly between 100.77 and 103.11 m depth, are smectitic in appearance; clay mineral analysis of samples from the core confirmed a relatively high proportion of smectite and mixed-layer illite-smectite in the upper part of the formation. Plastic limit and liquid limit test results, from a series of boreholes [0327 4732 to 0420 4768] drilled during site investigations for road improvements to the A17 trunk road west of Holdingham, showed differences in the properties of the clay in the topmost beds, compared with the lower ones. A borehole [0370 4754], commencing in orange-brown clay apparently at a horizon immediately below the Cornbrash, proved clay to at least 9.60 m depth. The value for the liquid limit is reported to approach 80%, and that for the plasticity index 55%, in the uppermost 1.2 to 1.5 m of clay; this was regarded as unsuitable for inclusion in construction of the embankment and problems with shrinking and swelling are likely. Records of a set of trial pits on Quarrington Hill [058 454] mention high plasticity in the clay of three of them.

The Blisworth Clay is of late Bathonian age. It is thought to span the *Oxycerites orbis* to *Clydoniceras discus* biozones (Cope et al., 1980a). Bivalves are abundant at the base and top of the formation, but otherwise, except for fish fragments and sparsely distributed shell debris, macrofossils are generally rare. Jukes-Browne (1885, p.62) mentions that *Placunopsis socialis* may form thin shelly seams. Small fragments of wood and comminuted plant debris occur; possible fossil carbonaceous material has been found in a sample of medium grey clay from an otherwise unfossiliferous exposure [0201 3867] north-west of Dembleby Thorns, and it was noted in Walks Farm Borehole particularly between 104.75 and 105.75 m depth.

The sparse fauna collected from outcrops of the Blisworth Clay is dominated by *Praeexogyra hebridica,* from near Dembleby Thorns [0279 3848], at Aisby [0148 3885] and near Bloxholm [0501 5374].

In Walks Farm Borehole, the basal calcareous mudstones, which pass down into the Blisworth Limestone, contain quite numerous macrofossils, but the fauna shows much less diversity than that from the uppermost beds, suggesting a more brackish-marine, lagoonal environment. *Praeexogyra hebridica subrugulosa* is particularly common, *Corbula* sp., *Corbis* sp., *Neomiodon cunninghami, Neomiodon* sp., *Placunopsis socialis,* and *Quenstedtia* sp. also occur.

Between 100.25 and 100.75 m depth, near the top of the formation, bivalves of mixed sizes and moderate diversity are fairly abundant, including *Catinula?, Corbula attenuata, Eomiodon angulatus, Eomiodon* sp., *Falcimytilus?, Gervillella ovata, Lucina* sp., *Meleagrinella echinata, Modiolus* sp., *Oxytoma* sp., *Placunopsis socialis* and *Pleuromya?.* Serpulid tubes, fragments of terebratulids and fish remains also occur.

Palynological analysis of samples from the Blisworth Clay of Walks Farm Borehole showed, in the samples from depths of 100.55, 105.05 and 107.05 m, abundant and diverse assemblages rich in marine species; *Ctenidodinium, Durotrigia, Jansonia, Leptodinium* cf. *subtile* and *Lithodinia reticulata,* found in these samples, are indicative of a Bathonian age. Two samples, taken from 101.77 and 102.87 m, are dominated by terrestrially derived species, and a rootlet and thin laminae of fine-grained sand were recorded from this section. The lower sample includes the freshwater/brackish alga *Botryococcus,* suggesting generally nonmarine deposition. Specimens from the highest beds show an increasing diversity of dinoflagellate cysts, indicating probable stable, open-marine conditions.

The calcareous microfauna in the lower part of the Blisworth Clay is sparse. However, a more diverse and well-preserved fauna occurred in a sample from the topmost 0.15 m, including *Micropneumatocythere falcata,* the index for the eponymous ostracod zone that equates with the *discus* ammonite Zone (Sheppard, 1981), and *Terquemula acutiplicata,* which indicates an age no younger than the basal part of that zone.

Cornbrash Formation

The Cornbrash is a predominantly limestone formation, lying between the Blisworth Clay and the Kellaways Formation. As considered here, it includes small thicknesses of highly calcareous mudstone at its base and top. The lower boundary is commonly gradational over a small thickness, but is locally erosional. Its upper boundary is gradational.

The Cornbrash Formation extends from Dorset to Yorkshire; in the Grantham district it is rarely more than 3 m, averaging about 2 m. Walks Farm Borehole proved 1.88 m. Although thin, the Cornbrash produces a strong scarp feature and an extensive dip slope. Isolated outliers, in some cases reduced to mere remnants of brash — as for example south of Cranwell — are found on the highest hilltops to the west of the main outcrop.

The Cornbrash occurs as very hard, fine- to coarse-sand grade, bioclastic (shell-fragmental), calcarenitic packstone, grading to sparry and crystalline grainstone in parts, appearing either thinly bedded and flaggy or rubbly. It is purplish to bluish grey, weathering to a characteristic rusty orange-brown brash at surface. It is sandy in places, for example at the base in a borehole [0799 3505] at Threekingham; near the top it passes into shell-grit at the base of the Kellaways Clay. Bored surfaces are seen in rubbly iron-stained brash in a field [054 447] east of Northfield Road, Quarrington; the borings are infilled with micritic limestone.

The main exposures of the formation are found in the ditches cut across the dip slope. Flaggy grey limestone is exposed in ditch sections at many localities, although at some, particularly those identified as Lower Cornbrash outcrops (for example the faulted outlier [039 528] at Warren Pit Plantation near Brauncewell) the brash is rubbly rather than flaggy. Douglas and Arkell (1932, pp.134–135) collected fossils from a shallow quarry at Quarrington (probably that [058 442] now degraded, on Stump Cross Hill). They describe a topmost bed, about 0.52 m thick, of flaggy, sandy limestone with abundant bivalves, separated by about 0.7 m of sandy marl also containing bivalves from underlying tough, grey-hearted, less fossiliferous limestone of more massive type. They recognised the uppermost, flaggy bed at another quarry [062 503], worked to about 0.8 m depth, by the Bloxholm–Leasingham road; this working has since been backfilled.

Marly and clayey partings and beds are common within the Cornbrash; these are 0.05 to 0.10 m thick in a borehole [0679 3810] at Osbournby, and 0.7 m in the quarry section at Quarrington mentioned above (Douglas and Arkell, 1932). A ditch section [0574 4396 to 0546 4392] south of Quarrington, within the Cornbrash, exposes 0.8 m of limestone with an irregular base, resting on 0.15 m of dark grey clayey silt with shells and shell debris increasing downwards. This passes down into 0.29 m of silty clay with abundant shell fragments; the sharp base of the clay rests on 0.54 m of bluish grey, massive limestone, which becomes rubbly with weathering. Moderately strong, rubbly, brown-stained grey-hearted, fine-grained, limestone was proved in a borehole [0706 4588] on the east side of Sleaford; it contains seams of firm sandy clay. In Walks Farm Borehole core, the matrix is generally muddy and a few centimetres of hard calcareous mudstone are present at the top and base of the formation.

The Cornbrash Formation straddles the Bathonian–Callovian stage boundary. It is divisible, on palaeontological evidence, into Lower Cornbrash (or Berry Member) of late Bathonian (*discus* Biozone) age and Upper Cornbrash (or Fleet Member) of early Callovian (Herveyi Zone) age (Page, 1989). There may be a nonsequence between the two divisions and locally the Lower Cornbrash may be absent (Douglas and Arkell,

1932; Page, 1989). This is true for at least part of this district as a *Macrocephalites* fragment, indicative of the Upper Cornbrash, was found at the very base of the formation [0344 4201] near Willoughby Walks Farm (Berridge, 1993). Faunas diagnostic of the Lower Cornbrash were, however, found elsewhere in Lincolnshire by Kent (1939a); fauna collected from borehole cores, ditch sections and field brash during this latest survey confirm that the Lower Cornbrash is present, at least sporadically, over a wide area in both the north and the south of this district. No attempt has been made to map the subdivisions of the Cornbrash because there is no consistent difference in lithology.

The localities in the district from which Cornbrash faunas have been obtained fall into 3 groups: those containing taxa exclusive to the Lower Cornbrash, those with taxa exclusive to the Upper Cornbrash and those comprising mixed Upper and Lower Cornbrash taxa. At Quarrington, Douglas and Arkell (1932, pp.134–135) collected Upper Cornbrash specimens; another site in the same general area, yielded probable Lower Cornbrash specimens. The following taxa indicating the Lower Cornbrash were collected in the district during the recent BGS survey: *Cererithyris intermedia, C.* cf. *dorsetensis, C.* sp., *Kallirhynchia yaxleyensis, Obovothyris* cf. *classis, O. magnobovata, O. obovata, O. obovata* var. *grandobovata, Liostrea* cf. *hebridica, Myophorella scarburgensis* and *Clydoniceras discus.* Taxa generally indicative of the Upper Cornbrash include: *Digonella [Microthyridina] lagenalis, D. siddingtonensis, Lopha marshii, Macrocephalites terebratus, M.* cf. *terebratus, M.typicus* (? = *M jacquoti* in Page, 1989) and *M.* sp. Many non-diagnostic specimens, mainly bivalves, with some echinoids, were also collected (Berridge, 1993; Samuel, 1992a, 1992b.).

No age-diagnostic macrofossil species were found in the Cornbrash of Walks Farm Borehole. Specimens of *Kallirhynchia* sp., *Entolium corneolum, Gervillella* cf. *aviculoides, Meleagrinella echinata, Modiolus* sp., ostreids and *Placunopis* sp. were recorded, in the basal bed. In higher beds, most of the shell material is in comminuted form, but some nearly complete valves of *Entolium corneolum* occur, also a colony of *Sarcinella* tubes, *Lopha?* and fragments of trigoniid bivalves, crinoids and other echinoderms (Ivimey-Cook et al., in preparation).

Palynological evidence from three samples of Cornbrash from Walks Farm Borehole shows that the formation there is mainly Upper Cornbrash, containing early Callovian dinoflagellate cysts. *Chytroeisphaeridia hyalina,* an early to mid-Callovian index, occurred in all the samples, together with five species having their range bases, and another one with its range top, in the Callovian. The diversity is relatively high, and overall there is an approximately equal division between marine microplankton and miospores; saccate gymnosperm pollen, for example *Callialasporites* spp., predominate over spores in the latter (Riding in Ivimey-Cook et al., in preparation). Calcareous macrofaunas in the Cornbrash are mainly long-ranging and of little biostratigraphical importance. The ostracod *Terquemula bradiana,* which was recorded at 98.30–98.40 m in Walks Farm Borehole, ranges from the *hodsoni* Biozone to the Herveyi Zone. However, the record of *Micropneumatocythere falcata* at (99.30–99.40 m) appears to be anomalous; this ostracod is indicative of the *discus* Biozone, it being the index species of the *falcata* Zone sensu Sheppard (1981).

The depositional environment deduced for the Cornbrash is a stable, open, low- to moderate-energy shallow shelf sea, with a supply of bioclastic debris from a carbonate shoal and of fine siliciclastic sediment from land not far distant. Periodic reworking by storm action would have transported coarser material to the district.

SIX

Middle to Upper Jurassic: Ancholme Group

ANCHOLME GROUP

All the solid strata above the Cornbrash in the district are referred to the Ancholme [Clay] Group (Table 9), a term originally proposed for the predominantly argillaceous Jurassic rocks between the Cornbrash and the Spilsby Sandstone in Humberside and north Lincolnshire (Gaunt et al., 1992). The group includes the Kellaways, Oxford Clay, West Walton, Ampthill Clay and Kimmeridge Clay formations which span the Callovian, Oxfordian and Kimmeridgian stages of the Middle and Upper Jurassic.

In this district, only the Kellaways and Oxford Clay formations are represented (Table 9); these have a combined total thickness of about 57 m. The outcrop forms a low-lying plain on the east side of the Cornbrash dip slope; the Kellaways Formation commonly forms hummocky ground near the eastern edge of that dip slope, but the Oxford Clay is largely drift-covered. The succession is known, in outline, from numerous water wells and boreholes drilled to the underlying Lincolnshire Limestone aquifer

The Ancholme Group of the district is entirely marine, and indicates a gradual deepening of the sea following the deposition of the Great Oolite and Inferior Oolite groups when shallow-water conditions prevailed and the area was subjected to periods of emergence and erosion. Terrestrial influences persisted during the deposition of the Kellaways Formation, but declined as sea-level rose. The inferred environment was a subtropical to warm temperate sea with neighbouring forested shores.

Exposure is poor, and where the strata are not covered by Quaternary deposits, they are commonly deeply weathered and decalcified, converting bedded, fossilifer-

Table 9 Stratal subdivisions of the Ancholme Group in the district.

Chronostratigraphy					Lithostratigraphy		
Series	Stage/ Substage		Standard ammonite-based		Member	Formation	Group
			Zone	Subzone			
UPPER JURASSIC	OXFORDIAN	LOWER	Cordatum	Bukowskii	Weymouth (formerly Upper Oxford Clay)	Oxford Clay	Ancholme
			Mariae	Praecordatum			
				Scarburgense			
MIDDLE JURASSIC	CALLOVIAN	UPPER	Lamberti	Lamberti	Stewartby (formerly Middle Oxford Clay)		
				Henrici			
			Athleta	Spinosum			
				Proniae			
				Phaeinum			
		MIDDLE	Coronatum	Grossouvrei	Peterborough (formerly Lower Oxford Clay)		
				Obductum			
			Jason	Jason			
				Medea			
		LOWER	Calloviense	Enodatum			
				Calloviense		Kellaways	
			Koenigi	Galilaeii	Kellaways Sand		
				Curtilobus			
				Gowerianus			
			Herveyi	Kamptus	Kellaways Clay		
				Terebratus		Cornbrash	Great Oolite
				Keppleri			

The Stewartby and Weymouth members have not been mapped separately, but a conjectural boundary between the two is shown in Figure 23.

ous mudstones into amorphous, apparently barren clays. Mapping has necessarily made use of relatively unweathered loose debris, assumed to have come out of nearby ditches, and vague discontinuous topographic features, the stratigraphical significance of which can only be inferred. Walks Farm Borehole [1534 4635], sited about 3 km east of the district, is a key reference section.

Kellaways Formation

The Kellaways Formation lies between the Cornbrash Formation below and the Oxford Clay above. In the original survey (Jukes-Browne, 1885), the formation was not differentiated from the Oxford Clay and appears thus on the Provisional Edition (1972) of the 1:50 000 Series Sheet 127 (Grantham). The term Kellaways Beds was first used in the Lincoln area for sands and sandstones (Kellaways Sand and Kellaways Rock) with an underlying thinner unit of 'black shales' resting on the Cornbrash (Ussher et al., 1888). The 'black shales' were subsequently named the Kellaways Clay (Woodward, 1895). This twofold division is maintained here; the Kellaways Clay and Kellaways Sand are regarded as members of the Kellaways Formation. The former is the Cayton Clay Formation of Page (1989). In this district, the combined thickness of the two members ranges from 6.5 m to 8 m. The formation belongs to the early Callovian Herveyi, Koenigi and Calloviense zones.

KELLAWAYS CLAY MEMBER

The base of the Kellaways Clay Member is taken at the base of a bed of coarse shell debris with mudstone matrix, overlying hard limestone of the Cornbrash Formation; a similar basal bed has been recorded elsewhere in eastern England (e.g. Horton, Lake, Bisson and Coppack, 1974; Horton, Shephard-Thorn and Thurrell, 1974). The junction with the overlying silt or fine-grained sand of the Kellaways Sand, is sharp and apparently locally channelled.

In Walks Farm Borehole, the basal bed comprises 0.20 m of a rough-textured shell-grit with an olive-grey, silty and finely sandy, muddy matrix. A sample from 0.07 m above the base was classified as a bioclastic mudstone (Folk, 1959) or bioclastic packstone (Dunham, 1962). The bioclastic debris consists of poorly sorted, fine to very coarse, sand-grade fragments of bivalves, echinoids and foraminifera; a layered structure indicates current action. Quartz of up to fine sand grade was also present, together with abundant pyrite. A similar depositional environment to that of the underlying Cornbrash is indicated for this part of the member, with low to moderate energy, shallow marine conditions; coarser material was probably storm-derived from nearby shoals. This basal bed, seen as a dark grey clay, gritty with shell fragments, was augered from a ditch [0706 5353] near Bloxholm Gorse. In several boreholes at Duke Street [069 460], Sleaford, it is the sole representative of the member.

At outcrop, the member is a smooth, dark grey to bluish grey or greenish grey clay with some orange mottling. It is locally silty, and commonly shelly at the base. It gives rise to a dull fawn-brown soil, which

contrasts with the orange-brown of the underlying weathered Cornbrash. It crops out as a very narrow strip between the broad dip slope of the Cornbrash and the gentle positive feature of the Kellaways Sand. Pockets of Kellaways Clay also occur as outliers resulting from minor faulting, or from down-warping of the Cornbrash surface.

Where fresh, as in Walks Farm Borehole, the member comprises mainly medium grey and olive-grey to pale olive-grey mudstone, with very thin partings of silty mudstone; small irregular inclusions of pale grey, fine-grained sandstone were recorded. Pyrite trails and small nodules occur near the base. A core sample taken from this borehole for clay mineral analysis consists of approximately half clay- (< 0.002 mm) and half silt- (0.063 to 0.002 mm) grade particles, with a trace of fine sand. Kaolinite is the predominant clay mineral, with some illite, smectite, and mixed-layer illite-smectite.

Within the district, the Kellaways Clay is commonly less than 1 m in thickness. Thicknesses proved by augering and by boreholes in the Dorrington–Ruskington area, in the north of the district, are about 0.6 m. Thicknesses of up to 1 m were proved west of Leasingham. Farther south, boreholes indicate that the clay is locally absent on the north side of Sleaford, but is present to the south. Thicknesses proved in boreholes and sections in the southern half of the district range from 0.9 m to 2 m. Walks Farm Borehole proved a thickness of 1.77 m.

The outcrops mapped during this survey yielded no identifiable macrofossils. In boreholes, bivalves dominate the macrofauna. Specimens collected from dark grey mudstone of the United Steel Co. Borehole NW155 [0900 3800], at Spanby, included *Meleagrinella* and *Modiolus*. In addition, the Kellaways Clay of Walks Farm Borehole yields *Bositra, Corbulomima, Entolium,* a nuculacean, *Pinna, Pleuromya* and *Protocardia; Dentalium, Procerithium* and serpulids were also collected, and fragments of the ammonite *Macrocephalites* provide zonal evidence. Palynological samples from Walks Farm Borehole show an abundant and diverse palynoflora. Marine microplankton averages 38%, but indications of a local source of fresh to brackish water are also found. Pollen grains strongly predominate over spores. Dinoflagellate cysts include *Chytroeisphaeridia hyalina* and abundant *Cleistosphaeridium varispinosum*; together, these indicate an early Callovian age. Although long-ranging forms dominate the calcareous microfauna, *Trochammina squamata* and *Reophax helveticus* occur, both of which are known to appear first in the Herveyi Zone, the latter in the upper part. Biostratigraphical evidence from this borehole endorses the assignment of the member to the Herveyi Zone, Kamptus Subzone (Page, 1989).

KELLAWAYS SAND MEMBER

The lower boundary of the Kellaways Sand, where fine sandstone or siltstone overlies mudstone of the Kellaways Clay, is generally clearly defined in this district, with channelling or a shell-bed. In Walks Farm Borehole, the lowest 0.75 m of the member comprises siltstone rather than sandstone. The shell content (whole bivalves and fragments) increases towards the base, where there is a

0.02 m-thick shelly bed directly overlying smooth mudstone of the Kellaways Clay. A sharp base, possibly channelled, was noted in ditch sections [0574 4396 to 0546 4392, and 0695 4458 to 0705 4448] south and east of Quarrington. At the more easterly locality, small calcareous nodules are locally present at the base. The upper boundary of the member (the base of the Oxford Clay Formation) is drawn at the top of the highest fine-grained sand or sandstone, and is also well defined. This sandstone, rich in *Gryphaea (Bilobissa) dilobotes,* was seen in a section [075 381] at South Beck in 1978.

Within the district, the member is typically 5.5 to 7.5 m in thickness; 5 m were proved in Walks Farm Borehole.

The Kellaways Sand is locally cemented, most commonly in its uppermost part, where it has been called the Kellaways Rock. This is, however, limited and irregular in extent, and is insufficiently well defined to be mapped separately in this district. In the Dorrington area, in the north of the district, some fragments of brash are seen, but the top of the member consisted mainly of sand. On the east side of Ruskington, a hard upper surface was encountered when augering in the base of a dried-up pond [0878 5111] and in ditches [0899 5046 and 0965 5005] near the sewage works.

According to Jukes-Browne (1885), the Kellaways Rock was seen in the stream-bed east of Swarby and in parts of the stream-bed in the valley between Quarrington and Silk Willoughby. During this survey, a section [0717 4953 to 0805 4925], about 1 km long, cut by the stream north of Deepdales was examined (Pattison, 1992). Flaggy to rubbly, bioturbated sandstone containing belemnites and bivalves, and some plant debris was exposed; interbedding of dark to greenish grey silty mudstone was found in parts. Cementation is probably not limited to the upper surface; the borehole [0671 3905] sunk at the Aswarby Hall Lodge appears to have encountered several hard bands in the 6.7 m of 'brown sandy clay and small boulders' which represents the Kellaways Formation. In Walks Farm Borehole, the topmost 0.18 m is moderately hard and calcareous; below, alternations of harder, calcareous, and less hard, non-calcareous layers occur in the uppermost 0.75 m but fade out downwards.

The sands of the member are generally loosely compacted but uncemented; in Walks Farm Borehole, they are friable and non-calcareous below the topmost 0.18 m. They comprise, predominantly, quartz of very fine sand to silt grade, and are well sorted. In colour, the sand is olive-grey to pale olive-grey; it weathers pale yellow to ochreous near the surface. Burrowing and bioturbation are common.

Analysis of the clay fraction of a sample from 0.82 m above the base of the member in Walks Farm Borehole shows kaolinite to be dominant, with moderate amounts of illite, some chlorite and mixed-layer illite-smectite, but no discrete smectite. A sample from 0.49 m below the top of the member again shows dominant kaolinite, with moderate illite and smectite, but no chlorite.

Clayey beds are recorded in the upper half of the member. Walks Farm Borehole proved a 0.45 m-thick bed, 0.68 m below the top; this consists mainly of mudstone containing silt and fine sand, and with one sandy intercalation. The South Beck section (see above) shows a slightly thinner bed of bluish grey mudstone at a similar horizon. Boreholes at Duke Street, Sleaford, proved 7.5 m of Kellaways Sand with 0.2 to 0.9 m of fissured and laminated, very silty clay, with sand partings and burrow infills in the upper part. In general, these clays are not mappable, but two thin clayey beds within the Kellaways Sand between Quarrington and Mareham Lane [066 440 to 075 446] were traced for over 1 km.

As in the Kellaways Clay, bivalves, particularly oysters, are the dominant macrofauna, although belemnites are also abundant. *Gryphaea (Bilobissa) dilobotes, Oxytoma expansa* and belemnite fragments were collected from sandstone, which also showed burrow structures and trace fossils, in a ditch section [075 446] west of Mareham Lane Farm, near Sleaford. Calcareous sandstone at the western end of the stream section near Deepdales, yielded a possible *Meleagrinella, Oxytoma inequivalve,* small oysters and belemnite fragments. Fragments of the belemnite *Cylindroteuthis,* valves of *Gryphaea dilobotes,* and *Discomiltha?* occur in sandstone debris [0966 5005] excavated from beneath Oxford Clay during installation of a high-pressure gas pipeline south-east of Ruskington. Walks Farm Borehole yields specimens of *Gryphaea,* including *Gryphaea (Bilobissa) dilobotes,* which forms a shell-bed in the topmost part of the member. Other bivalves include *Anisocardia, Bositra, Discomiltha, Entolium, Grammatodon?, Meleagrinella, Modiolus, Myopholas, Myophorella,* nuculaceans, *Oxytoma, Pleuromya* and *Protocardia. Procerithium,* a possible rhynchonellid brachiopod, belemnites and fossilised wood also occur. Two fragments of *Macrocephalites,* found about 0.9 m above the base, is consistent with regional evidence placing the basal part of the Kellaways Sand Member in the Koenigi Zone, Gowerianus Subzone (Page, 1989). An indeterminate kosmoceratid was found 0.85 m below the top.

Oxford Clay Formation

The Oxford Clay constitutes the youngest part of the Ancholme Group in the district, and it crops out in a 3 to 7 km-wide strip along the eastern border of the district (Figure 23). The outcrop is largely drift-covered and exposures are not common. The topographical features which facilitate the mapping of harder beds within the formation in the south Midlands are mostly undetectable. Knowledge of the local succession is therefore based largely on borehole evidence, especially from Walks Farm Borehole (Ivimey-Cook et al., in preparation). Using gamma-ray logs, this borehole succession has been tentatively correlated with other, mostly water authority, borehole sequences within the district (Figure 24).

The formation consists mostly of grey mudstones with subordinate limestones, and contains a varied molluscan fauna. It is between 60 and 70 m thick in south-west Lincolnshire; only the lowest 50 m of the formation is present in this district.

The Oxford Clay Formation is divided into three members—Peterborough (formerly Lower Oxford Clay), Stewartby (Middle Oxford Clay) and Weymouth (Upper

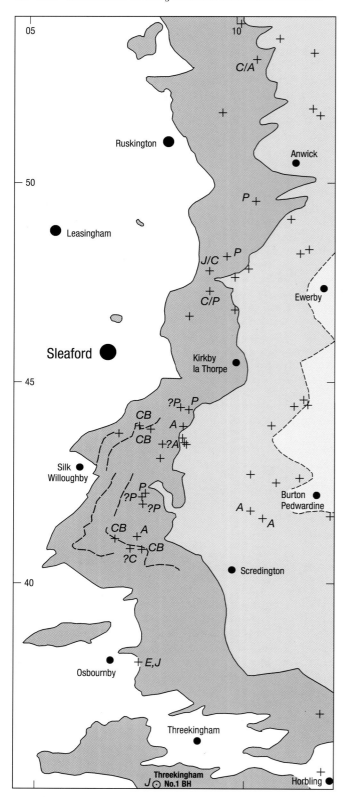

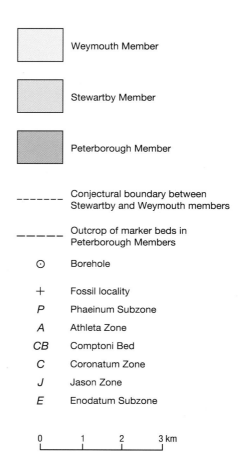

Figure 23 Sketch map showing outcrops of the Oxford Clay members and distribution of fossil localities.

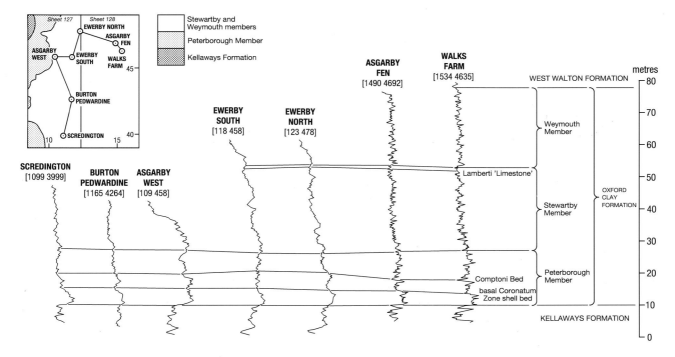

Figure 24 Correlation of gamma-ray logs from boreholes through the Oxford Clay in the eastern part of the district and the adjoining part of the Boston district (Sheet 128). The lithostratigraphical classification is based on the core from Walks Farm Borehole.

Oxford Clay) (Cox et al., 1992). These members are recognisable along much of the outcrop in England, as well as in cored or geophysically logged boreholes. However, it has not been possible to distinguish between the Stewartby and Weymouth members at outcrop within the district.

During the deposition of the Oxford Clay, water depth increased gradually on the East Midlands Shelf. Initially, bottom conditions were stagnant, although never anoxic, resulting in the deposition of organic-rich and fossiliferous, fissile mudstones of the Peterborough Member. Deeper, more restricted waters brought an increased benthos, with a consequent decrease in the carbonaceous content of the sediment.

The organic carbon content of the Peterborough Member is generally more than 3% (Hudson and Martill, 1991), in contrast with values of less than 1% for the younger members. Otherwise, the mineralogical content of the formation is fairly uniform. Quartz, clay minerals and calcitic shell material are predominant throughout, with shells also commonly preserved as primary aragonite or secondary pyrite. Disseminated pyrite is also common. X-ray diffraction analysis of the < 2 microgram fractions from Walks Farm Borehole shows a predominance of kaolinite (up to 80% of the clay minerals) over illite (up to 35%) with minor amounts of smectite and chlorite. This surprising result contrasts with the predominance of illite over kaolinite in most of the other Jurassic mudstone formations, and in the Oxford Clay elsewhere.

Biostratigraphical and chronostratigraphical classification of the formation is based largely on ammonites, and

Walks Farm Borehole yielded forms indicating the presence of the Jason, Coronatum, Athleta and Lamberti zones of the Callovian Stage and the Mariae and Cordatum zones of the Oxfordian (see Table 9). A few surface sections in the Peterborough Member of the district also yielded age-diagnostic ammonites (see below). In higher parts of the formation, *Gryphaea* are commonly found as field brash.

PETERBOROUGH MEMBER

This member typically comprises dark greenish grey, organic-rich, commonly pyritous, shelly mudstone, with a minor cyclicity involving the alternation of dark grey, very fissile units and firmer, blocky, slightly paler mudstones. The abundant fauna is characterised by *Gryphaea dilobotes*, crushed aragonitic ammonites (particularly *Kosmoceras)*, large belemnites, and thin-shelled bivalves, notably nuculaceans and *Meleagrinella*. Wood fragments, fish remains and sparse septarian nodules also occur. Preservation of the aragonitic shell material was facilitated by the dysoxic depositional environment and quick burial.

From the northern edge of the district to the neighbourhood of Aswarby [067 400], the outcrop of the member is from 1 to 3 km wide. It underlies a north–south-aligned vale and is largely concealed by Quaternary gravels. Minor hill-top outliers occur east of Leasingham and north-east of Sleaford. In the south-east of the district, the outcrop is wider and here, in particular, it is affected by faulting; it is partly overlain by till, and caps the low hills between Newton and Horbling. Mudstones of the member weather to dark greenish grey clay with streaks of diagenetic selenite, overlain by stiff, brown, clay soil.

The Peterborough Member is 17.55 m thick in Walks Farm Borehole. At outcrop in the district, it is estimated to be about 20 m thick, but correlation of borehole gamma-ray logs with that of Walks Farm Borehole (Figure 24) suggests a thickness nearer 17 m.

A section through the base of the member was seen in South Beck, Osbournby [0754 3806 to 0756 3818]. It shows:

	Thickness
	m
PETERBOROUGH MEMBER	
Mudstone, fissile, bluish and brownish grey with *Kosmoceras jason* and *K. gulielmi*; large septarian nodule and wood fragment in basal 0.2 m	1.0
Friable sand and silt with pyritous, shelly limestone concretions which yield rhynchonellide and terebratulide brachiopods, gastropods (*Dicroloma* and *Procerithium*), bivalves including abundant *Corbulomima macneillii*, belemnite fragments, fish teeth, and the ammonites *Cadoceras* sp., *Choffatia recuperoi, Macrocephalites tumidus* and *Sigaloceras (Catasigaloceras) enodatum*	0.2

KELLAWAYS FORMATION

Sandstone, hard, calcareous

A comparable basal boundary sequence was recorded in Walks Farm Borehole; at both localities, the thin basal bed belongs to the Enodatum Subzone. However, in a borehole [0799 3505] south-west of Threekingham, this bed is apparently absent; a sharp lithological break was recorded between fissile mudstones, with *Bositra buchii* and *Kosmoceras jason* (basal Peterborough Member) and hard, calcareous sandstone (Kellaways Formation).

Two marker beds can be mapped in the relatively drift-free outcrop of the lower part of the Peterborough Member between Sleaford and Aswarby. About 5 m above the base, a band of calcareous septarian nodules appears as field brash, in debris from ditches, and, most notably, from the stream [0605 4093 to 0683 4074] on the north side of Aswarby Park. This may correlate with a comparable band (Bed 10 of Callomon (1968)) in the lower part of the member (basal Jason Subzone) in the Peterborough district (Horton, 1989). Such a bed was not proved in Walks Farm Borehole where the most likely correlative is a partially pyritised shell-bed with bivalves, belemnites and *Kosmoceras*, 4.16 m above the base of the member (basal Coronatum Zone).

The higher marker bed occurs about 10 m above the base of the member. It is exposed in a ditch [0765 4391 to 0785 4387] east of Sleaford Lodge Farm where it is underlain and overlain by greyish brown, fissile mudstone. The marker bed (0.5 m thick) consists of pale grey, blocky mudstone with belemnites (*Cylindroteuthis puzosiana*) and abundant bivalves, including oysters and

nuculaceans (mainly *Palaeonucula triangularis* but also *Mesosaccella morrisi*). Ammonite fragments (*Erymnoceras* and *Kosmoceras*) were collected from a thin, cemented shell-layer. The bed is mappable as far south as the Scredington area, where similar faunal material was collected from a ditch section [0700 4112] and a river bank [076 408]. It is taken to be the Comptoni Bed and/or superjacent Acutistriatum Band, which mark the boundary between the Coronatum and Athleta zones throughout the East Midlands (Callomon, 1968). These were both recognised in Walks Farm Borehole. The Comptoni Bed comprises a pyritous shell-bed with the ammonite *Binatisphinctes comptoni* and, includes for convenience, the associated underlying mudstones with abundant nuculacean bivalves, totalling 0.39 m. The immediately overlying Acutistriatum Band is weakly developed as 0.13 m of shelly mudstone.

Brownish grey, fissile mudstones, probably belonging to the Jason Zone or Coronatum Zone, are exposed in the bed of the Old River Slea [0921 4779 and 0931 4790] north of Evedon. They yield fragmentary *Kosmoceras* and abundant *Meleagrinella*. Dark grey fissile mudstones in the river bed farther north-east [0964 4820 to 0999 4850] yield fossils characteristic of the Phaeinum Subzone of the Athleta Zone; these include *Kosmoceras phaeinum* and *K. acutistriatum*, as well as abundant *Bositra*. The cleanest section in Phaeinum Subzone mudstones is seen on the right bank of the New River Slea at Haverholme Lock [1051 4952] where about 1.5 m of mudstone are exposed. The top 1 m is weathered and brown, but the lowest 0.5 m consists of greenish grey, fissile mudstone with shell fragments, spat and foraminifera, yielding *Procerithium damonis, Bositra buchii, Mesosaccella morrisi, Parainoceramus subtilis, Binatisphinctes comptoni, Hecticoceras* sp. and *Kosmoceras* spp. with looped ribbing. This assemblage indicates an horizon close above the Acutistriatum Band. Similar fossiliferous mudstones of the Phaeinum Subzone were collected from debris of gas pipeline excavations [0854 4423], south-east of Sleaford, and [0766 4200 to 0782 4227], north-west of Scredington.

Two exposures of beds which are probably stratigraphically high in the Peterborough Member were recorded near Dorrington. An excavation [1010 5390] in Dalica Plantation showed no clean section but the debris, consisting of very fossiliferous weathered mudstone with race, yield nuculacean bivalves including *Mesosacella morrisi*, gastropods (*Procerithium damonis*) and belemnites. An auger sample from grey clay, poorly exposed in a stream [1045 5302] near Fen House, also yields *P. damonis*, as well as a foraminiferal assemblage, including *Triplasia acuta*, indicative of the youngest Coronatum Zone or Athleta Zone. Foraminifera are also present in the Peterborough Member of Walks Farm Borehole (Wilkinson, in Ivimey-Cook et al., in preparation). *Lenticulina ectypa* is recorded at 90.95 to 91.05 m depth, implying an age no older than the Calloviense Zone, and *Marginulina batrakiensis*, found at 89.95 to 90.05 m, is usually a good indicator of the Jason Zone. The latter zone and Coronatum Zone can be inferred by the appearance of a number of species between 86.95 to 87.05 m and 85.95 to 86.05 m, including *Epistomina* cf.

nuda, E. regularis and *Pseudolamarckina rjasanensis*. In the highest part of the member, *Triplasia kimmeridensis* and common *Nubeculinella bigoti* and *Ammobaculites coprolithiformis* (at 76.45 to 76.55 m) together with *Citharinella nikitini* (at 74.45 to 74.55 m) mark the Athleta Zone.

STEWARTBY AND WEYMOUTH MEMBERS

Above the Peterborough Member, about a further 30 m of Oxford Clay crop out in the district, although the highest 15 m are largely covered by till. In Walks Farm Borehole, the combined Stewartby and Weymouth members are 51.12 m thick. The two members are distinguishable in the borehole by a combination of biostratigraphical evidence, gamma-ray log correlation, and recognition of a correlative of the Lamberti Limestone, which is the highest bed of the Stewartby Member in areas to the south. Although this boundary is not mappable at outcrop in the district, it can be inferred that both members are present. The Stewartby Member is 25.8 m thick in Walks Farm Borehole.

The two members consist of pale olive-grey mudstones, silty in part, with some tough siltstone beds. They contain scattered shells (bivalves, gastropods, belemnites and ammonites) and plant stems, all commonly pyritised. Like the mudstones of the Peterborough Member, the strata show a minor cyclicity; fine-grained fissile beds alternate with tougher, silty and generally paler beds. The mudstones weather to stiff, grey-green clays which are overlain by brown clay soils with some *Gryphaea*.

The lowest 10 to 15 m of the Stewartby Member form fairly drift-free slopes on the west side of the till-capped hills near the eastern edge of the district. Two or three discontinuous linear topographical positive features are recognised on these slopes, at various places between the neighbourhood of Scredington [095 405] and the northern edge of the district, for example on the south side of the Slea valley between Evedon and Evedon Wood [about 103 482]. These may indicate *Gryphaea* beds; some are associated with *Gryphaea* brash. At least some of the loose *Gryphaea* valves (for example, from localities [1073 4391, 1120 4437] between Grange and Sardeson's farms near Kirkby la Thorpe) have been identified as *G. lituola* which is characteristic of the Stewartby Member. *Gryphaea* collected from brash [102 479] near Evedon were identified as forms intermediate between *G. dilobotes* and *G. lituola*, suggesting a low level within the Stewartby Member.

Pale to medium grey mudstone debris from Cliff Beck [1050 4158 and 1028 4180], west of Burton Pedwardine, also yield a macrofauna suggestive of a low level within the Stewartby Member; this includes *Bositra buchii, Pinna, Hecticoceras, Peltoceras* and loop-ribbed *Kosmoceras*. Ostracods extracted from a sample at the more southerly of the two localities include *Polycope sububiquita* and *Praeschuleridea caudata*, which also suggest the beds are part of the Stewartby Member.

Two brick-clay pits in the Oxford Clay of the district were mentioned by Jukes-Browne, (1885). The stratigraphical position of both is probably high in the Stewartby Member. One, in the valley south of Burton Pedwardine, is probably the now-flooded pit [121 416] next to the railway, and yielded 'Ammonites of the Ornati group' [= Kosmoceras] and 'Gryphaea dilatata'. The second pit [115 482], north-west of Ewerby, is also now flooded; Jukes-Browne recorded the belemnite *Hibolithes hastatus*, which is most characteristic of the upper part of the Stewartby Member and the Weymouth Member.

Auger samples from several localities yielded palynomorph assemblages indicative of the Stewartby Member: near Fen House, Dorrington [1108 5355], near Anwick Grange [1224 5161], near Haverholme Priory [1124 4904], at Brickyard Farm, Ewerby [1170 4832] and in North Beck, Burton Pedwardine [1249 4162]. A probable late Callovian age is indicated by the occurrence of *Ctenidodinium continuum, Gonyaulacysta centriconnata* and *Wanaea thysanota*. The first-named species, in England, has a range top within the late Callovian (Riding, 1987). A further factor supporting a late Callovian age is the presence of *Gonyaulacysta jurassica* subsp. *adecta* var. *adecta;* both the younger subspecies (*Gonyaulacysta jurassica jurassica*) and *Systematophora areolata*, which first appear in the early Oxfordian (i.e. Weymouth Member) are absent from these assemblages.

In Walks Farm Borehole, the inception of such ostracods as *Neurocythere interrupta interrupta* (at 72.45 to 72.55 m depth), *Lophocythere caesa caesa* (at 66.45 to 66.55 m), *Praeschuleridea caudata* (at 62.45 to 62.55 m), and *Lophocythere flexicosta lutzei* (at 58.45 to 58.55 m) are indicative of the Athleta and Lamberti zones. The foraminifer *Pseudolamarckina rjasanensis*, which is restricted to the Athleta Zone, ranges through to a depth of 53.42 to 53.49 m. The inception of *Neurocythere dorni*, at 48.45 to 48.55 m, is an excellent marker for the Lamberti Zone in the borehole.

The only biostratigraphical evidence for the presence of the Weymouth Member in the district comes from further palynological sampling and some doubtful finds of *Gryphaea dilatata*. The latter include specimens collected from soft, grey, weathered clay in a ditch [1185 5173 to 1174 5200] north of Anwick Grange; a belemnite (*Cylindroteuthis*?) was also found there. A palynomorph assemblage indicative of the Weymouth Member came from an auger hole [1157 4452] near Lodge Farm, Burton Pedwardine. The assemblage includes the dinoflagellate cysts *Crussolia deflandrei* and *Wanaea fimbriata*, the co-occurrence of which is characteristic of earliest Oxfordian strata.

The outcrop of the Weymouth Member in the district is probably confined to the hilltops around Ewerby and Burton Pedwardine and the inferred downthrown fault block between them. Walks Farm Borehole, within the same inferred fault block, proved 25.32 m of the member; the base is taken at the top of 1.76 m of very shelly mudstones which are regarded as the local development of the Lamberti Limestone. These contain a characteristic fauna including ammonites (*Hecticoceras, Peltoceras, Quenstedtoceras*) and bivalves (predominantly *Oxytoma inequivalve* and *Chlamys (Radulopecten) scarburgensis*) preserved as crushed mudstone casts with dull brown, pyritic coatings.

SEVEN

Quaternary

No rocks that are younger than the Oxford Clay and older than the Middle Pleistocene are known in situ in the district. Any deposits which were laid down during the intervening time (most of the Late Jurassic and the Cretaceous), were eroded during the Cainozoic Era. A postulated Palaeogene drainage system of parallel, east-flowing, master rivers was converted by the end of that period into a trellis-like pattern of major, north-flowing, subsequent rivers and minor eastward or westward flowing streams. They produced the basic scarp and vale landscape we see today (Straw and Clayton, 1979).

In Britain, the past 2 million years or so of the Quaternary Period have been characterised by marked climatic fluctuations with cold and temperate phases alternating with warm phases. These fluctuations are the basis of chronostratigraphical classification for the period. Only the last 0.5 Ma or so are represented in the local Quaternary succession. This includes deposits of the Anglian glaciation and the following warm and cold phases. There is no firm evidence anywhere in eastern England for a Quaternary glaciation prior to the Anglian. Any pre-Anglian glacial or interglacial sediments that may have been deposited have been removed, reworked or obscured by the Anglian ice or its deposits.

The Anglian ice-sheet is thought to have entered the district from the north-east, carrying material eroded from Upper Jurassic and Cretaceous outcrops. The most obvious local effect was deposition of till and associated water-laid sand and gravel. In addition, ice and associated meltwater streams cut deep valleys in the Lincolnshire Limestone upland, notably south of Grantham (Wyatt, 1971).

Since the Anglian glaciation, alternating cold and warm climatic phases have brought changes which have affected the landscape of the district. For example, rise and fall of sea-level, in response to glacio-eustatic variations as ice-sheets waxed and waned, changed the base level of the local rivers and streams: freeze–thaw and mass movement of surface regolith occurred in periglacial conditions established during the cold phases.

The named glacial and interglacial stages defined by Mitchell et al. (1973) (i.e. Hoxnian, 'Wolstonian', Ipswichian, Devensian, Flandrian; Table 10) are still the most commonly used classification for post-Anglian chronology in England, but neither 'Wolstonian' nor Devensian ice reached this district, and fluviatile sands and gravels are the most widespread deposits of this period. They occur in several discrete swathes across different parts of the district. Each swathe has a distinct lithological composition and topographical character and some have yielded fossil evidence of age. The most

evident geological process since the last (Devensian) cold stage has been increased alluviation as sea-level rose during the succeeding Flandrian.

TILL

Till is widespread in the east and south-east parts of the district (Figure 25). The overall present-day distribution suggests that it is a relict of a more or less continuous, largely easterly inclined sheet which at its western edge survives mostly on hilltops. Smaller patches occur west of the main outcrop and, apart from those near Gelston, they conform to the same easterly inclined pattern. The base of the till appears to be generally planar, but in the adjacent district to the south, till, containing abundant large erratic rafts of local provenance comparable with that near Gelston, fills deep buried channels in and around the upper Witham valley (Wyatt, 1971).

Along the eastern edge of the district, till caps the low hills which separate the north-trending vale through Ruskington [086 517], Sleaford and Osbournby [070 382] from the fen country to the east. These hills are dissected by west–east-trending valleys. In the north-east of the district, the top of the till sheet slopes gently eastward from over 20 m above OD to 2 m below OD beneath Flandrian fen deposits. In the south-east, the till sheet lies at over 80 m above OD near Braceby, dropping to about 10 m above OD in the Horbling area. Northwards from Braceby, the till caps the Blisworth Limestone outcrop almost as far as the Ancaster Gap, and west of Braceby, a separate patch on Ropsley Heath reaches over 100 m above OD. Only small patches of till occur on the upland north of the Ancaster Gap, and are associated with glaciofluvial sand and gravel on Caythorpe Heath.

West of the Lincoln Edge, till covers part of the upland area east and south of Gelston, at about 80 to 90 m above OD, but a strip south-south-west of the village descends along the western flank of the upland to about 60 m above OD just north of the River Witham.

Till does not appear to exceed 10 m in thickness within the district. In the east and south, the till seems to have a fairly uniform maximum thickness, ranging from about 5 to 9 m, and this is maintained where it disappears below younger deposits in the north-east. The greatest recorded thickness, of 9.14 m, is in a borehole [0400 3505] south-west of Newton. The till in the Gelston area is probably no more than 2 or 3 m thick on the hill tops, but to the south-south-west the thickness may be greater, although firm evidence is lacking.

The uniformity of the till in the east and south of the district reinforces the impression that it was deposited

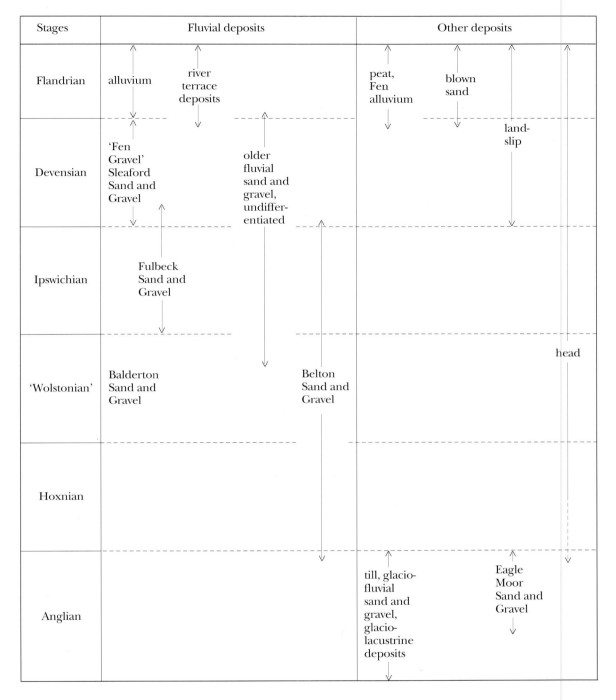

Table 10 Chronological classification of Quaternary deposits in the district.

Stages	Fluvial deposits		Other deposits		
Flandrian	alluvium	river terrace deposits	peat, Fen alluvium	blown sand	
Devensian	'Fen Gravel' Sleaford Sand and Gravel	older fluvial sand and gravel, undifferentiated			land-slip
Ipswichian	Fulbeck Sand and Gravel				
'Wolstonian'	Balderton Sand and Gravel	Belton Sand and Gravel			head
Hoxnian					
Anglian			till, glacio-fluvial sand and gravel, glacio-lacustrine deposits	Eagle Moor Sand and Gravel	

during a single glacial episode. It consists of a diamicton with a firm, mostly clay matrix, pale grey to bluish grey where fresh, and up to 15% of the volume made up of pebble-grade and larger clasts, although 5 to 10% is more typical. The most abundant clasts are subangular to rounded chalk pebbles, and finer-grained chalk material forms a large part of the matrix. Other clasts include angular, pebble-grade flints, limestone of various lithologies (probably including material of both Jurassic and Carboniferous derivation), mudstone, sandstone and ironstone (most of probable Jurassic provenance),

various igneous rocks and rounded quartzitic 'Bunter' pebbles. The last appear to be more common towards the west. Pebbles are more abundant than cobbles and cobbles more abundant than boulders. The boulders appear to include a greater proportion of limestone than is found among the smaller clasts.

The till weathers to a friable, yellowish brown stony clay, in which the effects of leaching, oxidation and decalcification deplete the chalk content and leave flints as the most common clasts visible at surface. There is a variable sand content in soils on the weathered till but

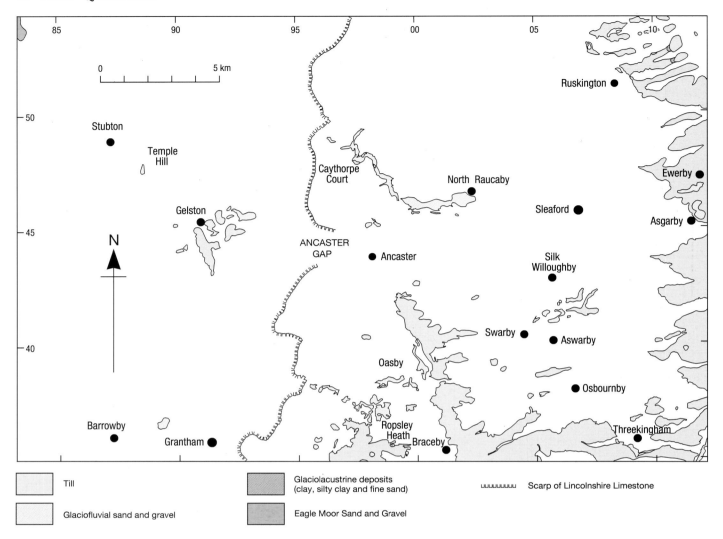

Figure 25 Distribution of till, glaciofluvial and glaciolacustrine deposits associated with the Anglian glaciation.

the variations may result from extraneous material, such as wind-blown sand, as well as differences in the till lithology. The soils on the till in the Gelston area appear to be particularly sandy. Discrete sand and gravel bodies, interpreted as glaciofluvial in origin, are found in contact with till between Asgarby and Ewerby in the eastern part of the district, near Threekingham in the south-east, and on Ropsley Heath. Otherwise, most of the inferred glaciofluvial deposits occur separately from till, although commonly not far removed from its outcrop.

In the Gelston area, till at one locality [909 446] was described by Kent (1943) as 'Boulder Clay consisting of a series of horizontal or gently dipping beds of Inferior Oolite, interleaved with glacial clay'. The most common erratics there are described as 'cementstones' and 'shelly Great Ponton Beds' from the Lincolnshire Limestone and also include Northampton Ironstone, a 'five feet long' piece of which was recorded as 'one of the smaller masses' at the locality. Erratics of this size and abundance

are probably unusual in the district, although clean exposures of till which is sufficiently fresh to show the nature and abundance of erratics in situ are uncommon.

The primary survey distinguished 'older' and 'newer glacial beds'; bluish grey till in the southern part of the district was included with the 'older' beds, and mottled red-brown and grey till in the east was included with the 'newer'. Straw (1969; 1991) recognised two tills, the Wragby Till and the Heath Till. The Wragby Till occurs on both sides of the lower Witham fens, and includes the till in the eastern part of this district. The Heath Till occurs on Lincoln Heath and includes the till in the southern part of the district. Straw believed these tills to be Wolstonian in age. However, more recent work on the pre-Devensian tills of eastern England (Perrin, Rose and Davies, 1979) shows that the till in south-west Lincolnshire and its extension into Leicestershire (where it is known as the Oadby Till) has been correlated with the 'chalky boulder clay' or Lowestoft Till of East Anglia

(Sumbler, 1983), and all these tills are now regarded as deposits of the Anglian glaciation.

With the exception of that in the Gelston area, the till in the district is taken to be a lodgement till deposited from an ice-sheet moving, generally, towards the south-west. The geographical and lithological distinctiveness of the Gelston till may indicate an origin associated with valley glaciers in the Witham valley or Ancaster Gap, although the unusually large erratics could merely be related to the effect of the westward passage of the main ice-sheet over the Marlstone and Lincolnshire Limestone scarps in the vicinity.

GLACIOLACUSTRINE DEPOSITS

Interbedded clay, silty clay and fine-grained sand occurring closely associated with till in the north-east part of the district are probably of glaciolacustrine origin. They have been proved by augering on the largely till-capped ridges east-north-east of Ruskington, but are not exposed. The deposits appear to consist of planar or lenticular bodies, which are interbedded with the till and dip eastward at about 1 in 50. There are up to three separate units, none of which exceeds 1.5 m in thickness. The easterly dip may indicate deltaic deposition in an ice-dammed lake.

GLACIOFLUVIAL DEPOSITS

All the glaciofluvial deposits of the district are regarded as having been associated with the Anglian glaciation. The deposits, laid down by meltwater from adjacent ice, are composed of sand and/or gravel in which the clasts are mostly of exotic (not local) origin. They include reddish sandstone/quartzite ('Bunter' pebbles), flint and a variety of igneous and metamorphic rocks. Pebbles and cobbles are generally well rounded. Glaciofluvial deposits can normally be distinguished from later fluvi-atile deposits by their composition, height of occurrence and spatial association with till. However, in low ground in the east of the district, some isolated outcrops cannot be classified with certainty, and have been mapped as sand and gravel of uncertain origin.

The present-day, patchy distribution of glaciofluvial deposits is a result both of original discontinuity and subsequent erosion of part of the deposits. Thus, to the west of the Lincoln Edge escarpment, the deposits are probably limited by later fluvial activity which gave rise to the numerous terrace deposits traversing this ground. Likewise, the lower levels of the Ancaster Gap must have been scoured by waters depositing the Belton Sand and Gravel deposits, even if an earlier, higher level gap had existed during Anglian times. East of the Lincoln Edge escarpment, it is possible that Anglian till and glacoflu-vial deposits once covered the entire area and were later removed where they were thin or where erosion processes were particularly concentrated, for example in the valleys in the north-east of the district.

West of the Lincoln Edge escarpment, noteworthy deposits are confined to the top of Temple Hill [8875 4735] (Figure 25), to a belt of high ground running east–west through Gelston, and to the small outcrop of Eagle Moor Sand and Gravel in the north-west which is described separately below. On Temple Hill much of the deposit is less than a metre thick, but at Gelston up to as much as 10 m are (or were) present, according to old records. Despite the presence of numerous old pits, no sections were seen at the time of this survey. Composition varies from gravelly sand to sandy gravel, with clast diameters up to 0.10 m, and the usual exotic pebble lithologies are present.

In the high ground running through the centre of the district, for the most part corresponding to the dip-slope surface of the Lincolnshire Limestone, glaciofluvial deposits are of two distinct types. In the south, between Oasby and Londonthorpe and thence southwards, comparatively abundant irregular spreads of sand with sparse pebbles mask the underlying limestone. On the heath between Londonthorpe, Harrowby and Ermine Street, large tracts of sandy soil indicate a thin cover of glaciofluvial and/or younger blown sand, but soil brash indicates limestone within ploughing depth. These sand deposits alternate with similar thin layers of till or, near Ropsley, occur within the till. They have little topographical effect and probably are rarely more than a metre thick, except at Oasby where old pits prove at least 1.5 m of gravel-poor sand. Though the sandy deposits on the Lincoln-shire Limestone of this southern area are undoubtedly mainly of glaciofluvial origin, they are vulnerable to deflation where cultivated and some of the sandy ground may therefore be redistributed blown sand. Isolated small patches of glaciofluvial sand occur northwards from Welby and Oasby to about National Grid northing 41, but beyond this a different kind of deposit prevails.

Very little till is preserved in the central part of the district (north of National Grid northing 42), but there are sporadic thin patches of pebble- to cobble-grade gravel. The most extensive of these is a near-continuous strip (Figure 26) which meanders 4 km south-eastward from Caythorpe Court [958 483], before veering eastwards along a ridge-top towards North Rauceby for a further 3 km. The incident angle of small tributary projections, and the general eastward increase in the width of the deposit, suggest that it is a remnant of an esker, deposited by an eastward-flowing englacial river. Small patches of till occur near its western end, confirming an association with the Anglian glaciation. The esker-like deposit has little or no topographical expression and appears to cross minor valley structures without deviation. It is composed almost entirely of exotic, well-rounded, hard-rock gravel. The dominant clast diameter varies between 40 and 50 mm, but ranges from 30 to 100 mm in parts. Sand is dominant over gravel only in the west, near Caythorpe Court. The deposit is generally less than 1 m in thickness. Similar gravel to that of the 'esker' occurs between Sudbrook and Ermine Street, and also south-west of Wilsford on the southern rim of the Ancaster Gap.

In the east of the district, glaciofluvial deposits occur in two main localities: between Ewerby and Asgarby, and between Silk Willoughby, Swarby and Aswarby; other occurrences are sparse and sporadic. The Ewerby–Asgarby deposits mostly overlie till and include both gravel rich in 'Bunter' pebbles and yellowish orange pebbly sand up to 6 m thick, but commonly of the order of only 1 m. The Silk Willoughby–Aswarby cluster of deposits consists of sand with relatively sparse gravel in spreads up to 1 m thick. Isolated patches of glaciofluvial deposits occurring at Highgate, south-east of Scredington, to the north of Scott Willoughby and to the south of Threekingham, are all likewise dominated by sand and do not greatly exceed a metre in thickness.

Eagle Moor Sand and Gravel

The Eagle Moor Sand and Gravel occurs in isolated hilltop patches, trending north-north-east from Newark towards a larger spread of the deposit on an undulating plateau at Eagle, about 7 km west-south-west of Lincoln (Brandon and Sumbler, 1991). Only a small outcrop, about 1 km long, occurs within the district (Figure 25) at about 30 to 35 m above OD. This is part of a larger patch occupying a ledge on top of the Penarth Group scarp east of Newark.

A borehole [8324 5359] near Coddington Windmill just outside the district proved sand and gravel, clayey at the top, to a depth of 3.9 m and an old pit [8287 5359] farther west showed 2.4 m of sand and gravel overlying mudstone. Thicknesses in excess of 5 m were recorded by Gozzard (1976) north-east of Newark. He described the deposit in the borehole near Coddington Windmill as 58% gravel, consisting of fine to coarse, subrounded to well-rounded quartz and quartzite, 30% sand, comprising medium, angular to subrounded quartz and rock fragments, and 12% fines (grains less than $1/16$ mm diameter). The gravel fraction of the Eagle Moor Sand and Gravel is dominated by 'Bunter-type' well-rounded quartzite and quartz pebbles, but also includes mudstone and pebble-grade subangular flints and chert.

The deposit is regarded as of late Anglian age, being outwards of the glaciation. It has been correlated with the upper part of the composite Hilton Terrace deposits of the River Trent, and its distribution in a discontinuous strip from near the Trent at Newark towards the gap through the Lincoln Edge at Lincoln indicates a former course of the Trent (Brandon and Sumbler, 1991). Waters (1992) inferred deposition in a flat-bottomed channel cut into the Lias bedrock, although erosion has removed most of the former banks. The flint content of the Eagle Moor Sand and Gravel was presumably derived from the Anglian icesheet.

OLDER RIVER TERRACE AND ASSOCIATED DEPOSITS

Sand and gravel not directly associated with glacial deposits occupy large areas of the district, in several discrete strips or patches (Figure 26). Each of these separate bodies is characterised by its own kind of lithology and topographical expression. Most, but not all, present a terrace-like appearance, which suggests deposition or reworking by a braided river. Most of them are clearly younger than the Anglian glacigenic deposits as they occur in valleys cut through the till or on plains well below the general level of the main till cover. Each of the larger bodies is identified by its own lithostratigraphical name; all except one of these names are based on localities within or close to the district. However, these names are primarily used to indicate contiguity of deposits, and it is not intended to imply that all deposits described under a particular name are necessarily of similar age and provenance, although such may be the case. Similarly, the order in which they are described below is based on location (generally west to east) rather than age.

Balderton Sand and Gravel

The Balderton Sand and Gravel is a terrace deposit of the early Trent (Brandon and Sumbler, 1991), covering about 5 sq km in the north-west of the district with a surface-level at 17 to 19 m above OD (Figure 26). In contrast to the patchy distribution of the glaciofluvial Eagle Moor deposits, it forms a continuous strip up to 3 km wide, which extends from the neighbourhood of Newark to the Lincoln Gap. The deposit occupies a flat-bottomed channel cut into the Lias bedrock and is generally 6 to 8 m in thickness; the greatest depth to which the deposit has been proved locally was 8.8 m in a borehole [8333 5188] at Balderton.

The sand and gravel consists mostly of gravel, made up of rounded quartzitic 'Bunter' pebbles (76%, by number) with subordinate pebble-grade subangular flints (16%) and reddish brown Triassic sandstone and siltstone (6%). An overall fining-upward trend is discernible, from poorly bedded gravels at the base to more distinctly bedded, sandier gravels at the top. At surface it forms a brown to orange-brown sandy, gravelly soil. Particle size analyses of the deposit (Gozzard, 1976) shows a gravel content (greater than 4 mm diameter) of 41 to 64%, a sand and fine gravel content (0.0625–4 mm) of 30 to 55%, and fines (less than 0.0625 mm) of 4 to 6%.

Exposures of the Balderton Sand and Gravel in the district are limited to ditch sections, but clean faces in several commercial workings farther north show cross-bedding, channels filled with silt and plant debris near the base of the deposit, and ice wedge casts higher up (Brandon and Sumbler, 1991). The cross-bedding, together with pebble imbrication, indicates deposition from currents flowing towards the north-north-east, parallel to the trend of the linear outcrop. The ice wedge casts, many of them truncated by syndepositional erosion, demonstrate a contemporaneous cold environment. This is supported by pollen and fauna collected mainly from the silts near the base. The fauna includes the bones and teeth of cold climate mammals such as mammoth, woolly rhinoceros and

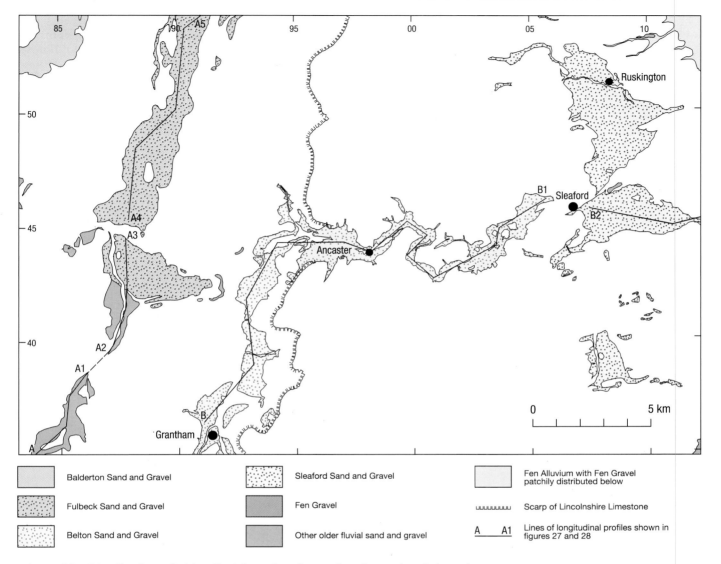

Figure 26   Distribution of older fluvial sand and gravel and associated deposits.

reindeer, but also the warmer climate, extinct forms *Palaeoloxodon antiquus* (the straight-tusked elephant) and *Stephanorhinus* cf. *hemitoechus* (a rhinoceros), suggesting probable interstadial conditions. Other cold climate faunal elements include molluscs, ostracods and beetles. A rubified palaeosol at the top of the deposit, indicates postdepositional temperate pedogenesis attributed to the Ipswichian interglacial stage. This palaeosol has locally been affected by Devensian cryoturbation.

The Balderton Sand and Gravel is thus shown to have been deposited in a cold environment prior to the last (Devensian) glaciation. Its surface profile, intermediate in elevation between those of the Fulbeck Sand and Gravel (with its Ipswichian fauna), and the presumed Anglian Eagle Moor Sand and Gravel, suggests a 'Wolstonian' age. This is supported by absolute age determinations: electron spin resonance tests on the mammoth and elephant teeth and amino acid analyses

of molluscs suggested a correlation with Oxygen Isotope Stage 6 (Brandon and Sumbler, 1991).

Fulbeck Sand and Gravel

The Fulbeck Sand and Gravel (Brandon and Sumbler, 1988), occurs in a north-north-east-trending strip, which extends from Hougham northwards to Brant Broughton, and for a farther 8 km north of the district to Aubourn. Thus, it stretches between two bends in the River Witham, suggesting deposition along an earlier course of that river. Sand and gravel deposits south of the River Witham, around Marston, are also included with the Fulbeck Sand and Gravel (Figure 26). The total outcrop is 23 km long and up to 2.5 km wide. The top of the sand and gravel forms a fairly flat terrace surface, the Fulbeck Terrace, which slopes gently towards the north from about 31 m above OD in the Marston area to about 7 m above OD at Aubourn. The isolated Temple Hill appears to have been an island in the middle of the former river and is surrounded by the sand and gravel. The surface of the outlier near Marston is steeper and reaches up to 40 m above OD (Figure 27). The deposit is incised into bedrock and the top commonly lies flush with the surrounding areas.

The dominant lithology of the deposit is sand, with scattered pebbles and subordinate pebble-grade gravel, with pebbles commonly ranging from 30 to 60 mm in diameter. The sand is typically clean, well sorted, medium-grained and orange-brown. The most abundant pebbles are derived from the Lias and Lincolnshire Limestone Formation. They include bioclastic limestone, siltstone and ironstone clasts, and phosphatic nodules. The gravel occurs mainly near the base of the deposit. Particle-size and lithological analyses of the deposit in the northernmost part of the district (Gozzard, 1976; Jackson, 1977) show a gravel content (greater than 4 mm diameter) varying from 3 to 22%, sand (0.0625–4 mm) from 60 to 86%, and fines (less than 0.0625 mm) from 2 to 37%. The gravel includes angular to subrounded quartz, quartzite, chert and 'rock'.

The Fulbeck Sand and Gravel is generally less than 2 m thick. Boreholes in the north of the district (Gozzard, 1976; Jackson, 1977) proved less than 1 m of the deposit. However, near Hougham and Marston, the thickness may be up to 5 m (Brandon, 1987).

The deposit has yielded mammalian remains, including hippopotamus, aurochs and/or bison, narrow-nosed rhinoceros and the straight-tusked elephant; these suggest a temperate climate. The presence of the hippopotamus (*Hippopotamus amphibius*), indicates an Ipswichian age (Brandon and Sumbler, 1988). These finds were all from gravels near the base of the deposit and the greater part of the deposit may be Devensian (Brandon and Sumbler *in* Bowen in press).

Belton Sand and Gravel, and the Ancaster Gap

The term Belton Sand and Gravel is here applied to a varied group of deposits which outcrops over the 25 km between Grantham and Sleaford. The outcrop forms a sinuous strip which is between 200 and 1500 m wide, and passes through the Ancaster Gap (Figure 26). To the south of the district, the deposit extends for two to three kilometres in the valley of the River Witham and its tributary the Mow Beck.

Throughout, the sand and gravel appear to lie directly on bedrock. The varied nature of both the lithology and topographical distribution of the deposits point to their having a complex origin and postdepositional history. They are assigned a single lithostratigraphical name merely for ease of description. This replaces other names used in a different way for some or all of these deposits, such as the Witham Gravels of Straw (1970) and the Ancaster Gravel of Dennison (1957).

The Ancaster Gap is a valley through the scarp of the Lincolnshire Limestone (Lincoln Edge) and the upland east of it the course of the Ancaster Gap follows incised meanders.

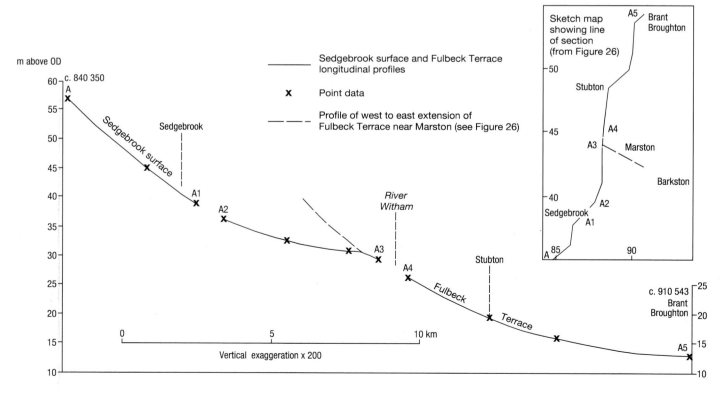

Figure 27 Longitudinal profiles of the Fulbeck Terrace and associated terrace surfaces.

South of Grantham in the upper Witham and Mow Beck valleys, the sands and gravels form an irregular-topped valley fill. Boreholes [9064 3516 and 9164 3511] have proved 12.9 m of sand and gravel in the Mow Beck valley and 8.53 m in the Witham valley. These thicknesses may provide evidence of a northward continuation of the buried drift-filled channels proved farther south (Wyatt, 1971).

From the centre of Grantham northwards, through Belton and Barkston, the main part of the outcrop appears to be a flat-topped or gently sloping terrace, incised by the River Witham. The deposit occupies a trench cut into the underlying bedrock (Brant Mudstone). On the west side, the top of the Belton Sand and Gravel is commonly flush with that of the adjacent solid strata. On the eastern side, tongues of sand with subordinate gravel extend above the terrace level up the lower slopes of the Marlstone Rock scarp. Bodies of sand and gravel in the Alma Park area of Grantham are of comparable composition and may be of similar age and provenance. They occur both below [935 372] and above [936 365] the Marlstone Rock scarp. A thickness of 4.50 m is recorded from a borehole [9137 3700] in the grounds of Grantham Hospital.

Although the main part of the deposit appears to have a planar, gently sloping top from the northern part of Grantham to just west of Sleaford, there is a distinct hump in the longitudinal profile where it crosses the present Witham/Slea watershed near Sudbrook (Figure 28). However, boreholes in Ancaster, which proved up to 10 m of sand and gravel without reaching bedrock, suggest that the base of the deposit continues to descend

eastward along the axis of the outcrop. A thickness of 2 to 3 m can be inferred in the Barkston area from the level of the mapped base of the deposit. A tongue of sand and gravel occupies the valley north of Carlton Scroop [948 460]. Peat and alluvial silt and clay overlie the sand and gravel on the floor of the Ancaster Gap both west and east of the watershed.

East of Ancaster, the sand and gravel occupies the valley bottom, through the incised meanders to Wilsford and on to Sleaford. The width of the outcrop is reduced to 200 m in places, but east of Wilsford it widens to 1 km. The longitudinal profile on the top surface of this stretch forms a generally east-sloping graded curve termed the 'Wilsford surface' (Figure 28). However, lateral extensions of the deposit are up to 25 m above the valley floor, notably to over 55 m above OD on the spur north of Wilsford, and to about 108 m above OD in the tributary valleys south of West Willoughby. Sand and gravel were proved to depths of 4.5 m at Wilsford and 4 m near Rauceby Station (Plate 9). Site investigations for the Sleaford north–south bypass, which provide a 1.2 km transverse section across the deposit, show from 1.2 to 5.0 m of sand and gravel between a flattish top and an undulating base. A pit [c.034 440], south-west of Rauceby Station, formerly exhibited cross-bedding, indicating deposition from a north-eastward flowing current. Just west of Sleaford, the sand and gravel is overlain by an eastwardly thickening and widening cover of peat and alluvium. At the Grantham end of its outcrop the Belton Sand and Gravel is mostly a fine- to medium-grained, pale brown to orange-brown, quartz-rich sand, with a gravel content of about 5%. The gravel consists largely of

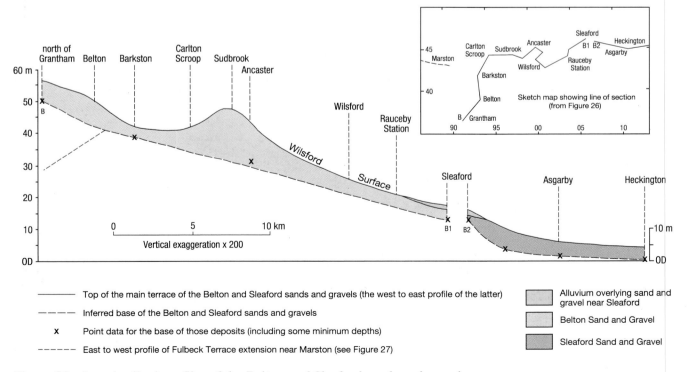

Figure 28 Longitudinal profiles of the Belton and Sleaford sands and gravels.

Plate 9 Belton Sand and Gravel, east of Rauceby Station [c.034 440].

Photographed in 1933. The section has since become degraded and partially overgrown. Note the dominance of gravel (mostly of Lincolnshire Limestone) over sand here, and also the prominent cryogenic involution piping down superficial sand deposits into the underlying gravel. (A6334)

pebbles, with a modal diameter of about 30 mm and buff Lincolnshire Limestone oolite as the dominant lithology, occurring as thin lenses or 'stringers', or scattered within the sand. Some thicker discrete beds of gravel occur, with a more varied composition, and include a basal bed which may be discontinuous. Other pebble lithologies include ironstone, quartzite ('Bunter'), chert and brown sandstone. From Ancaster eastward the proportion of gravel increases, with Lincolnshire Limestone pebbles constituting an even greater percentage of the clasts. They are commonly platy, angular to sub-rounded and up to 100 m in diameter, although 20 to 40 mm is more characteristic. In the pits near Rauceby Station (Plate 9), the deposit is largely a gravel, with interbedded lenses of sand up to 0.5 m thick. In some places, black manganiferous staining is associated variously with bedding planes, steep joints and undulose percolation fronts.

There are no definite records of faunal remains from the Belton Sand and Gravel. However, 'Antlers of Red Deer, and horn-core and leg-bone of Extinct Ox from the Alluvium of the Witham Valley near Grantham' cited by Preston (1918) may have come from the deposit.

The Belton Sand and Gravel has been discussed by many authors, commonly in conjunction with speculation about the evolution of the Witham valley and the Ancaster Gap; they include: Jukes-Browne (1885), Kent (1939b), Pocock (1954), Dennison (1957), Straw (1970) and Wyatt (1971). In the absence of any new direct evidence for the age of these sediments, their history remains uncertain, although there is now more precise dating evidence for the associated deposits.

The distribution of the channel in which the Belton Sand and Gravel lies, and the longitudinal profile of its base (Figure 28), indicate that it was cut by a forerunner of the River Witham which, at that time, flowed through the Ancaster Gap. The profile stands well above that of the Fulbeck Sand and Gravel (Brandon and Sumbler, 1988), implying a pre-Ipswichian age (see above), and it is likely that much of the downcutting within the Ancaster Gap relates to late Anglian and 'Wolstonian' processes. The Belton Sand and Gravel itself includes the ancient deposits of the Witham, as well as younger head gravels and blown sand, which accumulated after the Witham had assumed its more westerly course by Ipswichian times. The present profile of the top surface (Figure 28), including the development of the 'Wilsford Surface' represents relatively recent modification by the headwaters of the eastward-flowing River Slea, and the westward-flowing Honington Beck, both of which rise near Ancaster.

Sleaford Sand and Gravel

The Sleaford Sand and Gravel occupies the broad, strike-aligned valley between the dip slope of the Cornbrash and the low till-capped hills on the east of the district. It occurs in three main outcrops (Figure 26): around Ruskington (the Ruskington Gravel of Dennison, 1957), east of Sleaford (part of Dennison's 'Ancaster Gravel'), and east of Osbournby, with some isolated patches to the north-east of Scredington. Each of these outcrops slopes gently eastward, and the widths are 5 km, 4 km and 1.5 km from west to east, respectively. The sand and gravel around Ruskington and east of Sleaford extends eastward along valleys in which the deposits are progressively overlain by alluvium and/or peat. The valleys drain towards the Lincolnshire Fenland, and the sand and gravel deposited in them is probably contiguous with similar deposits in the Fenland (here referred to the 'Fen Gravel'), which are mostly covered by fen peats, silts and clays.

The composition of the Sleaford Sand and Gravel is typically either a well-sorted, pebble gravel with subordinate sand beds, or a pebbly sand. Within the southern part of the Ruskington outcrop and in the outcrop east of Sleaford, it is predominantly a well-sorted pebble gravel, with rounded to subrounded, clasts 10 to 40 mm long. The most common pebble lithology in that area (as in the Belton Sand and Gravel) is pale grey or buff limestone, much of it ooidal, probably of local provenance and mostly derived from the Lincolnshire Limestone. Flint, ironstone and sandstone pebbles are less abundant and locally, adjacent to the Cornbrash outcrop, cobble-grade clasts of Cornbrash limestone occur. In the northern part of the Ruskington outcrop, the deposit is mainly fine- to medium-grained, quartz sand with subordinate gravel; the latter is mostly limestone pebbles with some flint and quartzite. The deposit east of Osbournby, and the smaller patches to the north-east, are mostly gravel, with angular to subangular, pebble-grade flints as the most common clasts.

The maximum recorded thicknesses of the Sleaford Sand and Gravel are in the outcrop east of Sleaford, where sand and gravel was proved to a depth of 6.71 m in a borehole [0841 4512] at Sleaford South railway junction. An average thickness of 4 to 5 m prevails elsewhere in this area, and in the southern part of the northern outcrop. In the latter the deposit thins northward to about 3 m at Ruskington. The average thickness of the sand and gravel deposit between Osbournby and Scredington is about 1 m.

Several records of mammalian remains in the Sleaford area are probably from the Sleaford Sand and Gravel: Mammoth teeth and tusk, and 'Rhinoceros (teeth and leg bone)' from 'Pleistocene Gravels of Sleaford' by Preston (1918); and a mammoth tooth possibly from a Ruskington gravel pit (Dennison, 1957). They suggest a cold-climate environment. These finds, and the knickpoint at Sleaford, indicating deposition or reworking subsequent to the grading of the Wilsford Surface and, point to a Devensian age for the Sleaford Sand and Gravel.

Locally, especially near the western edge of the outcrop, scattered marine mollusc shells, including cockles and oysters, occur on the surface at about 12 to 13 m above OD. However, no shells have been recorded within exposed sections and the shells may have been spread for liming arable land.

'Fen Gravel'

The apron of sand and gravel deposits, to which the name 'Fen Gravel' was first applied, flanks the landward side of the Fenland alluvium and peat, in a long, discontinuous outcrop from central Lincolnshire to north-west Norfolk. Most of the Fen Gravel of the Peterborough district was referred to the 'First Terrace deposits' by Horton (1989) it is probably largely of Devensian age, but may include Ipswichian deposits. 'Fen Gravel' crops out in the south-east corner of this district [c.122 350], east of Horbling. There, the deposit is up to 1.2 m thick and consists of gravelly sand overlying gravel. The surface of the outcrop is at about 8 m above OD, from which the top of the deposit falls eastward and is overlain by progressively thicker silt and clay.

Sand and gravel which may also be assigned to 'Fen Gravel' occur, below the fen alluvium and peat, in the north-eastern corner of the district. A bed up to 1.5 m thick has been recorded in ditch sections and boreholes, below 0.4 to 1.4 m of younger deposits. It has a patchy distribution under parts of Dorrington Fen [c.121 540] within the district and of Anwick Fen and Ewerby Waithe Common just to the east. The lithological content is variable and includes pale grey, medium-grained sand and gravels, consisting variously of angular, pebble-grade flints to rounded limestone pebbles. Where seen in ditches, the underlying surface, commonly of till, is markedly cryoturbated, so that the thickness of the sand and gravel is very variable.

Older river terrace deposits, undifferentiated

The largest outcrops of unnamed fluvial sand and gravel deposits occur in the south and west of the district. One of these stretches south-south-westwards from a point [875 425] near Marston where it abuts the Fulbeck Sand and Gravel. It is broken by an approximately 1 km gap north of Sedgebrook, but otherwise continues to the southern edge of the district (Figure 26) and beyond it for about 4 km to the south. The outcrop is, thus, 32 km long, and up to 3 km wide. These unnamed deposits are less well sorted than the Fulbeck Sand and Gravel; they are fine- to coarse-grained, greyish brown sand, with a subordinate pebble gravel content, in which the most common clasts are ironstone, flint and 'Bunter' quartzite.

The thickness of the deposit is generally less than 2 m but exceeds 3 m around Sedgebrook. The top surface has a flat, terrace-like form; its longitudinal profile, the Sedgebrook surface, is shown in Figure 27, together with the profile of the Fulbeck Terrace. This illustrates the knickpoint between the two surfaces and suggests that the former is older than the latter.

Other patches of sand and gravel occur in the Barkston and Honington area between the terrace-like outcrops of the Fulbeck and Belton sands and gravels. Their heights vary from about 55 m above OD near Honington [927 439], which is above the main level of the Belton Sand and Gravel in the area, to 42 m above OD in Jericho Woods [909 418], which is approximately similar to that of the neighbouring Fulbeck Sand and Gravel. They are all largely composed of sand with subordinate gravel. The largest patch lies [c.918 423] west of

Barkston, mostly parallel to the River Witham and about 7 m above it, at about 44 m above OD. It is up to 1.1 m thick and consists of clayey, medium-grained sand with scattered angular ironstone fragments. The position of these deposits suggests that they might be relics of Belton Sand and Gravel, or derived from it during an intermediate phase of river capture.

Three hills in the Sleaford area are capped by gravels between about 17 to 23 m above OD. The highest of these deposits, on Galley Hill [067 463], was noted by Dennison (1954) but not mapped during this survey as it lies in an entirely built-up area and could not be distinguished from the underlying Kellaways Sand. Dennison described 1.8 m of gravel exposed in a pit at Carre's Grammar School as 'coarse unstratified marly', 'with many flat flakes of limestone, rounded brown quartzite pebbles near the surface and pipes and patches of sand.' The other hills [085 465 and 070 492], are west of the A17 road and next to Rigg Farm, Leasingham. The gravels on both include abundant 'Bunter' quartzite pebbles. The deposit at Rigg Farm also includes pebble-grade flints and is very thin. The deposit near the A 17 is thicker, up to 2 m, and more varied, with a large proportion of sand in parts, and locally containing abundant, buff, limestone pebbles. The 'Bunter' pebble content of these gravels indicates derivation from west of Lincoln Edge. Dennison (1957) interpreted the Galley Hill gravel as part of a terrace deposit associated with a proto-River Slea, draining the Ancaster Gap, but all three outcrops could be isolated patches of the more widely spread terraces in the lower Witham valley fenland.

SAND AND GRAVEL OF UNCERTAIN ORIGIN

Several discrete bodies of sand and gravel, which may be of glaciofluvial, fluviatile, aeolian or soliflucted origin, have been mapped in the eastern part of the district. They include patches near Digby, Ruskingon, Sleaford and Horbling, and are mostly adjacent to larger spreads of Sleaford Sand and Gravel or 'Fen Gravel', although at a higher level. The lithologies vary from clayey sand, to sand, to flint and 'Bunter' pebble gravels.

The patches near Digby, just north of the district [095 541 to 099 544], and at Ruskington, have generally terrace-like surfaces, and consist of fine- to medium-grained sand. The top surfaces of the two patches [088 465 and 095 467] east of Sleaford slope down to the Sleaford Sand and Gravel. They contain 'Bunter' pebbles, as well as the pebble-grade flints, which are characteristic of the latter deposit, in a clayey sand matrix. In a deposit near Horbling, [123 358 to 118 349], clayey sand also occurs, together with gravelly clay. Its surface slopes down to that of the 'Fen Gravel'.

These isolated outcrops all appear to predate the adjacent, named, sand and gravel, terrace deposits but are topographically lower than the local till, and are thus presumably no older than the latter. Both the Sleaford Sand and Gravel and the 'Fen Gravel' are inferred to be of Devensian age, and the till is inferred to be Anglian, so that a wide range of age and depositional environment is possible for these deposits.

YOUNGER RIVER TERRACE DEPOSITS

Low sand and gravel terraces border the alluvial floodplain of the River Witham between Grantham and Barkston, and near Marston [898 432], Westborough [852 445] and Barnby in the Willows [860 524].

The terraces between Grantham and Barkston occur on both sides of the river. Up to three different levels are recognised around Manthorpe and Belton, but the highest terrace, up to 500 m wide on the west bank, is poorly defined. The younger second terrace surface lies some 1.0 to 3.0 m above the adjacent floodplain, and first terrace is from 0.5 to 1.5 m in height. The deposits underlying the terraces consist mostly of reworked Belton Sand and Gravel, with some minor additions of local material. As they generally rest on older sand and gravel deposits, it is difficult to ascertain their thickness, but deposits near Belton [926 397 to 924 388], which rest on Brant Mudstone bedrock, are up to 1.5 m thick, and consist of clayey sand, with abundant ironstone pebbles less than 10 mm diameter.

Traced downstream, both terraces appear to merge successively with the floodplain west of Barkston, and although it seems probable that they are represented in the terraces farther downstream, the lateral relationships are insufficiently clear for subdivision to be meaningful. Thus, beyond Barkston, the younger river terraces are shown undifferentiated on the map. Around Westborough, terraces up to about 1.5 m above the modern floodplain occur on both sides of the river. The deposits consist of sand with abundant pebbles of Jurassic limestone and flint, and exceed 1.3 m in thickness. The terrace surfaces adjacent to the River Witham around Barnby in the Willows are between 1.0 and about 3.5 m above the neighbouring floodplain. They are poorly defined and probably vary in age. The largest areas are to the east of Barnby in the Willows [861 524; 865 526] where the underlying deposits appear to consist of sand and gravel with rounded quartzite ('Bunter') pebbles and rare flints; they are probably no more than 2 m thick.

Smaller patches of terrace are cut into sand and gravel next to the Witham [917 430] near Barkston Gorse, and in a valley [101 532] east of Dorrington. Neither deposit is likely to exceed 1.5 m thickness.

No direct evidence for dating any of these terrace deposits has been obtained in the district, but their height and position, closely associated with present-day floodplains, suggest that they are of late Devensian to Flandrian age.

ALLUVIUM

Alluvium of freshwater origin underlies the modern floodplains of the district, and along the River Witham near Claypole, it is up to 1.5 km wide. It is also present on large areas east of the Lincolnshire Heath upland. Alluvium occurs in many of the minor valleys both east and west of the upland, and as patches in the Ancaster Gap.

The alluvium in the Witham valley and other valleys west of the Lincoln Edge commonly consists of silty clay overlying sand and gravel, with a total thickness of up to 3 m. The clay appears structureless or blocky, and is medium to dark brown in colour. Where it overlies, or is close to, the older fluvial sand and gravel deposits, the upper part of the alluvium is typically a sandy clay, for example between Grantham and Barkston next to the Belton Sand and Gravel outcrop, and where the Witham crosses the Fulbeck Sand and Gravel outcrop near Hougham. A discontinuous ridge, about 1 m high, which extends along the Witham floodplain near Claypole [833 490 to 850 518 and beyond] is composed of ochreous sandy gravel, comparable to the alluvial gravel below the flooplain clay. This underlying gravel consists mainly of pebbles of Lias ironstone and ferruginous limestones, with subordinate Lincolnshire Limestone and angular pebble-grade flints.

In floodplain areas where surface drainage is poor, or apparently has been deficient, the upper part of the alluvium is commonly dark and humic, grading to peat. Some of these areas may have been former lake sites; they include the flat hollows [873 520, 873 510] west of Sutton and Fenton, [865 514] south-east of Barnby in the Willows, and in the Ancaster Gap, west of Ancaster.

Much of the alluvium in the eastern part of the district overlies older sand and gravel deposits. The thickness of the alluvial clay and silt in these strips is unlikely to exceed 1 m. As in the western part of the district, the alluvium of floodplain areas where drainage has been restricted has a high organic content and may grade into peat, for example in the Slea valley, west of, and through the town of, Sleaford [055 458 to 070 457], and at localities [068 494 and 090 473], east of Old Hall Farm, and south of Evedon.

The only recorded faunal remains from the alluvium of the district are from localities in the lower Witham valley. They include mammalian bones, gastropod and bivalve shells from both an old channel-fill of the river [875 529] near Sutton (Sumbler, 1987), and a 1 m-thick clay section in the river bank [8795 4506] near Hougham (Brandon, 1987). The shells from the latter site were identified by Dr D H Keen, who commented that the fauna indicated a warm temperate climate, deposition in a large, well-oxygenated river, and an age (based on the presence of *Viviparus viviparus*) in the Mid or Late Flandrian. The clay at this locality is underlain by at least 1.5 m of pebble-grade gravel. A Late Devensian or early Flandrian age is inferred for the alluvial gravel at this locality, with the overlying clay probably dating from the increased alluviation which followed the Flandrian transgression from about 7000 years BP. This age range is likely to be applicable in general terms to most of the postglacial fluviatile deposition in the district.

Fen alluvium

The fenland in the north-east of the district, indicated as 'Marine and estuarine alluvium' on the map, was shown as peat on earlier editions of the Geological Survey maps. A thin cover of peat or peaty clay remains, but deep cultivation, biodegradation, improved drainage and subsequent desiccation and wind erosion have reduced its thickness to less than 0.5 m over most of the area. Peat wastage in these fenland areas has revealed the underlying deposits, which comprise mostly estuarine and marine clay and silt. It was inundated during the early Flandrian transgression and corresponds with the so-called 'Barroway Drove Beds' of the Cambridgeshire and southernmost Lincolnshire Fens (Gallois, 1979).

The fen sequence typically comprises peat overlying clay, which commonly rests on Fen Gravel (Figure 29). Discontinuous peat beds may also occur within the clay, and a more persistent one immediately overlies the gravel. Over a large part of the area this sequence is thin, even where complete, with the underlying, commonly cryoturbated, top of the till or Oxford Clay visible in ditches within 1 m of the surface. In some parts of Digby and Anwick fens, just to the east of the district, the surface peat lies directly on gravel. The clay part of the sequence thickens generally eastwards; in Digby Fen it may be as much as 2 m thick. In the more easterly part of the fenland within the district, the largely planar bedding of these deposits is disrupted by sinuous silt bodies along the channels of former tidal creeks. These are known as 'roddons' farther south.

The basal peat bed is no more than 0.3 m thick. Wood fragments occur within it, and larger pieces of wood, including tree stumps, have been dug out from the bed and dumped on the side of ditches, notably on Dorrington Fen [around 122 532]. This bed probably equates with the Lower Peat of the Peterborough district, which has been dated at between 7690 and 3390 years BP (Horton, 1989).The clay is grey and greenish grey to chocolate brown, soft to plastic, silty in part, and commonly contains *Phragmites* rootlets and stems. The interbedded peats occur within about 400 m of the western edge of the fen. In Dorrington Fen, two such beds (apart from the surface peat) were recorded in auger holes, for example [1156 5318]:

	Thickness m	Depth m
Peat	0.3	0.3
Clay, greenish grey, soft with some peat	0.7	1.0
Peat	0.3	1.3
Clay, chocolate brown, soft	0.4	1.7
Peat	0.2	1.9
Clay, pale grey, soft	seen to 0.1	2.0

The upper peat is rarely more than 0.5 m thick, although both the previous geological survey and the memory of local farmers testify to a greater thickness in the past. It is equated with the Nordelph Peat of the Peterborough district (Horton, 1989), which has yielded radiocarbon dates from 4460 to 1845 years BP.

The silt 'roddons' protrude 0.4 to 0.7 m above the general level of the fen (due to greater compaction and wastage of the adjacent clays and peats) and are 15 to

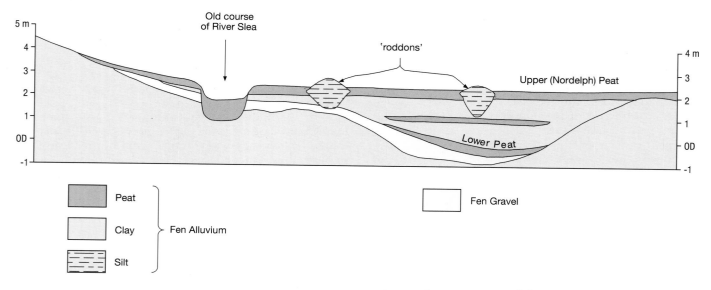

Figure 29 Diagrammatic section through the fen deposits in the north-eastern part of the district. The old channel of the River Slea is better developed in the Boston district (Sheet 128) to the east.

20 m wide. They converge in a dendritic pattern towards a 50 m-wide silt ridge that marks the site of a major channel which drained eastwards. The silt in the 'roddons' is typically pale brown, well sorted and generally shows no trace of bedding, although the basal 0.5 m or so of a roddon channel-fill in a ditch [1220 5409] in the north-eastern corner of the district was seen to consist of laminated peaty clay.

PEAT

The largest areas of peat mapped in the district are in the parallel valleys of the Old and New Slea rivers southeast of Ruskington, and at various places in the winding valley of the Ancaster Gap. Thin peat beds in the fenland area of the north-east of the district are discussed above.

The peat occurs where drainage is restricted, such as immediately west of Sleaford, or where it is sluggish, for example near the watershed at Sudbrook Moor, southeast of Carlton Scroop. Near Ancaster and Wilsford, the peat is mostly associated with clayey or silty alluvium, but locally lies directly on Belton Sand and Gravel. Thin-shelled gastropods were seen within the peat near Sleaford and Ancaster, and at Sudbrook Moor they form a gastropod-rich marl. Peat in the Ancaster Gap appears to be a remnant of a formerly more extensive cover which has been reduced by deep ploughing, improved drainage and deflation. That in Sleaford Fen, west of Sleaford, is thickest where the old railway embankment between Clay Hill and Drove Lane has acted as a dam and helped to maintain the moist environment in which the peat was formed. Thinner, unmapped, surface peat extends eastwards from there towards the town centre, where peat and peaty clay up to 0.9 m thick have been

proved below made ground and alluvium between South Gate and Carre Street.

The peat in the valleys of the Old and New Slea rivers near Ruskington thickens eastwards and appears to overlie Sleaford Sand and Gravel throughout. The thickest peat in the area is in the neighbourhood of Haverholme Priory and thence eastwards, especially in what appears to be a former channel of the Old River Slea. The peat in both valleys is continuous with the thin surface peat of the fenland to the east, and the inferred old river channel, in which the peat is up to a metre thick, can be traced north-north-eastwards across Anwick Fen in the adjoining Boston district (see Figure 29).

BLOWN SAND

Blown sand is the term used here to cover all mapped aeolian deposits. It is widely distributed in this region and commonly known as the 'Lincolnshire Cover Sands'. However, in comparison with east Lincolnshire, aeolian deposits are sparse in this district. A proportion of blown sand may be included with the sand-rich fluviatile and glaciofluvial outcrops, because it is not always practicable to distinguish the two unless dune structures are formed, as in the Long Hollow, south of Oasby, and in the Ancaster Gap, south-west of Rauceby Station.

The Blown Sand consists of fine-grained, well-sorted quartz sand and probably ranges in age from the end of the Devensian through to the present. Theories have been advanced for both western (Straw, 1963) and eastern (Catt, 1977) sources.

In other parts of Lincolnshire, the most favourable sites for blown sand accumulation are along the lower slopes of major west-facing escarpments. This applies within this district, but commonly the sand blown to the scarp foot has been converted to loam by cultivation. Patches of sand have nevertheless been mapped west of Londonthorpe and east of Belton. The area of most abundant blown sand deposition is further north around Caythorpe and Fulbeck villages, and upon the neighbouring 'heaths' at the scarp top to the east.

For the most part, the clay lowlands in the east of the district are devoid of blown sand, but several small patches, described as clayey sand and therefore likely to be mixed with underlying clay by ploughing, have been identified in the south-east of the district at Gorse Hill and Swaton Common, south-east of Scredington.

None of the blown sand deposits in the district is thought to exceed 2 m in thickness. Those at Fulbeck have been exploited in a number of small pits [e.g. 9427 4990].

HEAD

Head is the colluvial product of rock decomposition and mass movement, mainly under periglacial conditions. However, material of this origin is commonly inextricably mixed with minor proportions of a different origin, such as colluvium, blown sand and landslip. Thus, the mapped head probably includes deposits of diverse age, but it is locally possible to distinguish an 'older' head deposit from the remainder; the 'older' and 'younger' variants at one locality need not necessarily equate with those of another.

The composition of head deposits is as diverse as the source rocks from which they are derived. The deposits are typically poorly consolidated, unsorted, unbedded or with a crude stratification. Thicknesses probably do not exceed 2 m, and are generally less.

Two main types of deposit are present. The most extensive variant is widespread on the low Lias ground west of the Lincoln Edge escarpment. Isolated patches of head also occur on the low ground in the east of the district, near Dorrington, Leasingham Moor and Osbournby, and on higher ground at Cranwell.

The second type of head deposit is characteristic of the higher ground in the centre of the district, and is confined to strips along valley floors. It is especially common in dry valleys on the Lincolnshire Limestone outcrop, and is generally sandy in composition. This is particularly noticeable in the south of the district, where the head of ferruginous 'dirty' sand is probably mainly derived from glaciofluvial deposits, relics of which remain on neighbouring interfluves.

LANDSLIP

Landslipping, the downslope mass-movement of rock and soil, is extensive along the scarp slope of Lincoln Edge (Forster, 1992). The scarp is capped by the Lincolnshire Limestone Formation, with the thin underlying Northampton Sand and Grantham formations, but the greater part of the slope is formed by the Whitby Mudstone Formation. The strata which cap the scarp are permeable, but the underlying Whitby Mudstone impedes the downward percolation of groundwater. Whilst much of the water flows downdip to the east (Figure 30), some reappears as springs and seepages on the scarp face, and this wetting, accompanied by natural weathering processes, greatly weakens the Whitby Mudstone. Consequent structural failure and collapse of the mudstone under the influence of gravity, produces a landslip. The accompanying downslope cambering of the overlying water-bearing strata probably enhances the process by bringing progressively greater volumes of aquifer into a zone of westward water-flow.

Topographically, the Whitby Mudstone scarp slope is divisible into an upper steep slope of about 7° to 9°, characterised by rotational slippage cusps and a moundy surface, and a lower slope of 2° to 4°, characterised by mudflow lobes and subdued convex land forms. Both types of surface evidence are subject to degradation by ploughing, afforestation or civil engineering construction. Thus, on the geological map, areas shown as 'landslip' are not necessarily comprehensive. Such a warning is not merely academic or legalistic. Geotechnical calculations (Forster and Culshaw, 1994) indicate that the steeper upper slopes of the scarp are close to their threshold of stability and even the shallower lower slopes show the presence of shear surfaces in trenches dug into them. A farm worker reported that a steep, but smooth field he was ploughing would not retain trenches dug into it for any length of time. This means that the process of slippage can be restarted by any appropriate change in the status quo: for example, a rise in the water table, imposition of extra load at a critical site, or removal of support by excavation.

The scarp face below the Marlstone Rock, the second largest scarp in the district, also shows the local development of landslipped ground, notably at Barrowby, Great Gonerby and Syston. Traces of slippage involving clays of the Rutland Formation and Blisworth Clay were noted in the vicinity of Brauncewell, in the north of the district, but in general those formations show little evidence of landslip. Both commonly possess suitable composition, structural position and topographical attitude to favour landslip, and the absence of its surface expression may be in part due to the regular ploughing. The Blisworth Clay, in particular, is known to be prone to develop large contraction cracks during drought periods, a phenomenon that can lead to fracturing of constructions built upon it. The clay formations of the Ancholme Group and lower parts of the Lias are generally less prone to slippage, because of their subdued topography.

MADE GROUND AND LANDSCAPED GROUND

Most of the made ground and landscaped ground shown on the 1:50 000 geological map comprises either backfilled mineral workings or landscaped ground associated with industrial estates on urban fringes.

The partly or completely backfilled workings include the Lincolnshire Limestone quarries in the area south of Ancaster and Wilsford, the Marlstone Rock iron ore workings around Caythorpe, brick-clay pits in Grantham and excavations for sand and gravel in several parts of the district. The Lincolnshire Limestone quarries are commonly partly filled with rejected limestone and Rutland Formation overburden, usually from the same site, but overburden of Rutland Formation from Gregory's Quarry [990 410], Ancaster, has recently been used to cap landfill waste at Leadenham Quarry [962 523]. The former sand and gravel pits are similarly partly backfilled with rejected material. Most of the Marlstone Rock pits and many of the sand and gravel workings are unfilled; the latter are commonly flooded. The Grantham brick pits are now largely built over and the nature of the backfill, if any, is unknown.

The industrial estate landscaping includes areas around Dysart Road in west Grantham [c.908 358], Alma Park in north-east Grantham [937 374], and the area on the east side of Galley Hill in Sleaford [072 466]. Most of the material used in raising ground levels appears to have been obtained from elsewhere on the sites, although on part of Galley Hill there is rubble up to 4 m thick in and adjacent to what may have been old clay pits. Other areas of landscaped ground include the lagoons and embankments of the many sewerage works, notably the one [908 427] near Marston, which serves Grantham, and the Sleaford works [083 473] next to the A17.

Minor areas of made ground, mostly of insufficient extent to show on the 1:50 000 geological map, include road and railway embankments and banks associated with flood protection and drainage work. The latter are usually of locally derived clay from the till and the Jurassic clay formations. The road and rail construction has commonly employed a cut and fill process so that material dug from cuttings has been used to make adjacent embankments. The landscaped ground also includes archaeological sites, such as the old settlement at Burton Pedwardine [119 422] and the Iron Age fort [954 423] near Honington.

EIGHT

Economic geology

CLAY

In the past, bricks have been made from Lias clays and particularly from a horizon in the Brant Mudstone Formation, where the clay contains the optimum amounts of lime and quartz. However, none of the local brickworks survived beyond the end of the 1920s, their failure being attributed mainly to competition from large operations which worked Mercia Mudstone in the Newark area.

The longest surviving brickworks, in general, were those producing machine-made bricks, presumably on a substantial scale compared with the older hand-made brick producers. There were two such brickworks near Grantham; Gonerby Hill Foot Brickworks [c.905 376] at Gonerby, and Rudd & Son's Brickworks [912 353], Wharf Road, Grantham.

Brickworks producing hand-made bricks were recorded by Trueman (1917) at Brant Broughton [914 531], Broughton Mills [921 531], Allington [860 398] and Sedgebrook [855 387], but only Sedgebrook seems to have survived after 1914.

IRONSTONE

Bedded ironstones were formerly worked from the Marlstone Rock and Northampton Sand formations. The Marlstone Rock Formation has been exploited in several quarries, particularly around Caythorpe [938 485] and to a lesser extent between Honington and Barkston [942 418 to 945 428]. The Northampton Sand has been exploited only at Leadenham.

The Marlstone Rock at one time, formed an important iron resource extending throughout south Lincolnshire and north Leicestershire. The ore was first worked on a large scale in the 1870s and was the main source of iron for many blast furnaces in the Midlands. The average composition of the ore is approximately 25% Fe, 11% SiO_2, 15% CaO and 0.3% P (Goldring, 1974). Its relatively low iron content was offset to some extent by a high lime content which eliminated the need for a separate limestone flux in the smelting operation. The lime was present in excess and in practice the Marlstone Rock was often mixed with the siliceous Northampton Sand ironstone to provide a self-fluxing ore of optimum composition.

All British Jurassic iron ores suffer from the disadvantage of having a relatively low iron content, together with a phosphorous content sufficient to require a special separation step in the steel-making process. These two factors rendered domestic ironstones increasingly uncompetitive in the face of imported iron ore concen-trates, which could be imported cheaply as large bulk carriers were introduced and new deposits discovered abroad. UK production declined rapidly from the mid 1960s and the industry became defunct by the mid 1980s. It seems unlikely that these ironstones will have any future commercial value.

The history of the ironstone workings in the area has been recorded by Tonks (1991). After 1895, the operation of the deeper individual quarries is recorded in the lists of active quarries published by the Inspector of Mines and Quarries. A description of the operation carried out by the Stanton Ironworks Company was given by Hewlitt (1935). Descriptions of the operations were also provided by Whitehead (1952) and Hollingworth and Taylor (1951).

In the Caythorpe and Fulbeck areas, the Marlstone was first worked during the late nineteenth century by several companies, including the West Yorkshire Coal and Iron Company, the Yorkshire Iron and Coal Company, William Williams, M C Cohen and E P Davies. However, few of these companies survived into the present century. Walter Burke acquired Caythorpe Town Quarry [952 492] in 1897 and worked it until it closed during the First World War; the Butterley Iron Company worked Fulbeck Quarry [around 952 504] until 1930.

The largest operations in the area seem to have been those carried out by Walter Burke Ltd at Frieston Quarries [938 475 to 929 466], which commenced in 1916 and persisted until 1946, although there appear to be few records of these activities.

Honington Quarry [946 430] was opened in 1901 by Stanton Ironworks and operated until 1921. It worked an average thickness of 2.4 m of ironstone in an area between Honington and Barkston under an overburden thickness which eventually reached 4.3 m, when the workings were discontinued. The average composition of the ore, according to records held by British Steel, was 24.6% Fe, 9.7% SiO_2 and 21.7% CaO. Previously, between 1883 and 1897, the company had worked a small area known as Cliff Road Quarry [?937 468], approximately 1 km south of Caythorpe.

Leadenham Quarry [964 524], which more recently has produced limestone, was opened as an ironstone quarry owned by Major C Dove, circa 1896. Ownership passed to the Barnstone Blue Lias Company in 1920 and then to the Barnstone Cement Company, as the operation became more concerned with the production of limestone for cement-making, because of the increasing thickness of overburden above the ironstone. The ironstone was worked from the Northampton Sand Formation and was 2.1 m thick with an average grade of 30.5% Fe, 19.1% SiO_2 and 3.6% CaO on a dry basis. It was worked under a massive overburden, mainly of

Lincolnshire Limestone, and at one stage the quarry is said to have produced about 300 tonnes of limestone and 200 tonnes of ironstone per week. Ironstone production seems to have ceased at the end of the First World War, according to the Inspector of Quarries, although Hollingworth and Taylor (1951) suggest that it might have continued until 1925.

LIMESTONE

The Lincolnshire Limestone Formation has long been a source of building stone (Hunt, 1859) and more recently of crushed stone. It is currently (1993) worked within the area for aggregates at Brauncewell [027 518], Ancaster (Copper Hill) [978 426] and Ropsley [002 364] quarries. Until recently, it was also worked for aggregates at Leadenham Quarry. Crushed Lincolnshire Limestone does not, in general, provide aggregate suitable for use in concrete or as a Type 1 sub-base in roads. It suffers from a generally poor resistance to frost damage and a relatively low strength. Hence, it is used mainly as a selected fill. Fine material produced by the crushing operation is sold for agricultural lime.

In general, the Lower Lincolnshire Limestone is unsuitable for building stone because of its limited durability, although certain beds were selected for local use. The oolitic grainstones of the Upper Lincolnshire Limestone were widely exploited, however, and the outcrop is dotted with ancient quarries, mostly now infilled or ploughed over. Production of fine freestones was particularly concentrated around Ancaster, and 'Ancaster Stone' is found in many churches and other old buildings throughout the region. Most of the freestone quarries ceased production in the last century, but production continued at Copper Hill, Ancaster

(Plate 5) until relatively recently. Currently, the freestone is still worked by traditional methods from the topmost part of the Upper Lincolnshire Limestone, at Gregory's Quarry [990 410] (Plate 10) and an adjacent site at Wilsford Heath, Ancaster.

SAND AND GRAVEL

Sand and gravel deposits in the Grantham area occur in terraces associated with the Rivers Witham and Slea, and alongside the fens near Sleaford and Osbournby (Chapter Seven). There are also some small isolated deposits of glaciofluvial sand and gravel.

Until 1991, sand was worked from the Belton Sand and Gravel deposits in the valley of the River Slea between Ancaster and West Willoughby (Figure 26). However, this site has been closed and restored, and no active workings in sand and gravel deposits remain in the district.

The sand and gravel resources of the northern part of the district were described by Gozzard, (1976) and Jackson, (1977). These mineral assessment surveys showed that the Balderton Sand and Gravel is mostly between 5 and 7 m thick and consist of roughly equal proportions of gravel (greater than 4 mm) and sand (less than 4 mm) grade particles. The gravel consists mainly of quartz and quartzite pebbles, together with minor amounts of flint, while the sand fraction consists largely of quartz.

In the Fulbeck Sand and Gravel near Stragglethorpe and Brant Broughton, mineral assessment work has shown the deposits to be very thin and not a viable mineral resource. In the north-east of the area near Ruskington, mineral assessment work on the Sleaford Sand and Gravel has shown the deposits to be relatively

Plate 10   Gregory's Quarry, Wilsford Heath, Ancaster.

View looking east of north from about [9894 4104], showing worked Upper Lincolnshire Limestone, with overburden of Rutland and basal Blisworth Limestone formations. The extracted rock is from the 'Weather Bed') ('Rag' or 'Ragstone'), cross-bedded coarse- to very coarse-grained grainstones, 'blue'-hearted in part and spanned by the ladder in the photograph; the Weather Bed is underlain by 'Hard White', passing down to softer 'Freestone', both well-sorted, even-grained, coarser-grained oolite grainstones ('Ancaster Stone'). (A15106)

thin (1 to 3 m). The proportion of sand to gravel is somewhat variable and the pebbles consist mainly of shelly and oolitic limestone together with minor amounts of ironstone, sandstone and flint.

Elsewhere, there is relatively little information on the sand and gravel deposits. However, it may be inferred from field observation that the Fulbeck Sand and Gravel is relatively thin and unimportant as a mineral resource throughout the area, whereas both the Belton Sand and Gravel and the Sleaford Sand and Gravel can be expected to have more potential. With respect to petrographic composition, the gravels in the part of the area tend to contain abundant limestone and flint pebbles, whereas the Baldereton Sand and Gravel in the west predominantly contain quartzite and quartz and is broadly comparable to those found in the Trent Valley.

BUILDING STONE

The district has three principal sources of building stone which have been widely exploited for local building. Geologically, the oldest stone for building was obtained in the past from the limestone bands in the Lower Jurassic (Lower Lias) succession, outcropping in the western part of the district. This succession provided the grey limestone blocks which can be seen, for example, in the walls of churches, older houses and barns in and around the villages of Long Bennington, Dry Doddington and Fenton. These limestones provided a poor-quality building stone which has generally weathered badly.

Higher in the Lower Jurassic succession occur the dark orange-brown stones of the Marlstone Rock Formation. This ironstone bed was quarried extensively along its outcrop for building stone prior to its perhaps better known and more recent exploitation as an iron ore. In many of the villages along its outcrop, houses and churches are commonly built of ironstone rubble blocks with quoins, door frames and window mouldings fashioned from more-readily worked Middle Jurassic freestone. The ironstone, which sometimes weathers badly, is well displayed in the walls of houses and churches in, for example, the villages of Barrowby, Marston and Barkston. In Caythorpe the ironstone is commonly interbanded with paler Ancaster Stone in the walls of the buildings.

The pale grey to yellow, oolitic and shelly limestones of the overlying Middle Jurassic Lincolnshire Limestone Formation form the best and most widely used building stones of the district. The most famous of the many quarries that have operated in the area were those around Ancaster. Ancaster Stone has been quarried as a freestone there since Roman times (Alexander, 1996) and most of the older buildings (particularly the churches) in villages along the outcrop use Ancaster Stone, either as ashlar blocks or carved for window dressings and mouldings, for example at Grantham, Welby, Ancaster, Fulbeck and Leadenham. Most of the impressively tall church spires, for which Lincolnshire is justly famous, are constructed of Lincolnshire Limestone, much of it from the quarries of the Ancaster area. Belton House, the late seventeenth century mansion, now the property of the National Trust, however, was constructed of Lincolnshire Limestone from quarries at nearby Heydour.

The success of the Ancaster quarries can be attributed not only to the quality of the stone but to the development, using the local river systems, of a good transport system reaching more distant markets (Alexander, 1996). The importance and longevity of the Ancaster quarries is demonstrated by the extensive use of the stone outside the immediate district. Many important buildings dating from the twelfth to nineteenth centuries were constructed using Ancaster Stone. These include Newark Castle (twelfth century), the principal churches in Norwich (fifteenth century — Purcell, 1967), Tattershall Castle (fifteenth century), the Elizabethan Wollaton Hall in Nottingham (late sixteenth century) where the stone was apparently traded for coal, Belvoir Castle (seventeenth century) and Harlaxton Manor (nineteenth century).

Following improvements in the transportation system since the nineteenth century, most notably the development of the modern rail network, the stone can be found even further afield. For example, it was used in the late nineteenth century for several college buildings at Cambridge University (Purcell, 1967), for restorations at St Alban's Cathedral, dressings and mouldings at the buildings for the original University College of Nottingham (1888), in 1909 at St John's, Oxford University (Arkell, 1947) and intermittently throughout this period for restorations at Lincoln Cathedral.

Quarrying of the Lincolnshire Limestone for building stone is still active in the Ancaster area today and the stone remains much in demand for building and conservation work.

GEOTHERMAL ENERGY

The geothermal resources of eastern England have been reviewed by Gale and Holliday (1985), Holliday (1986) and Smith (1986). This section summarises these earlier accounts.

Because of their relatively low porosity and permeability values (Holliday, 1986), the Carboniferous rocks of the region were thought by Gale and Holliday (1985) to have little or no potential as sources of commercial heat-bearing groundwater. These authors did not rule out the possibility that the pre-Permian rocks of the region might have 'hot dry rock' potential; this involves the extraction of heat from rocks at depth by injecting cold water into the strata via boreholes. However, later studies by Evans et al. (1988) have shown that surface heat flow in the region is generally too low for sufficiently high temperatures to be present at depths currently suitable for drilling. There is no indication that the rocks of the district will behave differently from those of the rest of the region.

The Permo-Triassic sandstones (Smith, 1986) occur at relatively shallow depths within the district, mainly in the range 400 to 800 m below OD, and hence the groundwaters within them have attained relatively low temperatures, in the range 20 to 40°C. However, as Gale and Holliday (1985) have pointed out, their good to excellent porosity and permeability properties suggest that relatively large transmissivities, in excess of 10 Dm (Darcy-metres) at about 25°C, could be achieved in the Sherwood Sandstone Group.

Such quantities of groundwater, at the predicted relatively modest temperatures, are currently uneconomic. However, this situation may change in the future, due to technological advances and the exhaustion of presently cheaper fuels. In many parts of the world, similar low enthalpy geothermal sources are regarded as having considerable potential value to the agricultural industry in rural areas, such as the Grantham district, as a heat source for warming large greenhouses.

HYDROCARBON

The petroleum geology of the eastern England region has been discussed by Kirby et al. (1987), Scott and Colter (1987) and Fraser et al. (1990). This section, in part based on these accounts, reviews the hydrocarbon prospectivity of the East Midlands with particular reference to the district.

The area to the north and west of the district has been the subject of considerable exploratory activity for hydrocarbons since the late 1930s. Some notable discoveries, which comprise the East Midlands oilfields, have been made in these adjacent districts, where significant volumes of oil have been produced since 1939 (Huxley, 1983; Fraser et al., 1990). The Plungar Oilfield is located only 7 km west-south-west of the district. The district has been relatively little explored, with only four hydrocarbon exploration wells, at Claypole [84505 49334], Foston [8489 4145], Ruskington [0920 4974] and Long Bennington [83764 41577]; a similar number of coal exploration boreholes have been drilled. Several seismic reflection surveys, using both dynamite and vibroseis sources, have been carried out, and provide an open to sparse grid of data. No commercial discoveries have yet been made within the district, and exploration activity at the time of writing is at a low level.

Potential source rocks of Jurassic and Carboniferous age are present within the district. Organic-rich, potentially oil-bearing, source rocks occur in the Lias Group, particularly the Whitby Mudstone Formation, and in the Peterborough Member of the Oxford Clay. However, a number of studies, and unpublished BGS vitrinite reflectance data, have shown that the organic matter in these beds is immature (R_o less than 0.5%) in eastern England (Barnard and Cooper, 1983; Kirby et al., 1987). This, and their relatively shallow occurrence, precludes the possibility of economic accumulations having being derived from such sources within the district.

Comparison with neighbouring areas suggests that the concealed Upper Carboniferous rocks of the district are dominantly gas-prone. The main oil-prone source rocks of the East Midlands oilfields, the late Brigantian and early Pendleian Edale Shales, do not occur within the district, although they are present in districts to the west (Fraser et al., 1990). From published and unpublished vitrinite reflectance and coal rank data, it can be inferred that the Upper Carboniferous rocks of the district will have vitrinite reflectance values generally between 0.5 and 1.0%, at levels of organic maturity below peak oil generation. However, although local sources of hydrocarbons within the district may be inadequate, there is the possibility that oil, and perhaps gas, could have migrated from more deeply buried Upper Carboniferous source rocks in the Widmerpool Gulf to the west. On this argument, prospects for hydrocarbon accumulations in Carboniferous strata would be expected to be greater in the west and south-west than elsewhere in the district.

The reservoir properties of Carboniferous sandstones in the East Midlands oilfields have been extensively studied (Holliday, 1986; Fraser et al., 1990). They exhibit a wide range of porosity and permeability values, reflecting differing depositional environments and diagenetic and burial histories (Table 11). Although, overall, these values are relatively low, the Silesian sandstones of the East Midlands have proved adequate hydrocarbon reservoir rocks. Locally, better reservoir characters, including permeabilities locally around 400 mD (milliDarcys), have been found in the late Namurian–early Westphalian sandstones of the Welton Oilfield, north of Lincoln, which rest unconformably on Dinantian lime-

Table 11 Summary of porosity and permeability values from Carboniferous rocks of the East Midlands oilfields (data from Holliday, 1986).

	Porosity (%)		Permeability (mD)	
	Typical range	Mean	Typical range	Mean
Upper Coal Measures	12–19	15	< 160	60
Middle and Lower Coal Measures	7–20	12	< 37	13
'Millstone Grit'	< 20	12	< 30	14
Carboniferous Limestone	< 10	c.5	< 5.5	c.1.5

stones (Rothwell and Quinn, 1987). Similar sandstones may be present within the district, where Westphalian rocks overstep Namurian strata. Except where locally fractured, Dinantian limestones have extremely poor reservoir properties (Table 11) (Holliday, 1986) and have trapped only small amounts of oil in other districts (Huxley, 1983; Fraser et al., 1990). Good reservoir characters are to be found in several Mesozoic formations (Smith, 1986), but, as noted below, it is unlikely that much oil could have migrated into these beds.

The most favourable reservoir characters in Silesian rocks of the East Midlands commonly occur in sandstones of channel facies (Fraser et al., 1990). This indicates that depositional factors are an important contributor to the generation of closed structural traps in these oilfields. The main period of trap formation was in late Carboniferous to early Permian times, during Variscan earth movements and the related period of basin inversion. Some relatively minor modification of these structures, by faulting synchronous with Mesozoic deposition, is to be expected. A more important deformational phase, influencing structural traps and their areas of closure, resulted from Cainozoic uplift and eastward tilting.

Throughout the East Midlands there is clear evidence that the argillaceous beds, interbedded with the Upper Carboniferous sandstones, generally provide adequate seals to structural closures. Where Variscan uplift and erosion were most intense, as in the vicinity of the Foston High, the seals were breached and Upper Carboniferous rocks extensively removed prior to Permian deposition. Triassic and Jurassic argillaceous rocks provide good potential seals to any closed structures in Mesozoic rocks.

To the west of the district, Brigantian–Pendleian source rocks may have become mature during the later stages of Carboniferous deposition. Any oil that migrated into the district at that time probably escaped due to the paucity of trapping mechanisms. Except for areas such as the Foston High, where Variscan erosion was particularly extensive, the maximum depth of burial of Upper Carboniferous rocks was during late Mesozoic times (Fraser et al., 1990). Closed structures in Carboniferous rocks, which formed as a result of the Variscan movements, were available to receive any oil that formed within, or migrated into, the district. Any structural traps in Mesozoic rocks, resulting from syndepositional faulting or Late-Cimmerian (late Jurassic–early Cretaceous) movements, could also host oil formed at this time where the sealing influence of Upper Carboniferous argillaceous rocks was absent or inadequate. All structural traps were subject to the modifying influence of Cainozoic easterly tilting, which may have allowed significant quantities of hydrocarbons to escape.

Despite the presence of sealed structural closures, containing suitable reservoir rocks, it can be concluded from the above discussion, and from the lack of previous discoveries, that the prospects of finding major hydrocarbon accumulations within the district may not be great, because of the paucity of suitable source rocks in the vicinity. Prospects seem best in the south-west, where the Plungar Oilfield is in close proximity but, unfortunately,

the extensive Variscan erosion of Upper Carboniferous rocks in the vicinity of the Foston High restricts the likely occurrence of hydrocarbons in that area. However, very little drilling has been carried out in the district, and some areas have only skeletal seismic survey coverage. Therefore, not all possibilities have been eliminated, and the proximity to sites of previous or current successful oil extraction provides a stimulus to further investigation.

HYDROGEOLOGY

The district is bisected by the north–south-trending escarpment of the easterly dipping Lincolnshire Limestone Formation. The part of the district which lies to the west of this feature is drained by the River Witham, which here flows in a northward direction. The river subsequently turns eastwards through the Lincoln Gap. This, and the Ancaster Gap, in the centre of the district, are former glacial drainage channels which cut through the escarpment. Hydrogeologically significant deposits of glacially derived fluvial sands and gravels (see Chapter 7) occur along the course of the Ancaster Gap.

Average annual rainfall varies from less than 600 mm on either side of the escarpment to more than 650 mm along it. Evapotranspiration ranges from 430 to 510 mm per annum. Over 80 per cent of the total evaporation takes place during the summer months; thus winter rainfall is the main source of recharge to the groundwater system. The annual recharge to the Lincolnshire Limestone aquifer is estimated to be between 167 and 195 mm.

The main producing aquifer of the district is the Lincolnshire Limestone Formation (Downing and Williams, 1969). Smaller quantities of groundwater are obtained from late Quaternary fluvial sands and gravels and the Marlstone Rock Formation of the Lias Group. Some groundwater is also obtained from minor limestone units, for example the Blisworth Limestone and Cornbrash formations, while the Lias clays and Upper Jurassic clays form regional aquicludes. The main aquifer and aquiclude units, and groundwater flow pattern within the Lincolnshire Limestone Formation are shown on Figure 30.

The relative importance of the aquifer units is illustrated by licensed abstraction rates (Table 12). Nearly 80% of the total licensed abstraction is for public water supply. Anglian Water plc obtain up to 7.6 Mm^3/annum from the Lincolnshire Limestone aquifer via wellfields located at Kirkby la Thorpe [095 456], Aswarby [067 391] and Drove Lane [055 462]. The South Lincolnshire Health Authority is licensed to obtain up to 60 000 m^3/annum from the Lincolnshire Limestone aquifer via boreholes at Rauceby Hospital [041 440]. The Caythorpe Agricultural College [962 481] is licensed to abstract 26 367 m^3/annum from the Marlstone Rock aquifer of the Lias Group. Nearly 10% of the total licensed abstraction is used for spray irrigation. Of this amount, 398 000 m^3/annum comes from late Quaternary fluviatile sands and gravels and 523 000 m^3/annum from the Lincolnshire Limestone aquifer, with minor amounts

Figure 30
Main
hydrogeological
units of the
district.

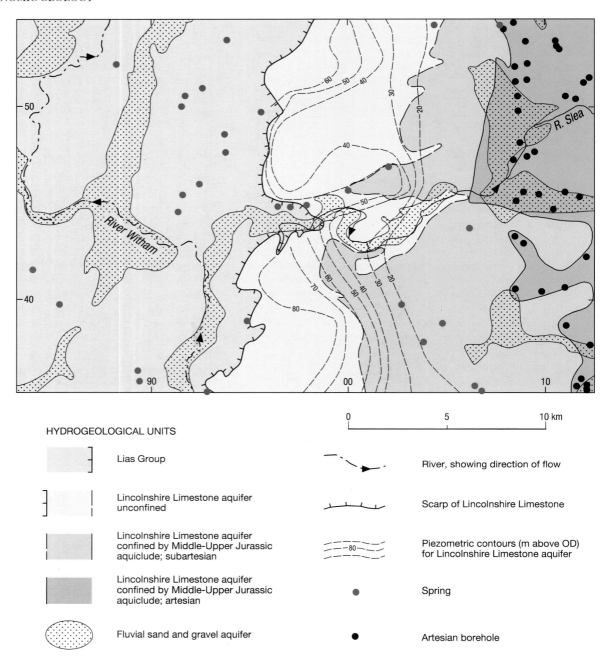

HYDROGEOLOGICAL UNITS

Lias Group

Lincolnshire Limestone aquifer
unconfined

Lincolnshire Limestone aquifer
confined by Middle-Upper Jurassic
aquiclude; subartesian

Lincolnshire Limestone aquifer
confined by Middle-Upper Jurassic
aquiclude; artesian

Fluvial sand and gravel aquifer

River, showing direction of flow

Scarp of Lincolnshire Limestone

Piezometric contours (m above OD)
for Lincolnshire Limestone aquifer

Spring

Artesian borehole

from the Marlstone Rock Formation and the Sherwood Sandstone Group. About 9% of the total licensed abstraction is used for industrial supply from the Lincolnshire Limestone aquifer. Individual farms form the bulk of the other licensed abstractors of groundwater within the district.

Sherwood Sandstone Group

West of the district, the highly productive eastward dipping Sherwood Sandstone aquifer is confined by the Mercia Mudstone Group. East of Newark, groundwater is obtained from the Sherwood Sandstone aquifer under flowing artesian conditions. Similar supplies should be

available at depth, within adjacent areas of the Grantham district.

Mercia Mudstone and Penarth groups

Strata of the Mercia Mudstone and Penarth groups dip to the east, overlying and confining the Sherwood Sandstone aquifer. They do not crop out within the district, but are overlain by clay of the Lias Group, and subcrop beneath Quaternary deposits in the extreme north-west. Although primarily composed of impermeable red and grey shaley marls with much gypsum, the 200 m-thick Mercia Mudstone Group includes discontinuous bodies of permeable sandstones from which small

Table 12 Groundwater abstraction licence data for the Grantham district.

Water use	General agriculture and domestic		Spray irrigation		Public supply		Industry		Totals	
Aquifer	m³/year	No. licences	m³/year	No. licences	m³/year	No. licences	m³/year	No. licences	m³/year	No. licences
Fluviatile sands and gravels	9106	14	398 323	13					407 429	27
Post Lincolnshire Limestone Middle–Upper Jurassic	4569	2							4569	2
Lincolnshire Limestone	90 075	42	522 801	13	7 629 658	4	854 213	5	9 096 747	64
Lower Jurassic	34 917	17	28 546	2	26 367	1			89 830	20
	138 667	75	949 670	28	7 656 025	5	854 213	5	9 599 711	114

Derived from data supplied by the National Rivers Authority, Anglian Region

quantities of very hard, fairly good quality groundwater can be abstracted. Yields of more than 1 l/sec have been obtained but these are rare.

Lias Group

The Lias Group is predominantly composed of impermeable mudstones with thin ironstone, limestone and sandstone horizons (Chapter 4). The Marlstone Rock Formation, up to 7 m thick, forms a locally important aquifer unit within the group. Groundwater abstraction from this formation is limited to a few boreholes supplying farms, with tested yields of 0.5 to 2 l/sec. Groundwater quality is generally good, but with high total hardness levels. The Marlstone Rock Formation is overlain by impervious mudstones of the Whitby Formation.

Inferior Oolite Group

The Northampton Sand and Grantham formations are a sequence of ironstone, mudstone and sandstone, up to 11 m thick, and are overlain unconformably by the Lincolnshire Limestone. Hydraulic continuity exists between these formations. Taken as a single unit, the higher, oxidised beds permit groundwater movement by both intergranular and fissure flow, while in the lower, unoxidised ferruginous sandstones, flow is primarily along fracture paths. Generally, yields in excess of 0.25 l/sec are obtained from boreholes drilled into the formations, although higher discharges have been recorded from several springs issuing at the base.

The Lincolnshire Limestone Formation is subdivided into an upper unit that is composed mainly of cross-bedded oolitic limestone, and a lower unit of carbonate mudstones, wackestones and packstones. The groundwater resources of the Lincolnshire Limestone aquifer have been extensively developed within the eastern half of the district. The hydrogeological nature of this important aquifer unit is described by Downing and Williams (1969). A north–south-trending regional groundwater divide crosses the central part of the area parallel to, and to the east of, the Lincolnshire Limestone escarpment (Figure 30). The water table declines from over 80 m above OD at the groundwater divide to less than 20 m above OD 10 km to the east, within the unconfined zone of aquifer recharge. Farther to the east, the Lincolnshire Limestone aquifer is confined by Middle Jurassic clays, and becomes increasingly artesian in nature towards the east. A large number of flowing artesian boreholes have been constructed in the easternmost part of the district (Figure 30).

The compact oolitic limestones that form much of the formation have low primary intergranular porosity and permeability (3×10^{-4} m/day) (Bird, 1974). High secondary fissure and micro-fissure permeabilities are present through much of the formation, being associated with a rectilinear fracture pattern of tectonic origin. The porosity and permeability of the fissure zones have been enhanced by karstic weathering, due to long-term changes in base-level water during successive Pleistocene glacial stages. Groundwater movement occurs by fissure flow along well-developed bedding plane fractures and joints. Aquifer transmissivity is generally about 1500 m²/day, but is locally as high as 5000–10 000 m²/day (Downing et al., 1977), depending upon degree of fissuring and karstic weathering. Aquifer pumping tests undertaken by Anglian Water at Kirkby la Thorpe, east of Sleaford, produced transmissivities of 700–1280 m²/day for the Lincolnshire Limestone aquifer. Production boreholes have an average yield of 25 l/sec. Borehole acidification has produced enhanced discharge rates.

The large groundwater storage of the aquifer system is reflected by delayed water-level response to infiltration and slow water level decline in drought periods as noted in response to the 1991–92 drought (Figure 31). Long-term changes in water level within the Lincolnshire

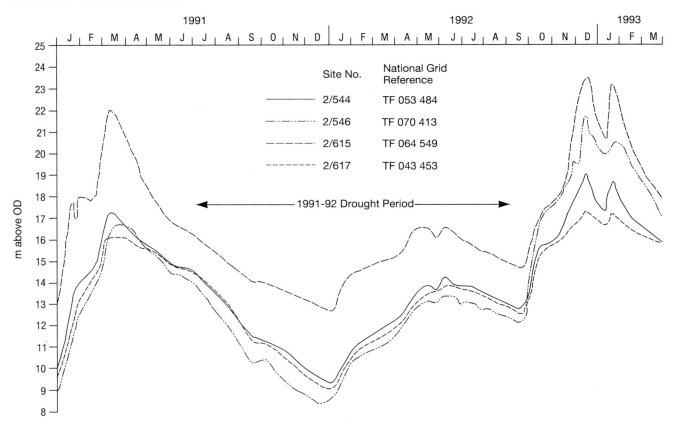

Figure 31   Borehole hydrographs of Lincolnshire Limestone aquifer.

Limestone aquifer have been monitored at the Silk Willoughby site [0429 4273] since 1972. Average monthly maximum and minimum water levels over that period vary from 23.07 to 6.07 m above OD. Maximum water levels were achieved in 1977 while minimum levels recorded in 1976 were lower than during the recent 1990–92 drought period, when the water table declined to 6.2 m above OD by January 1992.

The hydrogeochemistry of the Lincolnshire Limestone aquifer groundwaters is discussed by Lawrence, Lloyd and Marsh (1976), Edmunds and Walton (1983) and Walton (1980), who describe the various processes occurring along the unconfined–confined aquifer boundary, especially ion exchange. Recently recharged groundwaters within the unconfined zone are of calcium bicarbonate type, with carbonate hardness decreasing down dip from greater than 300 mg/l to less than 200 mg/l. Solution reactions predominate within the unconfined zone. In the confined zone, sodium becomes the dominant cation, and groundwater carbonate hardness is reduced to 100 mg/l. The apparent age of the groundwater was determined using the results of numerous radio-isotope and stable isotope studies. Total ionic concentrations tend to increase down dip from 500 mg/l in the unconfined aquifer to greater than 1500 mg/l within the confined aquifer to the east. Nitrate determinations as high as 50–70 mg/l, as NO_3, have been recorded within the unconfined zone, the highly fissured nature of the aquifer permitting rapid

movement of pollutants. Examples of groundwater hydrochemistry from the Lincolnshire Limestone aquifer are shown on Table 13.

Great Oolite Group

The Lincolnshire Limestone is unconformably overlain and confined by the mudstones and thin limestones of the Rutland Formation. Small quantities (0.6 l/sec) of variable quality water may be locally obtained from the Blisworth Limestone Formation. The Blisworth Clay Formation forms an impermeable seal between the Blisworth Limestone and Cornbrash formations. The Cornbrash Formation comprises permeable strata but because of its limited thickness it can store only low volumes of groundwater, so that only small yields of limited local value are available.

Ancholme Clay Group

The sandier portions of the Kellaways Formation can yield small local supplies, whereas the Oxford Clay Formation consists of thick impermeable mudstones.

Quaternary Sands and Gravels

The thicker Quaternary sands and gravels (Figures 26 and 30), are a potential source of groundwater for irriga-

Table 13 Hydrochemical analyses from the Grantham district.

Location		Barns Farm Nr Caythorpe	Cranwell Plantation	River Slea Augmentation b/h, Sleaford	Asgarby West Exploration
National Grif ref.		982 484	035 476	060 458	109 458
Type of source		Borehole	Borehole	Borehole (Artesian)	Borehole (Artesian)
Aquifer		Lincolnshire Limestone	Lincolnshire Limestone	Lincolnshire Limestone	Lincolnshire Limestone
Dates of analysis		01/01/92–30/04/93	01/01/92–30/04/93	01/01/92–30/04/93	01/01/92–30/04/93
pH		7.2	7.2	7.5	7.5
Eh mV		432.2	485.8	?	?
COND μmhos		1058.8	817.9	727.8	862.1
Calcium (Ca^{2+})	mg/l	145.3	146.4	127.4	8.9
Magnesium (Mg^{2+})	mg/l	7.1	4.3	7.2	13.2
Sodium (Na^+)	mg/l	35.0	22.9	18.7	151.0
Potassium (K^+)	mg/l	38.1	2.0	1.4	2.0
Bicarbonate (HCO_3^-)	mg/l	217.6	208.6	200.4	235.2
Sulphate (SO_4^{2-})	mg/l	108.7	97.6	120.2	1.0
Chloride (Cl^-)	mg/l	79.6	52.9	41.6	137.1
Nitrate (as N)	mg/l	23.2	17.0	0.1	0.12
Fluoride (F^-)		0.05	0.06	0.21	1.3
Iron (total Fe)		2.07	0.006	3.3	1.0
Manganese (total Mn)		0.04	0.005	0.03	0.13

tion. Examples are the Balderton Sand and Gravel in the north-west of the district, up to 8.4 m thick (Gozzard, 1976), and the Sleaford Sand and Gravel from Ruskington southwards to Sleaford, and east of Sleaford.

Landfill and waste disposal sites

Five of the 17 licensed landfill sites located within the district were completed before 1974. Three of seven sites receiving generally inert construction material are still in use. These are located at Carlton Scroop [936 455], Leadenham Quarry and Brauncewell Quarry. Domestic waste was dumped at five sites located at Sudbrook, near Ancaster [974 446] sited upon Pleistocene sands, Sedgebrook Tip [855 387] sited upon Lower Jurassic clays, Scredington [090 410] sited upon Middle to Upper Jurassic clays, Silk Willoughby [077 425] sited upon Middle to Upper Jurassic clays, and Holdingham [054 467] sited above Middle Jurassic clays. These five landfill sites are no longer in operation.

REFERENCES

Most of the references listed below are held in the Library of the British Geological Survey at Keyworth, Nottingham. Copies of the references can be purchased subject to current copyright legislation.

ALEXANDER, J. 1995. Building stone from the East Midlands quarries: sources, transportation and usage. *Medieval Archaeology*, Vol.39, 105–135.

ARKELL, W.J. 1946. *Oxford stone.* (London: Faber and Faber Ltd.)

ANON. 1896–1920, 1922, 1925, 1928, 1931, 1935, 1937, 1948. *List of quarries in the United Kingdom of Great Britain and Ireland and the Isle of Man.* (London: HMSO for Mines Department.)

ARTHURTON, R S. 1980. Rhythmic sedimentary sequences in the Triassic Keuper Marl (Mercia Mudstone Group) of Cheshire, northwest England. *Geological Journal*, Vol. 15, 43–58.

ASHTON, M. 1977. The stratigraphy and carbonate environments of the Lincolnshire Limestone Formation (Bajocian) in Lincolnshire and parts of Leicestershire. Unpublished PhD thesis, University of Hull.

ASHTON, M. 1979. A re-appraisal of the value of *Acanthothiris crossi* (Walker) in the correlation of the Lincolnshire Limestone Formation (Bajocian, Jurassic). *Transactions of the Leicester Literary and Philosophical Society*, Vol. 73, 65–76.

ASHTON, M. 1980. The stratigraphy of the Lincolnshire limestone Formation (Bajocian) in Lincolnshire and Rutland (Leicestershire). *Proceedings of the Geologists' Association*, Vol. 91, 203–224.

BALCHIN, D A, and RIDD, M F. 1970. Correlation of the younger Triassic rocks across eastern England. *Quarterly Journal of the Geological Society of London*, Vol. 126, 91–101.

BARNARD, P C, and COOPER, B S. 1983. A review of the geochemical data related to the northwest European Gas Province. 19–33 *in* Petroleum geochemistry and exploration of Europe. BROOKS, J (editor). *Special Publication of the Geological Society of London*, No. 12.

BATE, R H. 1978. The Jurassic, Part II—Aalenian to Bathonian. 213–258 *in* A stratigraphical index of British Ostracoda. BATE, R H, and ROBINSON, E (editors). *Geological Journal Special Issue*, No. 5.

BATE, R H, and COLEMAN, B E. 1975. Upper Lias Ostracoda from Rutland and Huntingdonshire. *Bulletin of the Geological Survey of Great Britain*, No. 55, 1–42.

BERRIDGE, N G. 1993. Geological notes and local details for 1:10 000 sheets SK93NE, SK94NE and SE, TF03NW, TF04NW and SW: Welby, Normanton Heath, Ancaster, Haceby, Rauceby and Culverthorpe. *British Geological Survey Technical Report*, WA/92/44.

BIRD, M J. 1974. Core Analysis Laboratory: Report No. 16. Physical properties of the Lincolnshire Limestone. *Unpublished Report of the Institute of Geological Sciences*, No. WD/ST/74/4.

BOWEN, D Q, HUGHES, S, SYKES, G A, and MILLER, G H. 1989. Land-sea correlations in the Pleistocene based on isoleucine epimerization in non-marine molluscs. *Nature, London*, No. 340, 49–51.

BRADSHAW, M J. 1978. A facies analysis of the Bathonian of eastern England. Unpublished DPhil. thesis. Oxford.

BRANDON, A. 1987. *Geological notes and local details for 1:10 000 sheets: SK 84 NE (Stubton).* (Keyworth, Nottingham: British Geological Survey.)

BRANDON, A, and SUMBLER, M G. 1988. An Ipswichian fluvial deposit at Fulbeck, Lincolnshire and the chronology of the Trent terraces. *Journal of Quaternary Science*, Vol. 3, 127–133.

BRANDON, A, and SUMBLER, M G. 1991. The Balderton Sand and Gravel: pre-Ipswichian cold stage fluvial deposits near Lincoln, England. *Journal of Quaternary Science*, Vol. 6, 117–138.

BRANDON, A, SUMBLER, M G, and IVIMEY-COOK, H C. 1990. A revised lithostratigraphy for the Lower and Middle Lias (Lower Jurassic) east of Nottingham, England. *Proceedings of the Yorkshire Geological Society*, Vol. 48, 121–141.

BRODIE, P B. 1850. Sketch of the geology of the neighbourhood of Grantham, Lincolnshire; and a comparison of the Stonesfield Slate at Collyweston in Northamptonshire with that in the Cotswold Hills. *Annals of Natural History*, Series 2, Vol. 6, 256–266.

BRODIE, P B. 1875. On the Lower Lias at Eatington and Kineton, and on the Rhaetics in that neighbourhood, and their further extension in Leicestershire, Nottinghamshire, Lincolnshire, Yorkshire, and Cumberland. *39th Annual report of the Warwickshire Natural History Society*, 6–17.

BURGESS, I C. 1982. The stratigraphical distribution of Westphalian volcanic rocks to the east and south of Nottingham. *Proceedings of the Yorkshire Geological Society*, Vol. 44, 29–44.

CALLOMON, J H. 1968. The Kellaways Beds and the Oxford Clays. 264–290 in *The geology of the East Midlands*. SYLVESTER-BRADLEY, P C, and FORD, T D (editors). (Leicester: University Press.)

CALVER, M A. 1968. Distribution of Westphalian marine faunas in northern England and adjoining areas. *Proceedings of the Yorkshire Geological Society*, Vol. 37, 1–72.

CATT, J A. 1977. Loess and coversands. 221–229 in *British Quaternary studies recent advances*. SHOTTON, F W (editor). (Oxford: Clarendon Press.)

CHARSLEY, T J, RATHBONE, P A, and LOWE, D J. 1990. Nottingham: A geological background for planning and development. *British Geological Survey Technical Report*, WA/90/1.

CLAYTON, K M. 1953. The glacial chronology of part of the middle Trent basin. *Proceedings of the Geologists' Association*, Vol. 64, 198–207.

COPE, J C W, DUFF, K L, PARSONS, C F, TORRENS, H S, WIMBLEDON, W A, and WRIGHT, J K. 1980a. A correlation of Jurassic rocks in the British Isles. Part 2: Middle and Upper Jurassic. *Special Report of the Geological Society of London*, No. 15.

COPE, J C W, GETTY, T A, HOWARTH, M K, MORTON, N, and TORRENS, H S. 1980b. A correlation of Jurassic rocks in the

British Isles. Part 1: Introduction and Lower Jurassic. *Special Report of the Geological Society of London*, No. 14.

COPESTAKE, P, and JOHNSON, B. 1989. The Hettangian to Toarcian (Lower Jurassic). In *Stratigraphical atlas of fossil foraminifera*. JENKINS, D G, and MURRAY, J W (editors). British Micropalaeontological Society Publication Series. (Chichester: Ellis Horwood.)

CORNWELL, J D, and WALKER, A S D. 1989. Regional geophysics. In *Metallogenic models and exploration criteria for buried carbonate-hosted ore deposits — a multidisciplinary study in eastern England*. PLANT, J A, and JONES, D G (editors). (Keyworth, Nottingham: British Geological Survey; London: The Institution of Mining and Metallurgy.)

COX, B M, HUDSON, J D, and MARTILL, D M. 1992. Lithostratigraphic nomenclature of the Oxford Clay (Jurassic). *Proceedings of the Geologists' Association*, Vol. 103, 343–345.

DAWN, A. 1993. Brittlestars from the Bathonian of Lincolnshire and Northamptonshire. *Mercian Geologist*, Vol. 13, 79–82.

DENNISON, V D. 1954. Geology. *Transactions of the Lincolnshire Naturalists' Union*, Vol. 13, 191–193.

DENNISON, V D. 1957. Notes on the course of the River Slea. *Transactions of the Lincolnshire Naturalists' Union*, Vol. 14, 87–94.

DOUGLAS, J A, and ARKELL, W J. 1932. The stratigraphical distribution of the Cornbrash: II The Northeastern area. *Quarterly Journal of the Geological Society of London*, Vol. 88, 112–170.

DOWNING, R A, SMITH, D B, PEARSON, F J, MONKHOUSE, R A, and OTLET, R L. 1977. The age of groundwater in the Lincolnshire Limestone, England, and its relevance to the flow mechanism. *Journal of Hydrology*, Vol. 33, 201–216.

DOWNING, R A, and WILLIAMS, B P J. 1969. *The groundwater hydrology of the Lincolnshire Limestone with special reference to the groundwater resources*. (Reading: Water Resources Board.)

DUNHAM, R J. 1962. Classification of carbonate rocks according to deposited texture. 108–121 *in* Classification of carbonate rocks. HAM, W E (editor). *American Association of Petroleum Geologists Memoir*, No. 1.

EBDON, C C, FRASER, A J, HIGGINS, A C, MITCHENER, B C, and STRANK, A R E. 1990. The Dinantian stratigraphy of the East Midlands: a seismostratigraphical approach. *Journal of the Geological Society of London*, Vol. 147, 519–536.

EDMUNDS, W M, and WALTON, N R G. 1983. The Lincolnshire Limestone — hydrogeochemical evolution over a ten year period. *Journal of Hydrology*, Vol. 61, 201–211.

ELLIOTT, R E. 1961. The stratigraphy of the Keuper Series in southern Nottinghamshire. *Proceedings of the Yorkshire Geological Society*, Vol. 33, 197–234.

EMERY, D, and DICKSON, J A D. 1991. The subsurface correlation of the Lincolnshire Limestone Formation in Lincolnshire. *Proceedings of the Geologists' Association*, Vol. 102, 109–122.

EVANS, C J, and ALLSOP, J M. 1987. Some geophysical aspects of the deep geology of eastern England. *Proceedings of the Yorkshire Geological Society*, Vol. 46, 321–333.

EVANS, C J, KIMBELL, G S, and ROLLIN, K E. 1988. *Hot dry rock potential in urban areas. Investigation of the geothermal potential of the UK*. (Keyworth, Nottingham: British Geological Survey.)

EVANS, W D. 1952. The Jurassic rocks of the Lincoln district. *Proceedings of the Geologists' Association*, Vol. 63, 316–335.

FALCON, N C, and KENT, P E. 1960. Geological results of petroleum exploration in Britain 1945–1957. *Geological Society of London Memoir*, No. 2.

FISHER, M J. 1986. Triassic. 113–132 in *Introduction to the petroleum geology of the North Sea* (2nd edition). GLENNIE, K W (editor). (Oxford: Blackwell Scientific Publications.)

FOLK, R L. 1959. Practical petrographic classification of limestones. *Bulletin of the American Association of Petroleum Geologists*, Vol. 43, 1–38.

FORSTER, A. 1992. The slope stability of the Lincolnshire Limestone escarpment between Welbourne and Grantham. 1:50 000 Geological Map Sheet 127. *British Geological Survey Technical Report*, WN/92/5.

FORSTER, A, and CULSHAW, M G. 1994. Slope instability assessment from geotechnical and slope data for planning purposes. 1771–1175 in *Proceedings of the Seventh International Congress, International Association of Engineering Geology*. OLIVEIRA, R, RODRIGUES, L F, COELHO, A G, and CUNHA, A P (editors). (Rotterdam: A A Balkema.)

FRASER, A J, and GAWTHORPE, R L. 1990. Tectono-stratigraphic development and hydrocarbon habitat of the Carboniferous in northern England. 49–86 *in* Tectonic events responsible for Britain's oil and gas reserves. HARDMAN, R F P, and BROOKS, J (editors). *Special Publication of the Geological Society of London*, No. 55.

FRASER, A J, NASH, D F, STEELE, R P, and EBDON, C C. 1990. A regional assessment of the intra-Carboniferous playa of northern England. 417–439 in Classic petroleum provinces. BROOKS, J (editor). *Special Publication of the Geological Society of London*, No. 50.

GALE, I N, and HOLLIDAY, D W. 1985. The geothermal resources of Eastern England. 55–63 in *European geothermal update*. STRUB, A S, and UNGEMACH, P (editors). (Dordrecht: D. Reidel Publishing Company.)

GALLOIS, R W. 1979. Geological investigations for the Wash Water Storage Scheme. *Report of the Institute of Geological Sciences*, No. 78/19.

GAUNT, G D, FLETCHER, T P, and WOOD, C J. 1992. Geology of the country around Kingston upon Hull and Brigg. *Memoir of the British Geological Survey*, Sheets 80 and 89 (England and Wales).

GEORGE, T N, JOHNSON, G A L, MITCHELL, M, PRENTICE, J E, RAMSBOTTOM, W H C, SEVASTOPULO, G D, and WILSON, R B. 1976. Dinantian (L. Carboniferous). *Special Report of the Geological Society of London*, No. 7, 1–87.

GLENNIE, K W. 1986. Early Permian Rotliegende. 63–85 in *Introduction to the petroleum geology of the North Sea*. (2nd edition). GLENNIE, K W (editor). (Oxford: Blackwell Scientific Publications.)

GOLDRING, D C. 1974. British iron ores: their future use. *Proceedings of the Royal Society of London*, Series A, Vol. 339, 313–324.

GOZZARD, J R. 1976. The sand and gravel resources of the country east of Newark upon Trent, Nottinghamshire: description of 1:25 000 resource sheet SK 85. *Mineral Assessment Report, Institute of Geological Sciences*, No. 20.

HALLAM, A. 1960. *Kulindrichnus langi*, a new trace fossil from the Lias. *Palaeontology*, Vol. 3, 64–68.

HALLAM, A. 1964. Origin of the limestone–shale rhythm in the Blue Lias of England: a composite theory. *Journal of Geology*, Vol. 72, 157–169.

HALLAM, A. 1968. The Lias. 188–210 in *The geology of the East Midlands*. SYLVESTER-BRADLEY, P C, and FORD, T D (editors). (Leicester: Leicester University Press.)

HEWLITT, H B. 1935. *Stanton Ironworks Co. Ltd. The quarries — ironstone, limestone and sand*. (Rochester: Stanhope Press.)

HOLLIDAY, D W. 1986. Devonian and Carboniferous basins. 84–110 in Geothermal energy — the potential in the United Kingdom. DOWNING, R A, and GRAY, D A (editors). (London: HMSO for British Geological Survey.)

HOLLINGWORTH, S E, and TAYLOR, J H. 1951. The Northampton Stone Ironstone, stratigraphy, structure and reserves. *Memoir of the Geological Survey.*

HORTON, A. 1989. Geology of the Peterborough district. *Memoir of the British Geological Survey*, Sheet 158 (England and Wales).

HORTON, A, IVIMEY-COOK, I C, HARRISON, R K, and YOUNG, B R. 1980. Phosphatic ooids in the Upper Lias (Lower Jurassic) of central England. *Journal of the Geological Society of London*, Vol. 137, 731–740.

HORTON, A, LAKE, R D, BISSON, G, and COPPACK, B C. 1974. The geology of Peterborough. *Report of the Institute of Geological Sciences*, No. 73/12.

HORTON, A, and POOLE, E G. 1977. The lithostratigraphy of three geophysical marker horizons in the Lower Lias of Oxfordshire. *Bulletin of the Geological Survey of Great Britain*, No. 62, 13–24.

HORTON, A, SHEPHARD-THORN, E R, and THURRELL, R G. 1974. The geology of the new town of Milton Keynes. *Report of the Institute of Geological Sciences*, No. 74/16.

HOWARD, A S, YOUNG, S R, and PHAROAH, T C. In preparation. Geology of the Nottingham district. *Memoir of the British Geological Survey*, Sheet 126 (England and Wales).

HOWARTH, M K. 1980. The Toarcian age of the upper part of the Marlstone Rock Bed of England. *Palaeontology*, Vol. 23, 637–656.

HOWARTH, M K. 1992. The ammonite family Hildoceratidae in the Lower Jurassic of Britain. *Monograph of the Palaeontographical Society*, Part 1.

HOWITT, F, and BRUNSTROM, R G W. 1966. The continuation of the east Midlands Coal Measures into Lincolnshire. *Proceedings of the Yorkshire Geological Society*, Vol. 35, 549–564.

HUDSON, J D, and MARTILL, D M. 1991. The Lower Oxford Clay: production and preservation of organic matter in the Callovian (Jurassic) of central England. 363–379 in Modern and ancient continental shelf anoxia. TYSON, R V, and PEARSON, T H (editors). *Special Publication of the Geological Society of London*, No. 58.

HUNT, R. 1859. Mineral statistics of the United Kingdom of Great Britain and Ireland for the year 1858. Part II. *Memoir of the Geological Survey of Great Britain.*

HUXLEY, J. 1983. *Britain's onshore oil industry.* (London: MacMillan.)

IRVINE, T N, and BARAGAR, W R A. 1971. A guide to the chemical classification of the common volcanic rocks. *Canadian Journal of Earth Sciences*, 8, 523–548.

IVIMEY-COOK, H C, and DONOVAN, D T. 1983. Appendix 3. The fauna of the Lower Jurassic. 126–130 in The geology of the country around Weston-Super-Mare. *Memoir of the Geological Survey of Great Britain.*

IVIMEY-COOK, H C, and others. (in preparation). The stratigraphy of the Fulbeck, Copper Hill and Walks Farm boreholes. *British Geological Survey Research Report.*

JACKSON, I. 1977. The sand and gravel resources of the country west and south of Lincoln, Lincolnshire: description of 1:25 000 resource sheets SK 95, 96 and 97. *Mineral Assessment Report, Institute of Geological Sciences*, No. 27.

JUDD, J W. 1875. The geology of Rutland. *Memoir of the Geological Survey of England and Wales*, Sheet 64 (Old Series).

JUKES-BROWNE, A J. 1885. The geology of the south-west part of Lincolnshire. *Memoir of the Geological Survey of England and Wales*, Sheet 70 (Old Series).

KENT, P E. 1937. The Lower Lias of south Nottinghamshire. *Proceedings of the Geologists' Association*, Vol. 48, 163–174.

KENT, P E. 1938. A borehole at Foston. *Transactions of the Lincolnshire Naturalists Union* [for 1937], 167–168.

KENT, P E. 1939a. New records of Lower Cornbrash in Mid-Lincolnshire. *Transactions of the Lincolnshire Naturalists' Union*, 1938, 220–221.

KENT, P E. 1939b. Notes on the river systems and glacial retreat stages in south Lincolnshire. *Proceedings of the Geologists' Association*, Vol. 50, 164–167.

KENT, P E. 1943. Geology. Glacially transported Inferior Oolite at Hougham. *Transactions of the Lincolnshire Naturalists' Union* for 1942, 40–41.

KENT, P E. 1953. The Rhaetic Beds of the north-east Midlands. *Proceedings of the Yorkshire Geological Society*, Vol. 29, 117–139.

KENT, P E. 1964. The basal Lias near Long Bennington. *Transactions of the Lincolnshire Naturalists' Union*, Vol. 16, 20–22.

KENT, P E. 1966. A review of the correlation of the Lincolnshire Limestone (Inferior Oolite). *Transactions of the Leicester Literary and Philosophical Society*, Vol. 60, 57–69.

KENT, P E. 1967. A contour map of the sub-Carboniferous basement surface in the north-east Midlands. *Proceedings of the Yorkshire Geological Society*, Vol. 36, 127–133.

KENT, P E. 1968a. The buried floor of eastern England. 138–148 in *The geology of the East Midlands.* SYLVESTER-BRADLEY, P C, and FORD, T D (editors). (Leicester: University Press.)

KENT, P E. 1968b. The Rhaetic Beds. 174–187 in T*he geology of the East Midlands.* SYLVESTER-BRADLEY, P C, and FORD, T D (editors). (Leicester: University Press.)

KENT, P E. 1970. Problems of the Rhaetic in the East Midlands. *Mercian Geologist*, Vol. 3, 361–373.

KENT, P E. 1975. The Grantham Formation of the east Midlands, revision of the Middle Jurassic Lower Estuarine Beds. *Mercian Geologist*, Vol. 5, 305–327.

KENT, P E. 1980. *British regional geology: Eastern England from the Tees to The Wash* (2nd edition). (London: HMSO for Institute of Geological Sciences.)

KIRBY, G A, SMITH, K, SMITH, N J P, and SWALLOW, P W. 1987. Oil and gas generation in eastern England. 171–180 in *Petroleum geology of North West Europe.* BROOKS, J, and GLENNIE, K W (editors). (London: Graham and Trotman.)

KIRTON, S R. 1984. Carboniferous volcanicity in England with special reference to the Westphalian of the East and West Midlands. *Journal of the Geological Society of London*, Vol. 141, 161–170.

LAMPLUGH, G W, GIBSON, W, SHERLOCK, R L, and WRIGHT, W B. 1908. The geology of the country between Newark and Nottingham. *Memoir of the Geological Survey*, Sheet 126 (England and Wales).

LAMPLUGH, G W, WEDD, C B, and PRINGLE, J. 1920. Iron ores. Bedded ores of the Lias, Oolites and later Formations in England. *Special Report on the Mineral Resources of Great Britain, Memoir of the Geological Survey of Great Britain*, Vol. 12.

LAWRENCE, A R, LLOYD, J W, and MARSH, J M. 1976. Hydrochemistry and groundwater mixing in part of the

Lincolnshire Limestone Aquifer, England. *Ground Water,* Vol. 14, No. 5, 320–327.

LEE, M K, PHARAOH, T C, and GREEN, C A. 1991. Structural trends in the concealed basement of eastern England from images of regional potential field data. *Annales de la Societé Géologique de Belgique,* Vol. 114, 45–62.

LEE, M K, PHARAOH, T C, and SOPER, N J. 1990. Structural trends in central Britain from images of gravity and aeromagnetic fields. *Journal of the Geological Society of London,* Vol. 147, 241–258.

LOTT, G K, and WARRINGTON, G. 1988. A review of the latest Triassic succession in the U.K. sector of the Southern North Sea Basin. *Proceedings of the Yorkshire Geological Society,* Vol. 47, 139–147.

MADER, D. 1992. Nottingham area (England): Buntsandstein-facies and Keuper-facies. 155–226 in *Evolution of palaeoecology and palaeoenvironment of Permian and Triassic fluvial basins in Europe. Volume 1.* MADER, D (editor). (New York, Stuttgart: Gustav Springer Verlag.)

MAYALL, M J. 1983. An earthquake origin for synsedimentary deformation in a late Triassic (Rhaetian) lagoonal sequence, southwest Britain. *Geological Magazine,* Vol. 120, 613–622.

MITCHELL, G F, PENNY, L F, SHOTTON, F W, and WEST, R G. 1973. A correlation of Quaternary deposits in the British Isles. *Special Report of the Geological Society of London,* No. 4.

MORRIS, P H, and COLEMAN, B E. 1989. The Aalenian to Callovian (Middle Jurassic). 189–236 in: *Stratigraphical atlas of fossil foraminifera* (2nd edition). JENKINS, G, and MURRAY, J W (editors). British Micropalaeontological Society Series. (Chichester: Ellis Horwood.)

NOBLE, S R, TUCKER, R D, and PHARAOH, T C. 1993. Lower Palaeozoic and Precambrian igneous rocks from eastern England, and their bearing on late Ordovician closure of the Tornquist Sea: constraints from U-Pb and Nd isotopes. *Geological Magazine,* Vol. 130, 737–749.

OWENS, B, RILEY, N J, and CALVER, M A. 1985. Boundary stratotypes and new stage names for the early and middle Westphalian sequences in Britain. *Compte Rendu, 10th International Congress of Carboniferous Stratigraphy and Geology (Madrid 1983),* 1, 35–44.

PAGE, K N. 1989. A stratigraphical revision for the English Lower Callovian. *Proceedings of the Geologists' Association,* Vol. 100, 363–382.

PATTISON, J. 1992. Geological notes and local details for 1:10 000 Sheet TF 04 NE: Sleaford. *British Geological Survey Technical Report,* WA/92/45.

PEARCE, J A. 1982. Trace element characteristics of lavas from destructive plate boundaries. 525–548 in *Orogenic andesites.* (Chichester: J Wiley and Sons.)

PEARCE, J A, HARRIS, N B W, and TINDLE, A G. 1984. Trace element discrimination diagrams for the tectonic interpretation of granitic rocks. *Journal of Petrology,* Vol. 25, 956–983.

PENN, I E, COX, B M, and GALLOIS, R W. 1986. Towards precision in stratigraphy: geophysical log correlation of Upper Jurassic (including Callovian) strata of the Eastern England Shelf. *Journal of the Geological Society of London,* Vol. 143, 381–410.

PERRIN, R M S, ROSE, J, and DAVIES, H. 1979. The distribution, variation and origins of pre-Devensian tills in eastern England. *Proceedings and Philosophical Transactions of the Royal Society,* Vol. 287, Series B, Vol. 1024, 535–570.

PHARAOH, T C, MERRIMAN, R J, EVANS, J A, BREWER, T S, WEBB, P C, and SMITH, N J P. 1991. Early Palaeozoic arc-related volcanism in the concealed Caledonides of southern Britain. *Annales de la Societé Géologique de Belgique,* Vol. 114, 63–92.

PHARAOH, T C, MERRIMAN, R J, WEBB, P C, and BECKINSALE, R D. 1987a. The concealed Caledonides of eastern England: preliminary results of a multidisciplinary study. *Proceedings of the Yorkshire Geological Society* 46, 355–369.

PHARAOH, T C, WEBB, P C, THORPE, R S, and BECKINSALE, R D. 1987b. Geochemical evidence for the tectonic setting of late Proterozoic volcanic suites in central England. 541–552 in Geochemistry and mineralisation of Proterozoic volcanic suites. PHARAOH, T C, BECKINSALE, R D, and RICKARD, D (editors). *Special Publication of the Geological Society of London,* No. 33.

PLANT, J A, and JONES, D G (editors). 1989. *Metallogenetic models and exploration for buried carbonate-hosted ore deposits — a multidisciplinary study in eastern England.* (London: The Institute of Mining and Metallurgy.)

POCOCK, T J. 1954. The rivers Witham and Devon in the glacial period. *Zeitschrift fur Gletscherkunde und Glazialgeologie,* Band 3, Heft 1, 47–54.

POSNANSKY, M. 1960. The Pleistocene succession in the middle Trent basin. *Proceedings of the Geologists' Association,* Vol. 71, 285–311.

POWELL, J H. 1984. Lithostratigraphical nomenclature of the Lias Group in the Yorkshire Basin. *Proceedings of the Yorkshire Geological Society,* Vol. 45, 51–57.

POWELL, J H. GLOVER, B W, and WATERS, C N. 1992. A geological background for planning and development in the 'Black Country'. *British Geological Survey Technical Report,* WA/92/33.

PRESTON, H. 1918. Geological report. *Transactions of the Lincolnshire Naturalists' Union,* Vol. 4, 115–116.

PURCELL, D. 1967. *Cambridge stone.* (London: Faber and Faber Ltd.)

RAMSBOTTOM, W H C, CALVER, M A, EAGER, R M C, HODSON, F, HOLLIDAY, D W, STUBBLEFIELD, C J, and WILSON, R B. 1978. A correlation of Silesian rocks in the British Isles. *Special Report of the Geological Society of London,* No. 10, 1–87.

REES, J G, and WILSON, A A. 1998. Geology of the country around Stoke-on-Trent. *Memoir of the British Geological Survey,* Sheet 123 (England and Wales).

RIDING, J B. 1987. Dinoflagellate cyst stratigraphy of the Nettleton Bottom Borehole (Jurassic; Hettangian to Kimmeridgian), Lincolnshire, England. *Proceedings of the Yorkshire Geological Society,* Vol. 46, 231–266.

RIDING, J B, and THOMAS, J E. 1992. Dinoflagellate cysts of the Jurassic System. 7–97 in A stratigraphic index of dinoflagellate cysts. POWELL, A J (editor). *British Micropalaeontological Society Publication Series.* (London: Chapman and Hall.)

RILEY, N J. 1993. Dinantian (Lower Carboniferous) biostratigraphy and chronostratigraphy in the British Isles. *Journal of the Geological Society of London,* Vol. 150, 427–446.

ROLLIN, K E. 1978. Interpretation of the main features of the Humber–Trent 1:25 000 Bouguer gravity anomaly map. *Institute of Geological Sciences, Applied Geophysics Unit Report,* No. 74.

ROTHWELL, N R, and QUINN, P. 1987. The Welton Oilfield. 181–189 in *Petroleum geology of North West Europe.* BROOKS, J, and GLENNIE, K W (editors). (London: Graham and Trotman.)

SAMUEL, M D A. 1992a. Geological notes and local details for 1:10 000 Sheet TF 05 SW (Brauncewell). *British Geological Survey Technical Report,* WA/92/63.

SAMUEL, M D A. 1992b. Geological notes and local details for 1:10 000 Sheet TF 05 SE (Ruskington). *British Geological Survey Technical Report*, WA/92/64.

SCOTT, J, and COLTER, V S. 1987. Geological aspects of current onshore Great Britain exploration plays. 95–107 in *Petroleum geology of North West Europe*. BROOKS, J, and GLENNIE, K W (editors). (London: Graham and Trotman.)

SHARP, S. 1870. The oolites of Northamptonshire. *Quarterly Journal of the Geological Society of London*, Vol. 26, 358–380.

SHEPPARD, L M. 1978. The exploration application of the range tables. In *A stratigraphical index of British Ostracoda*. BATE, R H, and ROBINSON, E (editors). *Geological Journal Special Issue*, No. 8.

SHEPPARD, L M. 1981. Bathonian ostracod correlation north and south of the English Channel with the description of two new Bathonian ostracods. 73–89 in *Microfossils from fossil and recent shelf seas*. NEALE, J W, and BRASIER, M D (editors). (Chichester: Ellis Horwood for British Micropalaeontological Society.)

SMITH, D B. 1989. The late Permian palaeogeography of north-east England. *Proceedings of the Yorkshire Geological Society*, Vol. 47, 285–312.

SMITH, D B, BRUNSTROM, R G W, MANNING, P I, SIMPSON, S, and SHOTTON, F W. 1974. A correlation of Permian rocks in the British Isles. *Special Report of the Geological Society of London*, No. 5.

SMITH, D B, HARWOOD, G M, PATTISON, J, and PETTIGREW, T H. 1986. A revised nomenclature for Upper Permian strata in eastern England. 9–17 in The English Zechstein and related topics. HARWOOD, G M, and SMITH, D B (editors). *Special Publication of the Geological Society of London*, No. 22.

SMITH, E G, and WARRINGTON, G. 1971. The age and relationships of the Triassic rocks assigned to the lower part of the Keuper in north Nottinghamshire, north-west Lincolnshire and south Yorkshire. *Proceedings of the Yorkshire Geological Society*, Vol. 38, 201–227.

SMITH, I F. 1986. Mesozoic basins. 42–83 in *Geothermal energy — the potential in the United Kingdom*. DOWNING, R A, and GRAY, D A (editors). (London: HMSO for British Geological Survey.)

SOMERVILLE, I D, and STRANK, A R E. 1984. Discovery of Arundian and Holkerian faunas from a Dinantian platform succession in North Wales. *Geological Journal*, Vol. 19, 85–104.

STEVENSON, I P, and MITCHELL, G H. 1955. Geology of the country between Burton upon Trent, Rugeley and Uttoxeter. *Memoir of the Geological Survey*, Sheet 140 (England and Wales).

STRANK, A R E. 1987. The stratigraphy and structure of Dinantian strata in the East Midlands, UK. 157–175 in *European Dinantian environments*. MILLER, J, ADAMS, A E, and WRIGHT, V P (editors). (Chichester: John Wiley and Sons.)

STRAW, A. 1958. The glacial sequence in Lincolnshire. *East Midlands Geographer*, Vol. 2, 29–40.

STRAW, A. 1963. The Quaternary evolution of the lower and middle Trent. *East Midlands Geographer*, Vol. 3, 171–189.

STRAW, A. 1969. Pleistocene events in Lincolnshire: a survey and revised nomenclature. *Transactions of the Lincolnshire Naturalists' Union*, Vol. 17, 85–98.

STRAW, A. 1970. Wind-gaps and water-gaps in eastern England. *East Midlands Geographer*, Vol. 5, 97–106.

STRAW, A. 1991. Glacial deposits of Lincolnshire and adjoining areas. 213–222 in *Glacial deposits in Great Britain and Ireland*. EHLERS, J, GIBBARD, P L, and ROSE, J (editors). (Rotterdam: Balkema.)

STRAW, A, and CLAYTON, K M. 1979. Eastern and Central England. In *Geomorphology of the British Isles*. (London: Methuen.)

SUMBLER, M G. 1983. A new look at the type Wolstonian glacial deposits of Central England. *Proceedings of the Geologists' Association*, Vol. 94, 23–31.

SUMBLER, M G. 1987. *Geological notes and local details for 1:10 000 sheet SK 85 SE (Beckingham)*. (Keyworth, Nottingham: British Geological Survey.)

SUMBLER, M G. 1993a. The Lias succession between Fulbeck and the Vale of Belvoir. *Mercian Geologist*, Vol. 13, 87–94.

SUMBLER, M G. 1993b. Geological notes and local details for 1:10 000 Sheet SK 95 SE (Leadenham). *British Geological Survey Technical Report*, WA/93/3.

SUMBLER, M G, and IVIMEY-COOK, H C. 1996. Temporary sections in Jurassic strata near Leadenham, Lincolnshire. *Mercian Geologist*, Vol. 14.

SUMBLER, M G, LOTT, G K, and BERRIDGE, N G. 1990. The Lincolnshire Limestone Formation (Middle Jurassic) near Grantham, Lincolnshire. *13th International Sedimentological Congress (Nottingham) Field Guide*, No. 6.

SWINNERTON, H H. 1918. The Keuper basement beds near Nottingham. *Proceedings of the Geologists' Association*, Vol. 29, 16–28.

SWINNERTON, H H, and KENT, P E. 1949. *The geology of Lincolnshire. Lincolnshire natural history brochure No. 1* (1st edition). (Lincoln: Lincolnshire Naturalists' Union.)

SWINNERTON, H H, and KENT, P E. 1976. The geology of Lincolnshire from the Humber to the Wash. *Lincolnshire natural history brochure No. 7* (2nd edition). (Lincoln: Lincolnshire Naturalists' Union.)

SYKES, J H, CARGILL, J S, and FRYER, H G. 1970. The stratigraphy and palaeontology of the Rhaetic Beds (Rhaetian: Upper Triassic) of Barnstone, Nottinghamshire. *Mercian Geologist*, Vol. 3, 233–262.

SYLVESTER-BRADLEY, P C, and FORD, T D. 1968. *The geology of the East Midlands*. (Leicester: University Press.)

TAYLOR, F M. 1968. Permian and Triassic formations. 149–173 in *The geology of the East Midlands*. SYLVESTER-BRADLEY, P C, and FORD, T D (editors). (Leicester, Leicester University Press.)

TAYLOR, F M. 1974. Permian and Lower Triassic landscapes of the East Midlands. *Mercian Geologist*, Vol. 5, 89–100.

TAYLOR, S R. 1983. A stable isotope study of the Mercia Mudstones (Keuper Marl) and associated sulphate horizons in the English Midlands. *Sedimentology*, Vol. 30, 11–31.

TONKS, E. 1991. Ironstone quarries of the Midlands, Part VIII, S Lincolnshire. (Cheltenham: Runpast Publishing.)

TORRENS, H S. 1968. The Great Oolite Series. 227–263 in *The geology of the East Midlands*. SYLVESTER-BRADLEY, P C, and FORD, T D (editors). (Leicester: University Press.)

TRUEMAN, A E. 1915. Fauna of the Hydraulic Limestones in south Nottinghamshire. *Geological Magazine*, Decade VI, Vol. 2, 150–152.

TRUEMAN, A E. 1917. The Lias brickyards of south-west Lincolnshire. *Transactions of the Lincolnshire Naturalists' Union*, Vol. 4, 48–53.

TRUEMAN, A E. 1918. The Lias of south Lincolnshire. *Geological Magazine*, Decade VI, Vol. 5, 64–73; 100–111.

USSHER, W A E, JUKES-BROWNE, A J, and STRAHAN, A. 1888. The geology of the country around Lincoln. *Memoir of the Geological Survey*, Sheet 83 (England and Wales).

VERSEY, H C. 1925.   The beds underlying the Magnesian Limestone in Yorkshire.   *Proceedings of the Yorkshire Geological Society*, Vol. 20, 200–214.

WALTON, N R G. 1980.   Summary of unpublished hydrogeochemical data on the Lincolnshire Limestone for studies between 1969 and 1980.   *Institute of Geological Sciences Technical Report*, WT/ST/80/9.

WARRINGTON, G, AUDLEY-CHARLES, M G, ELLIOTT, R E, EVANS, W B, IVIMEY-COOK, H C, KENT, P E, ROBINSON, P L, SHOTTON, F W, and TAYLOR, F M. 1980.   A correlation of Triassic rocks in the British Isles.   *Special Report of the Geological Society of London*, No. 13.

WARRINGTON, G, and IVIMEY-COOK, H C. 1992.   Triassic. 97–106 *in* Atlas of palaeogeography and lithofacies. COPE, J C W, INGHAM, J K, and RAWSON, P F (editors). *Memoir of the Geological Society of London*, No. 13.

WATERS, C N. 1992.   Geology of the Balderton district.   *British Geological Survey Technical Report*, WA/92/02.

WHITCOMBE, D N, and MAGUIRE, P K H. 1981.   A seismic refraction investigation of the Charnian basement and granitic intrusions flanking Charnwood Forest.   *Journal of the Geological Society of London*, Vol. 138, 643–651.

WHITEHEAD, T H, ANDERSON, W, WILSON, V, and WRAY, D A. 1952. The Mesozoic Ironstones of England: the Liassic Ironstones. *Memoir of the Geological Survey of Great Britain*.

WILLS, L J. 1970.   The Triassic succession in the central Midlands in its regional setting.   *Quarterly Journal of the Geological Society of London*, Vol. 126, 225–283.

WILLS, L J. 1978.   A palaeogeological map of the Lower Palaeozoic floor beneath the cover of Upper Devonian, Carboniferous and later formations.   *Memoir of the Geological Society of London*, No. 8.

WINCHESTER, J A, and FLOYD, P A. 1977.   Geochemical discrimination of different magma series and their differentiation products using immobile trace elements. *Chemical Geology*, Vol. 20, 325–343.

WOODWARD, H B. 1895.   The Jurassic rocks of Britain. Vol. V. The middle and upper oolitic rocks of England (Yorkshire excepted).   *Memoir of the Geological Survey of Great Britain*.

WYATT, R J. 1971.   New evidence for drift-filled valleys in north-east Leicestershire and south Lincolnshire.   *Bulletin of the Geological Survey of Great Britain*, No. 37, 29–55.

APPENDIX 1

List of 1:10 000 and 1:10 560 maps

Geological National grid 1:10 000 and 1:10 560 maps included wholly or in part in Sheet 127 are listed below, together with the initials of the surveyors and the date of survey.

The surveyors were K Ambrose (KA), N G Berridge (NGB), A Brandon (AB), T P Fletcher (TPF), A S Howard (ASH), J Pattison (JP), J H Powell (JHP), M D A Samuel (MDAS), M G Sumbler (MGS), C N Waters (CNW), F B A Welch (FBAW), R B Wilson (RBW), V Wilson (VW), D A Wray (DAW), R J Wyatt (RJW) and S R Young (SRY).

SK 83 NW	Bottesford	AB	1991
SK 83 NE	Sedgebrook and Barrowby	MDAS, JP	1991–92
SK 83 SE	Harlaxton	DAW	1939–40
		FBAW	1940
		RBW	1952
		RJW	1968
	minor revision by	MDAS	1992
SK 84 NW	Long Bennington	ASH	1991–92
SK 84 NE	Stubton	AB	1986–87
SK 84 SW	Staunton-in-the-Vale	SRY	1991–92
SK 84 SE	Foston	AB	1990
SK 85 SW	Balderton	CNW	1991
SK 85 SE	Beckingham	MGS	1986
SK 93 NW	Grantham and Belton	JP	1989–90
SK 93 NE	Welby	NGB	1989–90
SK 93 SW	Great Ponton	DAW	1940
		FBAW	1940–41
		RBW	1952
		RJW	1968
	minor revision by	JP	1992
SK 93 SE	Ropsley	FBAW	1940–41
		RBW	1952

		RBW	1968
	minor revision by	NGB	1992
SK 94 NW	Caythorpe	AB	1986–87
SK 94 NE	Normanton Heath	NGB	1990–91
SK 94 SW	Barkston	KA, NGB, JP	1991
SK 94 SE	Ancaster	NGB	1990–91
SK 95 SW	Brant Broughton	MGS	1986
SK 95 SE	Leadenham	MGS	1987, 1992
TF 03 NW	Haceby	NGB	1989
TF 03 NE	Osbournby	TPF	1978
TF 03 SW	Ingoldsby and Pickworth	RBW	1952–53
		RJW	1961, 1968
	minor revision by	NGB	1992
TF 03 SE	Folkingham	RBW	1952–53
		RJW	1961–69
	minor revision by	TPF	1978
TF 04 NW	Rauceby	NGB	1992
TF 04 NE	Sleaford	JP	1991
TF 04 SW	Culverthorpe	NGB	1991–92
TF 04 SE	Silk Willoughby	KA	1989
TF 05 SW	Brauncewell	MDAS	1990–91
TF 05 SE	Ruskington	MDAS	1991
TF 13 NW	Swaton and Horbling	TPF, JHP	1978l
TF 13 SW	Billingborough	RBW	1953
		VW	1961
		RJW	1970
	minor revision by	TPF	1978
TF 14 NW	Ewerby	JP	1990–91
TF 14 SW	Heckington and Helpringham	JP	1990
TF 15 SW	Anwick and Digby Fen	JP	1991

APPENDIX 2

Availability of BGS Technical reports

The BGS Technical reports listed below are details accounts of the geology of the constituent 1:10 000 sheets of the 1:50 000 Series Sheet 127, Grantham. The full title is given for the first report; the others all carry analogous titles. Copies may be ordered from the British Geological Survey, Keyworth, Nottingham.

SK 83 NE Samuel, M D A, and Pattison, J. 1992. Geological notes and local details for 1:10 000 Sheet SK83NE (Sedgebrook and Barrowby). British Geological Survey Technical Report WA/92/65. (Keyworth, Nottingham: British Geological Survey.)

SK 84 NW	Long Bennington	Howard, A S. 1992. WA/92/48.
SK 84 NE	Stubton	Brandon, A. 1987.
SK 74 SE & SK 84 SW	Orston and Staunton-in-the-Vale	Young, S R. 1992. WA/92/47.
SK 85 SW	Balderton	Waters, C N. 1992. WA/92/02.
SK 85 SE	Beckingham	Sumbler, M G. 1987.
SK 93 NW	Grantham and Belton	Pattison, J. 1991. WA/91/54.
SK 93 NE, SK 94 NE & SE, TF 03 NW, TF 04 NW & SW	Welby. Normanton Heath, Ancaster, Haceby, Rauceby, and Culverthorpe	Berridge, N G. 1993. WA/92/44.
SK 94 NW	Caythorpe	Brandon, A. 1987.
SK 95 SW	Brant Broughton	Sumbler, M G. 1987.
SK 95 SE	Leadenham	Sumbler, M G. 1993. WA/93/03.
TF 05 SW	Brauncewell	Samuel, M D A. 1992. WA/92/63.
TF 05 SE	Ruskington	Samuel, M D A. 1992. WA/92/64.
TF 04 NE	Sleaford	Pattison, J. 1992. WA/92/45.
TF 14 NW & SW, and TF 15 SW	Helpringham to Digby Fen	Pattison, J. 1992. WA/92/4.

APPENDIX 3

Abstracts of boreholes cited in the text

Boreholes for which the logs are confidential are marked with an asterisk, and only site details and total depths are given. Non-confidential borehole records may be consulted at the National Geosciences Data Centre, BGS, Keyworth.

The boreholes are identified by their registered numbers in the BGS 1:10 000 sheet registration system, and are ordered by sheet and registered number.

SK73NE 3   Bottesford No. 4 (British Petroleum) [7859 3881] Surface level c.+ 28.9 m OD.

	Thickness m	Depth m
Scunthorpe Mudstone Formation	33.8	33.8
Penarth Group	4.6	38.4
Mercia Mudstone Group	242.0	280.4
Sherwood Sandstone Group	112.2	392.6
Permian	40.8	433.4
Barren Measures and Coal Measures	201.2	634.6
Fault breccia	11.6	646.2
Barren Measures and Coal Measures	279.8	926.0
Millstone Grit	57.3	983.3
Carboniferous Limestone	11.9	995.2

SK73SE 8   Plungar 8A (British Petroleum) [7745 3336] Surface level c.+ 56 m OD. Total depth 1071.37 m.

SK83NW 8   Bottesford (British Petroleum) [8043 3740] Surface level c.+ 37.5 m OD. Total depth 973.23 m.

*SK83NW 10   Cox's Walk (British Coal) [8411 3808] Surface level + 52.67 m OD. Total depth 800.65 m.

*SK83NW11   Stenwith (British Coal) [8335 3683] Surface level + 45.66 m OD. Total depth 720.26 m.

SK83NW 13   Redmile No. 2 (British Petroleum) [80698 36089] Surface level + 53.71 m OD. Total depth 648 m.

SK83SE 540   Great Ponton No. 1 (British Petroleum) [89400 30530] Surface level 130.6 m OD. Total depth 971 m.

SK83SE 540   Redmile No. 1 (British Petroleum) [8086 3440] Surface level + 60.53 m OD. Total depth 935.74 m.

*SK83SW 99   Woolsthorpe Bridge (British Coal) [8434 3488] Surface level + 65.70 m OD. Total depth 783.85 m.

SK83SW 106   Harston (British Petroleum) [84522 31657] Surface level + 101.2 m OD. Total depth 1084 m.

SK84NW 3   Claypole (British Petroleum) SK84NW 3 [84505 49334] Surface level c.+ 14.5 m OD. Total depth 669.3 m.

SK84SW 1   Bennington G1 (British Petroleum) [8376 4157] Surface level c.+ 22 m OD. Total depth 718.72 m.

SK84SW 3   Foston 1 (British Petroleum) [8489 4145] Surface level + 28.3 m OD. Total depth 748.28 m.

*SK84SW 21   Three Shire Oak Borehole (British Coal) [8221 4304] Surface level + 40.07 m OD. Total depth 982.41 m.

SK85SW 28   Bridge Farm, Balderton [8333 5188] Surface level + 18 m OD

	Thickness m	Depth m
Older river terrace deposits	8.8	8.8
Scunthorpe Mudstone Formation	1.7+	10.5

SK85SW 29   Coddington Windmill [8324 5359] Surface level + 35.7 m OD

	Thickness m	Depth m
Older river terrace deposits	3.9	3.9
Scunthorpe Mudstone Formation	1.6+	5.5

SK85SW 48   The Newark Borehole (British Petroleum) [8290 5244] Surface level + 19 m. Total depth 744 m

SK85SE 25   Fulbeck Borehole 1 [8889 5053] Surface level + 18.03 m OD

	Thickness m	Depth m
Lias Group		
Scunthorpe Mudstone Formation		
Foston Member	17.9	17.9
Beckingham Member	22.6	40.5
Granby Member	30.4	70.9
Barnby Member	21.9	92.8
Barnstone Member	8.1	100.9
Penarth Group		
Cotham Member	6.1	107.0
Westbury Formation	4.5	111.5
Blue Anchor Formation	6.0	117.5
Mercia Mudstone Group		
Cropwell Bishop Formation	36.6	156.1
Edwalton Formation	44.9	201.0
Gunthorpe Formation	86.3	287.3
Radcliffe Formation	14.3	301.6
Sneinton Formation	73.6	375.2
Sherwood Sandstone Group	20.9+	396.1

SK93NW 7 R   Hornby and Sons' Ironworks, Spittlegate [9164 3511] Surface level c.+ 57.9 m OD

	Thickness m	Depth m
Belton Sand and Gravel	8.53	8.53
Brant Mudstone Formation		
Scunthorpe Mudstone Formation	244.45	252.98
Penarth Group		
Mercia Mudstone Group	7.12	260.10
?Blue Anchor Formation		

SK93NW 9   Messrs Shaw's Tan Yard [9064 3516]
Surface level c.+ 59.7 m OD

	Thickness m	Depth m
Belton Sand and Gravel	12.2	12.2
Brant Mudstone Formation	18.3	30.5

SK93NW 45   Grantham Hospital, BH3A [9137 3700]
Surface level c.+ 52 m OD

	Thickness m	Depth m
Belton Sand and Gravel	4.5	4.5
Brant Mudstone Formation	7.5	12.0

SK94NE 6A   Caythorpe Pump House [9618 4817] Surface level + 97.5 m OD

	Thickness m	Depth m
Lower Lincolnshire Limestone	1.37	1.37
Northampton Sand Formation	1.37	2.74
Whitby Mudstone Formation	60.81	63.55
Marlstone Rock Formation	5.94	69.49
Brant Mudstone Formation	1.07	70.56

*SK94SW 4   Westfield Lane (British Coal) [9199 4172]
Surface level + 42.04 m OD. Total depth 679.58 m.

SK94SE 56   Copper Hill Borehole (**BGS**) [9787 4265] Surface level + 69.3 m OD

	Thickness m	Depth m
Open hole	0.95	0.95
Made ground (quarry rubble)	0.07	1.02
Lower Lincolnshire Limestone	2.74	3.76
Grantham Formation	13.55	17.31
Whitby Mudstone Formation	46.39	63.70
Marlstone Rock Formation	3.60	67.30
Brant Mudstone Formation	48.15	115.45
'Pecten Ironstone'	0.19	115.64
	51.81	167.45
Brandon Sandstone	4.43	171.88
	10.52	182.40
Glebe Farm Bed	0.20	182.60
Scunthorpe Mudstone Formation	5.71	188.31
Stragglethorpe Grange Limestone	0.35	188.66
	2.19	190.85
Highfield Farm Limestones	0.13	190.98
	6.02	197.00
Mill Lane Limestones	1.10	198.10
	2.40	200.50
Littlegate Limestones	1.61+	202.11

*SK95NW 16   Bassingham Fen (British Coal) [9319 5856]
Surface level + 7 m OD. Total depth 863.6 m.

*SK95SW 7   Broach Road (British Coal) [9292 5455]
Surface level + 10.5 m OD. Total depth 907.62 m.

*SK95SW 8   Stragglethorpe (British Coal) [9005 5183]
Surface level + 14.60 m OD. Total depth 845.6 m.

SK95SW 17   Fulbeck Borehole 5 [9061 5178]
Surface level + 14.48 m OD

	Thickness m	Depth m
Lias Group		
Brant Mudstone Formation	4.58	4.58
Scunthorpe Mudstone Formation		
Foston Member	30.07	34.65
Beckingham Member	22.10	56.75
Granby Member	30.60	87.35
Barnby Member	22.05	109.40
Barnstone Member	8.25	117.65
Penarth Group		
Lilstock Formation		
Cotham Member	6.80	124.45
Westbury Formation	4.00	128.45
Mercia Mudstone Group	9.80+	138.25

SK95SW 57   A17 Leadenham Bypass BH13 (D.o.T.) [94592 51279] Surface level + 30 m OD

	Thickness m	Depth m
Head		
Brant Mudstone Formation	5.0+	5.0

SK95SW 61 A17   Leadenham Bypass BH17A (D.o.T.) [94991 50962] Surface level + 53.92 m OD

	Thickness m	Depth m
Brant Mudstone Formation	6.4+	6.4

SK95SE 48 A17   Leadenham Bypass BH10 (D.o.T.) [9503 5113] Surface level + 54.34 m OD

	Thickness m	Depth m
Marlstone Rock Formation	2.5	2.5
Brant Mudstone Formation	12.0+	14.5

SK95SE 49 A17   Leadenham Bypass BH11R (D.o.T.) [9504 5110] Surface level + 54.65 m OD

	Thickness m	Depth m
Marlstone Rock Formation	2.8	2.8
Brant Mudstone Formation	17.2	20.0

SK95SE 50 A17   Leadenham Bypass BH18 (D.o.T.) [9502 5094] Surface level + 54.18 m OD

	Thickness m	Depth m
Marlstone Rock Formation	3.6	3.6
Brant Mudstone Formation	10.4+	14.0

*SK96SW 16   Bassingham 1 Borehole (British Coal) [9208 6060] Surface level + 13.12 m OD. Total depth 1398.2 m.

TF03NE 2   Osbournby [0679 3810] Surface level + 21.3 m OD

	Thickness m	Depth m
Kellaways Formation	5.8	5.8
Cornbrash Formation	1.9	7.7
Blisworth Clay	7.8	15.5
Blisworth Limestone	3.7	19.2
Rutland Formation	9.0	28.2
Lincolnshire Limestone	17.8+	46.0

TF03NE 5   Aswarby [0671 3905] Surface level + 22.9 m OD

	Thickness	Depth
	m	m
Oxford Clay Formation, undivided	1.8	1.8
Kellaways Formation	6.7	8.5
Cornbrash Formation	0.9	9.4
Blisworth Clay	6.7	16.1
Blisworth Limestone	4.9	21.0
Rutland Formation	8.9	29.9
Lincolnshire Limestone	33.5	63.4
Grantham Formation	8.2	71.6

TF03NE 10   Threekingham No. 1, United Steel Co., Ltd. NW134. [0799 3505] Surface level + 48.3 m OD

	Thickness	Depth
	m	m
Till	8.8	8.8
Oxford Clay Formation, undivided	1.3	10.1
Kellaways Formation	7.6	17.7
Cornbrash Formation	1.5	19.2
Blisworth Clay	8.2	27.4
Blisworth Limestone	2.8	30.2
Rutland Formation	9.0	39.2
Lincolnshire Limestone	30.7	69.9
Grantham Formation	2.0	71.9

TF03NE 17   Spanby, United Steel Co., Ltd. NW155. [0900 3800] Surface level + 12.8 m OD

	Thickness	Depth
	m	m
Drift	2.3	2.3
Oxford Clay Formation, undivided	4.9	7.2
Kellaways Formation	12.0	19.2
Cornbrash Formation	1.2	20.4
Blisworth Clay	7.6	28.0
Blisworth Limestone	6.5	31.5
Rutland Formation	10.6	42.1
Lincolnshire Limestone	35.2	77.3
Grantham Formation	0.6+	77.9

TF04NW 13   Windmill House (A17) Road Improvement [0370 4754] Surface level c.+ 15.2 m OD

	Thickness	Depth
	m	m
Blisworth Clay	9.6	9.6

TF04NE 1   Ruskington Borehole [0920 4974] Surface level + 11.0 m OD

	Thickness	Depth
	m	m
Kellaways Sand Formation	10.05	10.05
Cornbrash Formation	5.49	15.54
Blisworth Clay		
Blisworth Limestone		
Rutland Formation	20.12	35.66
Lincolnshire Limestone	31.70	67.36
Grantham Formation	6.70	74.06
Whitby Mudstone Formation	46.94	121.00
Marlstone Rock Formation	130.00	9.00
Brant Mudstone and Scunthorpe		
Mudstone formations	215.03	345.03
Penarth Group	2.44	347.47
Mercia Mudstone Group	216.41	563.88
Sherwood Sandstone Group	201.17	765.05
Permian	10.67	775.72

Barren Measures	86.86	862.58
Middle Coal Measures	121.01	983.59
Carboniferous Limestone	18.90+	002.49

TF04NE 8   LNER Railway, Sleaford [0841 4513] Surface level + 14.2 m OD

	Thickness	Depth
	m	m
Made ground	3.35	3.35
Sleaford Sand and Gravel	3.36	6.71
Oxford Clay Formation, undivided	5.79	12.50
Kellaways Formation	6.85	19.35
Cornbrash Formation	1.99	21.34
Blisworth Clay	6.09	27.43
Blisworth Limestone	7.62	35.05
Rutland Formation	8.23	43.28
Lincolnshire Limestone	24.08+	67.36

TF04NE 23   Drove Lane [0552 4622] Surface level + 17.1 m OD Water well. No borehole log data available.

TF04NE 47   Holdingham Roundabout, Sleaford, Trial Pit 3 [0592 4720] Surface level c.+ 22 m OD

	Thickness	Depth
	m	m
Drift	0.9	0.9
Cornbrash Formation	0.3	1.2
Blisworth Clay	1.8+	3.0

TF04NE 61   Council Offices, Sleaford, BH 1 [0706 4588] Surface level + 13.81 m OD

	Thickness	Depth
	m	m
Made ground	0.8	0.8
Alluvium	0.5	1.3
Sleaford Sand and Gravel	1.9	3.2
Cornbrash Formation	1.0	4.2
Blisworth Clay	7.8+	12.0

TF04NE 95   Kirkby la Thorpe Test/Production Bore A (Anglian Water Authority) [095 456] Surface level + 9.39 m OD

	Thickness	Depth
	m	m
Sleaford Sand and Gravel	4.9	4.9
Oxford Clay Formation, undivided		
Kellaways Formation	21.6	26.5
Cornbrash Formation	3.1	29.6
Blisworth Clay	7.9	37.5
Blisworth Limestone	3.4	40.9
Rutland Formation	8.0	48.9
Lincolnshire Limestone	31.9	80.8
Grantham Formation	2.2	83.0

TF04SW 7A   Rauceby Hospital, Quarrington [0412 4399] Surface level c.+ 26 m OD

	Thickness	Depth
	m	m
Made ground	0.9	0.9
Blisworth Clay	7.3	8.2
Blisworth Limestone	4.6	12.8
Rutland Formation	8.5	21.3
Lincolnshire Limestone	30.9	52.3
?Grantham Formation		
?Northampton Sand Formation	2.3	54.6
Whitby Mudstone Formation	15.5+	70.1

*TF04SW 10   **Gables Farm** (British Coal)
Surface level + 22.57 m OD. Total depth 999.73 m.

*TF04SE 22   **Hurn Corner** (British Coal) [0907 4118]
Surface level + 8.13 m OD. Total depth 991.47 m.

*TF04SE 23   **Mareham Grange** (British Coal) [0845 4328]
Surface level + 8.06 m OD. Total depth 958.5 m.

TF05NE 1   Blankney No. 1 Borehole [0635 5967] Surface
level c.+ 24.4 m OD

	Thickness m	Depth m
Lincolnshire Limestone	29.9	29.9
Northampton Sand Formation	3.3	3.3
Whitby Mudstone Formation	49.1	82.3
Marlstone Rock Formation		
Brant Mudstone Formation	204.5	286.8
Scunthorpe Mudstone Formation		
Penarth Group	9.8	296.6
Mercia Mudstone Group	274.6	571.2
Sherwood Sandstone Group	158.2	729.4
Permian	156.9	886.3
?Barren Measures	10.4	896.7
Millstone Grit	11.3	908.0
Carboniferous Limestone	32.3+	940.3

TF05SE 16   Digby Test/Production Borehole (Anglian Water
Authority) [0776 5484] Surface level 21.0 m OD.

	Thickness m	Depth m
Cornbrash Formation	3.0	3.0
Blisworth Clay	7.4	10.4
Blisworth Limestone	6.6	17.0
Rutland Formation	6.0	23.0
Lincolnshire Limestone	30.0	53.0
Grantham Formation	1.0	54.0

TF13NE 9   Helpringham Trial No. 1 (British Petroleum)
[17530 38840] Rotary table elevation 7.1 m OD.
(Gamma log interpretation)

	Thickness m	Depth m
Till	15.24	15.2
Oxford Clay Formation, undivided	19.06	34.3
Kellaways Sand	3.1	37.4
Kellaways Clay	3.4	40.8
Cornbrash	1.3	42.1
Blisworth Clay	6.1	48.2
Blisworth Limestone	3.9	52.1
Rutland Formation	9.2	61.3
Lincolnshire Limestone	30.7	92.0
?Grantham Formation	6.2	98.2
Whitby Mudstone Formation	43.5	141.7
Marlstone Rock Formation	6.1	147.8
Brant Mudstone Formation		
Scunthorpe Mudstone Formation	221.0	368.8
Penarth Group	7.3	376.1
Mercia Mudstone Group	203.0	579.1
Sherwood Sandstone Group	86.6	665.7
Permian	62.2	727.9
Coal Measures	34.4	762.3

TF13NW 21   Scredington Observation Borehole 1 (Anglian
Water Authority) [1099 3999] Surface level 17.27 m OD.
(Gamma log interpretation to 58 m)

	Thickness m	Depth m
Till	5.7	5.7
Oxford Clay Formation, undivided	33.9	39.6
Kellaways Formation		
Kellaways Sand Member	4.8	44.4
Kellaways Clay Member	2.0	46.4
Cornbrash Formation	1.6	48.0
Blisworth Clay	7.0	55.0
Blisworth Limestone	4.5	59.5
Rutland Formation	10.0	69.5
Lincolnshire Limestone	29.5	99.0
Grantham Formation	1.0	100.0

TF14NW 6   Asgarby Fen (Anglian Water Authority) [1490
4962] Surface level + 5.78 m OD.

	Thickness m	Depth m
Ancholme Group (undivided)	75.5	75.5
Kellaways Formation	4.1	79.6
Cornbrash Formation	2.4	82.0
Blisworth Clay	8.6	90.6
Blisworth Limestone	4.4	95.0
Rutland Formation	7.7	102.7
Lincolnshire Limestone	30.3	133.0
Grantham Formation	3.2	136.2

TF14NW 8   Ewerby North (Anglian Water Authority) [123
478] Surface level + 15.7 m OD. (Gamma log interpretation)

	Thickness m	Depth m
Till	2.8	2.8
Ancholme Group (undivided)	48.2	51.2
Kellaways Sand	5.6	56.8
Kellaways Clay	0.8	57.6
Cornbrash Formation	3.6	61.2
Blisworth Clay	6.6	67.8
Blisworth Limestone	4.2	72.0
Rutland Formation	7.0	79.0
Lincolnshire Limestone	31.0	110.0
?Grantham Formation	2.0	112.0

TF14NW 9   Ewerby South (Anglian Water Authority) [118
458] Surface level + 19.9 m OD. (Gamma log interpretation)

	Thickness m	Depth m
Till	4.6	4.6
Oxford Clay, undivided	47.1	51.7
Kellaways Sand	5.6	57.3
Kellaways Clay	1.2	58.5
Cornbrash	2.9	61.4
Blisworth Clay	5.2	66.4
Blisworth Limestone	4.5	71.1
Rutland Formation	9.4	80.5
Lincolnshire Limestone		
?Grantham Formation		
?Northampton Sand Formation	41.5	122.0
?Whitby Mudstone Formation		

TF14NW 11   Asgarby West (Anglian Water Authority) [109 458] Surface level + 8.35 m OD. (Gamma log interpretation)

	Thickness m	Depth m
Sleaford Sand and Gravel	5.2	5.2
Oxford Clay, undivided	27.4	32.6
Kellaways Sand	7.0	39.6
Kellaways Clay	1.1	40.7
Cornbrash Formation	2.0	42.7
Blisworth Clay	6.5	49.2
Blisworth Limestone	4.0	53.2
Rutland Formation	7.8	61.0
Lincolnshire Limestone		
Grantham Formation	38.0	99.0

TF14NE 18   Walks Farm Borehole (BGS) [1534 4635] Surface level c.+ 3 m OD

	Thickness m	Depth m
No core	5.42	5.42
Till	3.08	8.50
No core	0.16	8.66
West Walton Formation	14.27	22.93
Oxford Clay: Weymouth Member	25.32	48.25
Stewartby Member	25.80	74.05
Peterborough Member	17.55	91.60
Kellaways Sand Member	5.00	96.60
Kellaways Clay Member	1.77	8.37
Cornbrash Formation	1.88	100.25
Blisworth Clay	6.98	107.23
Blisworth Limestone	3.64	110.87
Rutland Formation	7.66	118.53
Upper Lincolnshire Limestone	3.76+	122.29

TF14SW 16   Burton Pedwardine [1165 4264] Surface level + 12.67 m OD

	Thickness m	Depth m
Ancholme Group undivided	5.0	55.0
Cornbrash Formation	3.0	58.0

Blisworth Clay	3.0	71.0
Blisworth Limestone	3.5	74.5
Rutland Formation	11.5	89.5
Lincolnshire Limestone	8.5	114.5
Grantham Formation	1.5	116.0

*TF14SW 13   Burton Lodge (British Coal) [1142 4384] Surface level + 15.61 m OD. Total depth 984.55 m.

TF23NW 17   Well at Bicker [247 385] Surface level + 2.9 m OD

	Thickness m	Depth m
Drift		
Peat and alluvium	7.6	7.6
Older river terrace and associated deposits ('Fen Gravel')	0.4	8.0
?Till	8.0	16.0
West Walton Formation	5.0	21.0
Oxford Clay Formation		
Weymouth Member	18.0	39.0
Stewartby Member	24.0	63.0
Peterborough Member	17.5	80.5
Kellaways Formation		
Kellaways Sand	4.0	84.5
Kellaways Clay	2.5	87.0
Cornbrash Formation	2.0	89.0
Blisworth Clay	5.0	94.0
Blisworth Limestone	3.0	97.0
Rutland Formation	8.5	105.5
Lincolnshire Limestone	23.5	129.0
Grantham Formation	10.0	139.0
Whitby Mudstone Formation	touched	

APPENDIX 4

Geophysical data

AEROMAGNETIC DATA

West of National Grid line 500 kmE the aeromagnetic data (Figure 8b) were acquired by a survey flown in 1955 with a mean terrain clearance of 305 m. The east–west flight line spacing was 2.45 km with north–south tie lines at 14.5 km intervals.

East of National Grid line 500 km E, the aeromagnetic survey was flown in 1956 at a constant barometric height of 457 m, overlapping the 1955 survey on its eastern margin by about 2 km. The north–south flight line spacing was 2 km with east–west tie lines at 10 km intevals.

In both surveys the total magnetic field was measured to one nanotesla (1 nT) precision. Work sheet compilations, showing flight lines, contour cuts and contoured field, have been digitised using contour cuts, areas of low gradient and turning points of the total field along each flight line. The validated digitisation products now form part of the BGS National Aeromagnetic data bank.

GRAVITY DATA

Gravity data (Figure 8a) have been collected over the past 40 years and now exist in processed digital form as the BGS National Gravity data bank. The average station spacing in the area of the Grantham district is about one station per 1.4 km². In the west of the district several gaps of up to 3 km diameter exist in the data coverage.

BOREHOLE LOGS AND SEISMIC DATA

A dense network of seismic reflection data exists over much of the district and surrounding area. Depth converted sections have been gridded for five reflectors, numbered in the left hand column of Table 1. The general agreement at boreholes of the depth converted data is better than 5 per cent of depth. Table 1 summarises the borehole data for five wells for which geophysical logs were available.

PHYSICAL PROPERTIES OF ROCKS

Although geophysical data exist for many boreholes in the Grantham district, there are none from which reliable rock densities can be recovered. However, the surrounding area has been extensively drilled for hydrocarbon exploration and reliable compensated formation density logs are available for the boreholes listed in Table 1. These logs were analysed over intervals represented in Table 1 using the BGS 'Wellog' program suite. Supplementary density and magnetic susceptibility data were taken from Plant and Jones (1989; tables 4.1, 4.4 and appendix 2). A summary of the densities used for gravity stripping of the effects of the major lithostratigraphical units down to the base of the Carboniferous is given in Table 2.

APPENDIX 5

Geological Survey photographs

Photographs illustrating the geology of the Grantham district are deposited for reference in the headquarters library of the British Geological Survey, Keyworth, Nottingham NG12 5GG; in the library at the BGS, Murchison House, West Mains Road, Edinburgh EH9 3LA; and in the BGS Information Office at the Natural History Museum Earth Galleries, Exhibition Road, London SW7 2DE. They belong to the A Series and most were taken during and following the 1989–1992 survey. The photographs depict details of the various rocks and sediments exposed and also include general views and scenery. A list of titles can be supplied on request. The photographs can be supplied as black and white or colour prints and 2×2 colour transparencies, at a fixed tariff.

AUTHOR CITATIONS FOR FOSSIL SPECIES

To satisfy the rules and recommendations of the international codes of botanical and zoological nomenclature, authors of cited species are listed below.

Chapter 3 Concealed strata

Agathammina pusilla (Geinitz, 1848)
Anthrocosia aquilina (J de C Sowerby, 1840)
Anthrocosia lateralis (Brown, 1843)
Anthrocosia ovum Trueman & Weir, 1951
Anthrocosia phrygiana (Wright, 1929)
Anthrocosia regularis (Trueman, 1929)
Aulophyllum redesdalense Smith, 1913

Bakevellia binneyi (Brown) Logan, 1967

Calcinema permiana (King) Podemski, 1970
Carbonicola cristagalli Wright, 1936
Carbonicola os-lancis Wright, 1929
Clisiophyllum rigidum Lewis, 1930

Dainella holkeriana Conil & Longerstacey *in* Conil, Longerstacey & Ramsbottom, 1979
Davidsonina carbonaria (McCoy, 1855)
Dibunophyllum bourtonense Garwood & Goodyear, 1924
Dictyotriletes karadenizensis Artuz, 1959

Eotrapezium concentricum (Moore, 1861)
Eotrapezium germari (Dunker, 1846)
Euestheria minuta (Zeiten, 1833)

Geisina arcuata (Bean, 1836)
Gigantoproductus maximus (McCoy, 1844)
Gyrolepis alberti L Agassiz, 1833

Koninckophyllum vaughani Fedorowski, 1971

Lingula credneri Geinitz, 1848
Lingula mytilloides J Sowerby, 1812
Linoprotonia corrugatohemisphaerica (Vaughan *in* Dixon & Vaughan, 1911)
Lonsdaleia duplicata (Martin, 1809)
Lycospora pusilla (Ibrahim) Schopf, Wilson & Bentall, 1944

Monotaxinoides subplana Brazhnikova & Yartsheva, 1956
Mooreisporites fustis Neves, 1958
Mooreisporites trigallerus Neves, 1961

Naiadites quadratus (J de C Sowerby, 1840)
Permophorus costatus (Brown, 1841)

Protocardia rhaetica (Merian, 1853)
Pseudomonotis speluncaria (Schlotheim, 1820)
Pseudovoltzia liebeana (Geinitz) Florin, 1927
Rhaetavicula contorta (Portlock, 1843)

Schizodus obscurus (J Sowerby, 1821)

Chapter 4 Lower Jurassic: Lias Group

Acanthopleuroceras valdani (d'Orbigny, 1844)
Agassiceras scipionianum (d'Orbigny, 1844)
Alsatites laqueolus (Schloenbach, 1865)
Amaltheus gibbosus (Schlotheim, 1820)
Amaltheus margaritatus de Montfort, 1808
Amaltheus wertheri (Lange, 1932)
Ammodiscus siliceus (Terquem, 1862)
Ammodiscus yonsnabensis Nagy, Løfaldi & Bomstad, 1983
Androgynoceras maculatum (Young & Bird, 1822)
Arnioceras miserabile (Quenstedt, 1856)
Arnioceras semicostatum (Young & Bird, 1828)
Astacolus semireticulata (Fuchs, 1970)

Caenisites turneri (J de C Sowerby, 1824)
Calcirhynchia calcaria S S Buckman, 1918
Caloceras johnstoni (J de C Sowerby, 1824)
Camptonectes subulatus (Münster, 1836)
Cardinia crassiuscula (J Sowerby, 1817)
Cardinia hybrida (J Sowerby, 1817)
Cardinia hybrida var. *depressa* (Zeiten, 1833)
Cardinia insignis Martin, 1863
Cardinia lanceolata (Stutchbury, 1842)
Cardinia listeri (J Sowerby, 1817)
Cardinia ovalis (Stutchbury, 1842)
Chlamys textoria (Schlotheim, 1820)
Citharina collietzi (Terquem, 1866)
Cleviceras elegans (J Sowerby, 1815)
Cleviceras exaratum (Young & Bird, 1828)
Coroniceras hyatti Donovan, 1952
Coroniceras kridion (Hehl *in* Zieten, 1830)
Coroniceras lyra Hyatt, 1889
Cristacythere crassireticulata Michelsen, 1975
Crucilobiceras crucilobatum S S Buckman, 1920
Cytherella concentrica Field, 1966
Cytherelloidea circumscripta (Blake, 1876)

Dacryomya gaveyi Cox, 1960
Dentalina matutina d'Orbigny, 1850
Dentalina terquemi d'Orbigny, 1849
Dentalina varians hauesleri (Schick, 1903)

Euagassiceras donovani Guérin-Franiatte, 1966
Euagassiceras resupinatum (Simpson, 1843)
Euagassiceras subtaurus (Reynès, 1879)
Euagassiceras terquemi (Reynès, 1879)

Gagaticeras exortum (Simpson, 1855)
Gagaticeras gagateum (Young & Bird, 1828)

Gagaticeras neglectum (Simpson, 1855)
Gammacythere ubiquita Malz & Lord, 1976
Gleviceras victoris (Dumortier, 1867)
Gramannella apostolescui (Gramann, 1962)
Grammatodon insons Melville, 1956
Gryphaea arcuata Lamarck, 1801
Gryphaea arcuata incurva J Sowerby, 1815
Gryphaea gigantea J de Sowerby, 1823
Gryphaea maccullochii J de C Sowerby, 1827
Gryphaea maccullochii arcuatiforme Hallam, 1968
Gryphaea maccullochii maccullochii Hallam, 1968

Haplophragmoides lincolnensis Copestake, 1986
Harpoceras falciferum (J Sowerby, 1820)
Hippopodium ponderosum J Sowerby, 1819

Isobythocypris elongata (Blake, 1876)
Isocrinus psilonoti (Quenstedt, 1858)

Kinkelinella foveolata (Michelsen, 1975)
Kinkelinella intermedia (Gramann, 1962)
Kinkelinella intrepida Bate & Coleman, 1975
Kinkelinella persica Bate & Coleman, 1975
Kinkelinella sermoisensis (Apostolescu, 1959)
Kinkelinella translucens (Blake, 1876)
Kinkelinella triebeli (Klingler & Neuweiler, 1959)
Kinkelinella vitiosa (Apostolescu, 1959)

Lenticulina varians (Bornemann, 1854)
Leptechioceras nodotianum (d'Orbigny, 1844)
Lingulina collenoti (Terquem, 1866)
Lingulina tenera subprismatica (Franke, 1936)
Lingulina tenera substriata (Nørvang, 1957)
Liostrea hisingeri (Nilsson, 1831)
Liostrea irregularis (Münster, 1833)
Lobothyris punctata (J Sowerby, 1813)
Lucina limbata Terquem & Piette, 1868

Mactromya arenacea (Terquem, 1855)
Mactromya subglobosus (Tate, 1876)
Marginulina prima d'Orbigny, 1849
Marginulina prima interrupta (Terquem, 1866)
Modiolus hillanoides (Chapuis & Dewalque, 1855)
Modiolus hillanus J Sowerby, 1818
Modiolus minimus J Sowerby, 1818
Modiolus scalprum J Sowerby, 1819
Montlivaltia haimei Chapius & Dewalque, 1853

Nanacythere aequalicostata Park, 1987
Nanocythere elegans (Drexler, 1958)
Nodosaria issleri Franke, 1936
Nuculana ovum (J de C Sowerby, 1824)

Ogmoconcha contractula Triebel, 1941
Ogmoconcha hagenowi Drexler, 1958

Ogmoconchela aspinata Drexler, 1958
Ogmoconchella danica Michelsen, 1975
Oistoceras angulatum (Frebold, 1922)
Ophthalmidium liasicum (Kübler & Zwingli, 1866)
Oppelismilia mucronata (Duncan, 1868)
Oxynoticeras oxynotum (Quenstedt, 1843)
Oxytoma inequivalve (J Sowerby, 1819)

Palaeoneilo galatea (d'Orbigny, 1850)
Paltechioceras rothpletzii (Bösc, 1894)
Paracypris redcarensis (Blake, 1876)
Pholadomya ambigua (J Sowerby, 1819)
Piarorhynchia juvenis (Quenstedt, 1852)
Plagiostoma giganteum J Sowerby, 1814
Planularia inaequistriata (Terquem, 1863)
Platypleuroceras brevispina (J de C Sowerby, 1827)
Pleurifera harpa (Klingler & Neuweiler, 1959)
Pleuroceras spinatum (Bruguière, 1789)
Pleuromya tatei Richardson & Tutcher, 1914
Pleurotomaria anglica (J Sowerby, 1816)
Plicatula calloptycus (Deslongchamps, 1860)
Plicatula spinosa J Sowerby, 1819
Polycope cerasia Blake, 1876
Polymorphites confusus (Quenstedt, 1856)
Polymorphites lineatus (Quenstedt, 1884)
Polymorphites quadratus Tutcher & Trueman, 1925
Praeschuleridea pseudokinkelinella Bate & Coleman, 1975
Progonoidea reticulata (Klingler & Neuweiler, 1959)
Promicroceras capricornoides (Quenstedt, 1884)
Protocardia truncata (J de C Sowerby, 1827)
Pseudolimea acuticostata (Münster *in* Goldfuss, 1836)
Pseudolimea pectinoides (J Sowerby, 1815)
Pseudopecten dentatus (J de C Sowerby, 1827)
Pseudopecten equivalvis (J Sowerby, 1816)
Psiloceras planorbis (J de C Sowerby, 1824)
Psilophyllites hagenowi (Dunker, 1847)
Ptychomphalus solarioides (J Sowerby, 1821)

Reinholdella macfadyeni (Ten Dam, 1947)
Reinholdella planiconvexa (Fuchs, 1970)
Ryderia doris (d'Orbigny, 1850)

Schlotheimia angulata (Schlotheim, 1820)
Spiriferina walcotti (J Sowerby, 1822)

Tetrarhynchia dunrobinensis (Rollier, 1917)
Tetrarhynchia tetrahedra (J Sowerby, 1812)
Trochammina canningensis Tappan, 1955
Tropidoceras acteon (d'Orbigny, 1844)
Tutcheria richardsoni Cox, 1946

Uptonia jamesoni (J de C Sowerby, 1827)

Vaginulinopsis denticulatacarinata (Franke, 1936)
Vermiceras rouvillei (Reynès, 1879)

Vermiceras solaroides (da Costa, 1853)
Waehneroceras iapetus Spath, 1924
Waehneroceras portlocki (Wright, 1881)
Wicherella semiora kirtonensis Lord, 1972

Chapter 5   Middle Jurassic: the Inferior and Great Oolite groups

Acanthothiris crossi (Walker, 1870)
Ammodiscus siliceus (Terquem, 1862)

Bisulcocypris ancasterensis Bate, 1967

Cererithyris dorsetensis Douglas & Arkell, 1928
Cererithyris intermedia (J Sowerby, 1812)
Chytroeisphaeridia hyalina (Raynaud) Lentin & Williams, 1981
Clydoniceras discus (J Sowerby, 1813)
Conicospirillina trochoides (Berthelin, 1879)
Corbula attenuata Lycett, 1863
Cytherelloidea eastfieldensis Bate, 1963

Darwinula incurva Bate, 1967
Digonella digonoides S S Buckman, 1913
Digonella [*Microthyridina*] *lagenalis* (Schlotheim, 1820)
Digonella siddingtonensis (Walker, 1878)

Entolium corneolum (Young & Bird, 1828)
Eocytheridea carinata Bate, 1964
Eomiodon angulatus (Morris & Lycett, 1855)

Fastigatocythere juglandica (Jones, 1884)
Fossaterquemula blakeana (Jones, 1884)

Galliaecytheridea kingscliffensis Bate, 1967
Gervillella aviculoides (J Sowerby, 1814)
Gervillella ovata (J de C Sowerby, 1853)
Glyptocythere guembeliana (Jones, 1884)
Glyptocythere oscillum (Jones & Sherborn, 1888)

Kallirhynchia vagans (S S Buckman, 1917)
Kallirhynchia yaxleyensis (Davidson, 1878)
Kinkelinella triangulata (Brand, 1961)

Leptodinium subtile Klement, 1960
Liostrea hebridica (Forbes, 1851)
Liostrea undosa (Phillips, 1829)
Lithodinia reticulata (Dodekova) Gocht, 1976
Lopha marshii (J Sowerby, 1814)
Lophocythere batei Malz, 1975

Macrocephalites jacquoti (H Douvillé, 1878)
Macrocephalites terebratus (Phillips, 1829)
Macrocephalites typicus Blake, 1905
Marslatourella bullata Bate, 1967
Meleagrinella echinata (Wm Smith, 1817)
Micropneumatocythere brendae Sheppard, 1978
Micropneumatocythere convexa Bate, 1963
Micropneumatocythere falcata Sheppard, 1978
Micropneumatocythere globosa Bate, 1964
Micropneumatocythere postrotunda Bate, 1967

Micropneumatocythere quadrata Bate, 1967
Modiolus imbricatus (J Sowerby, 1818)
Myophorella scarburgensis (Lycett, 1863)

Neomiodon cunninghami (Forbes, 1851)
Obovothyris classis (Douglas & Arkell, 1928)
Obovothyris magnobovata S S Buckman, 1927
Obovothyris obovata (J Sowerby, 1812)
Obovothyris obovata var. *grandobovata* S S Buckman, 1927
Ophiohybris griesbachii (Wright, 1854)

Pholadomya deltoidea (J Sowerby, 1818)
Placunopsis socialis Morris & Lycett, 1853
Pleuromya calceiformis (Phillips, 1829)
Pneumatocythere bajociana Bate, 1963
Praeexogyra hebridica (Forbes, 1851)
Praeexogyra hebridica var. *subrugulosa* (Morris & Lycett, 1853)
Praeschuleridea confossa Sheppard, 1981
Praeschuleridea decorata Bate, 1968
Progonocythere acuminata Bate, 1965
Progonocythere laevigata Bate, 1967
Progonocythere polonica Blaszyk, 1959
Progonocythere reticulata Bate, 1963
Progonocythere triquetra Bate, 1967
Protoacanthocythere faveolata Bate, 1963

Systenocythere exilofasciata Bate, 1963

Terquemula acutiplicata (Jones & Sherborn, 1888)
Terquemula bradiana (Jones, 1884)
Trochammina canningensis Tappan, 1955

Vaginulina harpa (Roemer) sensu Cifelli, 1959
Vaginulina legumen (Linnaeus, 1758)
Vaugonia moretoni (Morris & Lycett, 1853)

Chapter 6   Middle to Upper Jurassic: Ancholme Group

Ammobaculites coprolithiformis (Schwager, 1867)

Binatisphinctes comptoni (Pratt, 1841)
Bositra buchii (Roemer, 1836)

Chlamys (Radulopecten) scarburgensis (Young & Bird, 1822)
Choffatia recuperoi (Gemmellaro, 1872)
Chytroeisphaeridia hyalina (Reynaud) Lentin & Williams, 1981
Citharinella nikitini (Uhlig, 1883)
Cleistosphaeridium varispinosum (Sarjeant) Woollam & Riding, 1983
Corbulomima macneillii (Morris, 1850)
Crussolia deflandrei Wolfand & van Erve, 1981
Ctenidodinium continuum Gocht, 1970
Cylindroteuthis puzosiana (d'Orbigny, 1860)

Epistomina nuda Terquem, 1883
Epistomina regularis Terquem, 1883

Gonyaulacysta centriconnata Riding, 1983
Gonyaulacysta jurassica (Deflandre) Norris
  & Sarjeant, 1965 subsp. *adecta*
  Sarjeant, 1982 [var. *edecta* (autonym)]
Gryphaea (Bilobissa) dilobotes Duff, 1978
Gryphaea dilatata J Sowerby, 1816
Gryphaea lituola Larmarck, 1819

Hibolithes hastatus Montfort, 1808

Kosmoceras acutistriatum (S S Buckman,
  1924)
Kosmoceras gulielmi (J Sowerby, 1821)
Kosmoceras jason (Reinecke, 1818)
Kosmoceras phaeinum (S S Buckman, 1924)

Lenticulina ectypa (Loeblich & Tappan,
  1950
Lophocythere caesa caesa Triebel, 1951
Lophocythere flexicosta lutzei Whatley, 1970

Macrocephalites tumidus (Reinecke, 1818)
Marginulina batrakiensis (Myatlivk, 1939)

Mesosaccella morrisi (Deshayes, 1853)

Neurocythere dorni (Lutze, 1960)
Neurocythere interrupta interrupta (Triebel,
  1951)
Nubeculinella bigoti Cushman, 1930

Oxytoma expansa (Phillips, 1829)
Oxytoma inequivalve (J Sowerby, 1819)

Palaeonucula triangularis Duff, 1978
Parainoceramus subtilis (Lahusen, 1883)
Polycope sububiquita Whatley, 1970
Praeschuleridea caudata (Donze & Enay,
  1962
Procerithium damonis (Lycett, 1860)
Pseudolamarckina rjasanensis (Uhlig, 1883)

Reophax helviticus (Haeusler, 1881)

Sigaloceras (Catasigaloceras) enodatum
  (Nikitin, 1881)

Triplasia acuta Bartenstein & Brand, 1951
Triplasia kimmeridensis Bielecka &
  Pozaryski, 1954
Trochammina squamata Jones & Parker,
  1860

Wanaea fimbriata Sarjeant, 1961
Wanaea thysanota Woollam, 1982

Chapter 7   Quaternary

Hippopotamus amphibius Linnaeus, 1758

Palaeoloxodon antiquus (Falconer &
  Cautley, 1847)

Stephanorhinus hemitoechus (Falconer, 1860)

Viviparus viviparus (Linnaeus, 1758)

INDEX

BRITISH GEOLOGICAL SURVEY

Keyworth, Nottingham NG12 5GG
0115 936 3100

Murchison House, West Mains Road, Edinburgh
EH9 3LA   0131 667 1000

London Information Office, Natural History Museum
Earth Galleries, Exhibition Road, London SW7 2DE
020 7589 4090

The full range of Survey publications is available through the
Sales Desks at Keyworth and at Murchison House, Edinburgh,
and in the BGS London Information Office in the Natural
History Museum (Earth Galleries). The adjacent bookshop
stocks the more popular books for sale over the counter. Most
BGS books and reports can be bought from The Stationery
Office and through Stationery Office agents and retailers.
Maps are listed in the BGS Map Catalogue, and can be bought
together with books and reports through BGS-approved
stockists and agents as well as direct from BGS.

*The British Geological Survey carries out the geological survey of Great
Britain and Northern Ireland (the latter as an agency service for the
government of Northern Ireland), and of the surrounding continental
shelf, as well as its basic research projects. It also undertakes
programmes of British technical aid in geology in developing countries
as arranged by the Department for International Development and
other agencies.*

*The British Geological Survey is a component body of the Natural
Environment Research Council.*

Published by The Stationery Office and available from:

The Publications Centre
(mail, telephone and fax orders only)
PO Box 276, London SW8 5DT
Telephone orders/General enquiries 0870 600 5522
Fax orders 0870 600 5533

The Stationery Office Bookshops
123 Kingsway, London WC2B 6PQ
020 7242 6393 Fax 020 7242 6394
68–69 Bull Street, Birmingham B4 6AD
0121 236 9696 Fax 0121 236 9699
33 Wine Street, Bristol BS1 2BQ
0117 926 4306 Fax 0117 929 4515
9–21 Princess Street, Manchester M60 8AS
0161 834 7201 Fax 0161 833 0634
16 Arthur Street, Belfast BT1 4GD
028 9023 8457 Fax 028 9023 5401
The Stationery Office Oriel Bookshop
18–19 High Street, Cardiff CF1 2BZ
029 2039 5548 Fax 029 2038 4347
71 Lothian Road, Edinburgh EH3 9AZ
0131 228 4181 Fax 0131 622 7017

The Stationery Office's Accredited Agents
(see Yellow Pages)

and through good booksellers